S0-CPT-027

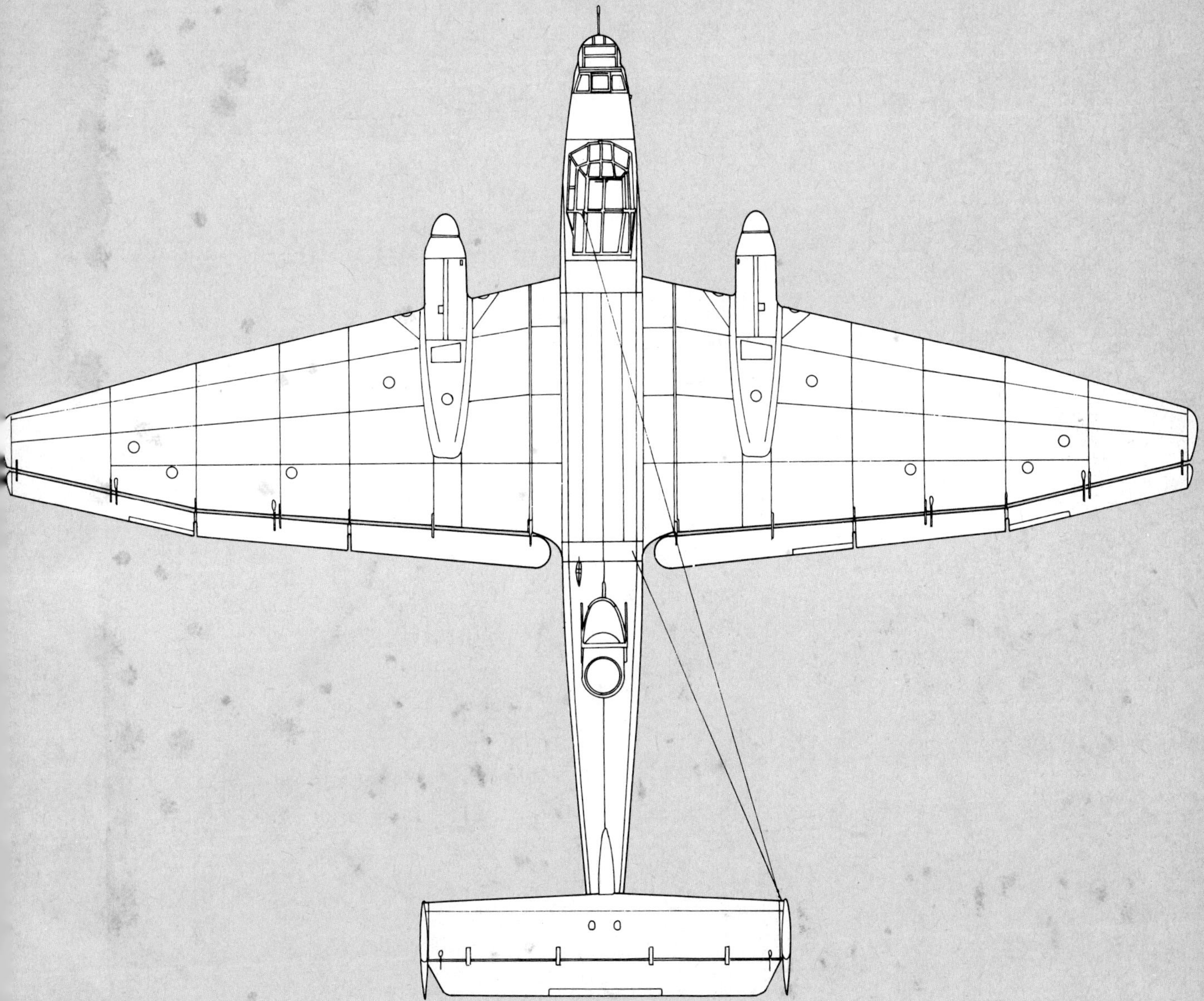

The Illustrated Encyclopedia of 20th Century WEAPONS AND WARFARE

CAUTION
LEFT
HAND
DRIVE

The Illustrated Encyclopedia of 20th Century WEAPONS AND WARFARE

COLUMBIA HOUSE/New York

Editor: Bernard Fitzsimons
Consultant Editors: Bill Gunston (Aviation)
Ian V. Hogg (Land Weapons)
Antony Preston (Naval)
Deputy Editor: Suzanne Walker
Copy Editor: Michael Maddison
Assistant Editors: Will Fowler, Richard Green, Corinne Benicka, John Liebmann, Michael de Luca
Editorial Assistant: Julie Leitch
Art Editor: David Harper
Assistant Art Editor: John Bickerton
Design Assistants: Jeff Gurney, John Voce
Production: Sheila Biddlecombe
Picture Research: Jonathan Moore
Contributors: Chaz Bowyer, David Brown, Mark Hewish, Ian V. Hogg, Bill Gunston, John Jordan, Pamela Matthews, Kenneth Munson, Antony Preston, John A. Roberts, Anthony J. Watts, John S. Weeks
Illustrator: John Batchelor

Cover Design: Harry W. Fass
Production Manager: Stephen Charkow

Distributed by Columbia House, a Division of CBS Inc.,
1211 Avenue of the Americas, New York, New York 10036
Printed in the U.S.A.

"Praise the Lord and pass the ammunition."

—Howell M. Forgy at Pearl Harbor, 7 December 1941.

INTRODUCTION

The fascinating range of twentieth-century military hardware is clearly demonstrated in Volume 14 of *The Illustrated Encyclopedia of 20th Century Weapons and Warfare.* One aspect of this variety is the unpredictability of developments, and the way in which concepts —and even actual hardware—which have come to be considered obsolete can suddenly find new applications.

One case in point is the battleship. The first USS ***Iowa*** was the fourth battleship built for the US Navy, following the *Indiana* Class of the early 1890s. Reflecting the political preoccupation with coastal defense which had made the coast artillery the best-equipped branch of the US Army, *Iowa,* like her predecessors, was designed as a "coastline" battleship. Even without this constraint, the revolution in battleship design embodied by the British *Dreadnought,* launched in 1906, would have rendered her obsolete by the First World War; she played no part in that conflict and ended her life as a target for her successors in 1923.

No constraints inhibited the design of the later ***Iowa* Class,** designed in the shadow of the approaching Second World War as a consequence of the Japanese non-participation in the London naval treaty of 1936. In fact, *Iowa* and her sisters corresponded to the traditional battlecruiser, reversing the true battleship's order of priorities of armor protection, armament and speed to place the emphasis on speed and range.

In doing so, they reflected the growing dominance of the aircraft carrier in naval warfare: the capital ship of the past would no longer be the kingpin of the battle fleet, but would itself become part of the escort for the new main instrument of power at sea. They also reflected the expansion of the military horizons of the United States. Their sphere of action extended far beyond the coastal waters of their nineteenth-century namesakes, and the four members of the class served across the Pacific to Japan and subsequently off Korea.

But the most remarkable part of the history of the class came when the day of the battleship seemed to be gone forever. In 1968 *New Jersey* was recommissioned for shore bombardment of Vietnam, and while this was hardly the role for which she had been designed, she demonstrated the power and precise accuracy of the big naval gun, both far greater than that provided by the carriers' attack bombers. As the table accompanying the entry shows, the Mk VII 16-in gun could deliver a 2700-lb shell over a range of 24 miles—an awesome prospect with three triple turrets turning out a total of 18 rounds per minute.

The first battlecruiser had been the British ***Invincible,*** launched in 1907 and inspired by studies of the sea battles of the Russo-Japanese War. *Invincible* was intended to be the first of a new type of warship, fast and powerful enough to catch and destroy the armored cruisers which she superseded and able to evade any vessel more powerful than herself—qualities which are, of course, nullified if the enemy also builds battlecruisers.

In addition to the above, Volume 14 contains some familiar names: the whole range of German **Junkers** aircraft; the **Jeep,** one of Eisenhower's answers when asked what three weapons had done most to win the Second World War, and the universal light military vehicle for many years; and the **Kalashnikov** range of small arms, including the AK assault rifle, made in uncounted millions and in terms both of design and sales one of the most successful weapons ever made.

Invincible

British battlecruiser class. The *Invincible* Class were the world's first battlecruisers and were contemporaries of *Dreadnought*, the first all-big-gun battleship. In fact they could be described as all-big-gun armoured cruisers because they were intended to replace existing armoured cruisers in much the same way as *Dreadnought* was to replace existing battleships.

The idea for the design originated in the fertile mind of Admiral Sir John Fisher, who began with the logical idea of producing an armoured cruiser of 25 knots armed with 9.2-in (234-mm) and 7.5-in (190-mm) guns compared with 23 knots and 6-in (152-mm) guns of existing ships. All that remained was to add a uniform 9.2-in gun armament to provide a ship which would be a valuable addition to the future *Dreadnought*-orientated fleet. Unfortunately, Fisher was subsequently influenced by the battles of the Russo-Japanese war, which emphasized the value of speed and gunpower, and the construction for foreign navies of heavily-armed cruising ships. He concluded that 12-in (305-mm) armament was essential for his new ships, on the general principle that they could then provide a 'fast wing' to the battlefleet, capable of bringing heavy-gun support wherever it was needed, especially in encircling movements across the van of an enemy fleet. At the same time the new ships would be capable of catching and destroying any existing armoured cruiser while being fast enough to escape from more heavily armed battleships. The flaw in the argument was the assumption that the enemy did not possess similar vessels of high speed and heavy armament. Since the new ships retained the scale of protection of the old-style armoured cruisers, they could not stand up to heavy gunfire. Once Germany began to build battlecruisers the value of the new ships diminished substantially.

When Fisher became First Sea Lord in 1904 one of his first actions was to set up a Committee on Designs, the principal object of which was to make recommendations on the designs of future British warships. In the case of the armoured cruiser they recommended a vessel of 17 000 tons armed with eight 12-in (305-mm) guns and capable of 25 knots, to be powered, like *Dreadnought*, by steam turbines. This proposal was approved by the board in March 1905 and detailed design begun for three vessels to be included in the 1905-06 Estimates.

The three armoured cruisers (reclassified in 1913 as battlecruisers), *Invincible* (built by Armstrong), *Indomitable* (built by Fairfield), and *Inflexible* (built by John Brown), were laid down in 1906, launched in 1907 and completed in 1908. As finally designed, they were of 17 250 tons displacement, had machinery of 41 000 shp for 25 knots speed and were protected by 6-in (152-mm) side armour. The armament consisted of four twin 12-in (305-mm) gun turrets, mounted forward, aft and en echelon amidships, and 20 12-pdr anti-torpedo-boat guns (replaced by 16 4-in [102-mm] while under construction). *Invincible* was experimentally fitted with electrically-powered turrets but these were not successful and were converted to hydraulic power in 1914. The ships had Parsons turbines, as in *Dreadnought*, and 31 boilers. On full-power trials all three greatly exceeded their designed power producing between 46 500 and 47 800 shp giving speeds of 26.1 knots *(Indomitable)*, 26.48 knots *(Inflexible)* and 26.6 knots *(Invincible)*. *Indomitable* made a record passage between Canada and Britain in 1908 averaging 25.3 knots with 43 700 shp over a period of three days.

The ships' three funnels were originally of equal height, but during 1910-11 the fore-funnels of *Indomitable* and *Inflexible* were raised to reduce the effects of smoke interference on the bridge. (*Invincible* had hers raised in 1915.) During 1914-15 the 4-in (102-mm) guns mounted on the turret roofs were transferred to positions in the superstructure, and director control was added for the main armament. During 1915-16 two 3-in (76-mm) AA guns were added amidships. After the Battle of Jutland (Skagerrak), where *Invincible* was sunk, the two surviving ships had additional armour plating added on their turret roofs and over the crowns of the magazines. During 1917-18 one of the 3-in (76-mm) AA guns was replaced by a 4-in (102-mm) AA, the bridge and foretop were enlarged, and aircraft platforms were added on the wing turrets.

On completion, the three ships joined the Home Fleet where they remained until 1912-13 when they transferred to the Mediterranean Fleet, though *Invincible* returned to Home Waters at the end of 1913. On the outbreak of war in 1914, *Inflexible* and *Indomitable* took part in the hunt for the German battlecruiser *Goeben* and in the blockade of the Dardanelles, before returning to Home Waters in November and December 1914 respectively. In November, *Invincible*, flying the flag of Vice Admiral Sturdee, and *Inflexible* were despatched to the south Atlantic to search for Admiral Maximilian von Spee's cruiser squadron and avenge the loss of Vice Admiral Christopher Craddock's cruiser squadron at the Battle of Coronel. They arrived at the Falkland Islands on December 7 and by an incredible stroke of luck von Spee's squadron appeared off the islands on the following day. In the ensuing action the British battlecruisers sank von Spee's two armoured cruisers with little damage to themselves, though *Inflexible* was hit three times and *Invincible* 22 times. This

The battlecruiser HMS *Invincible*. The *Invincible* Class were the world's first battlecruisers and marked a revolution in cruiser design

action was seen as a vindication of the battlecruiser principle, but the fact that the two British ships expended most of their 12-in (305-mm) ammunition and took nearly five hours to sink their two inferior adversaries seems to have been overlooked. Shortly after the action, *Invincible* returned to Home Waters for repairs and *Inflexible* transferred to the Mediterranean where she took part in the initial stages of the bombardment of the Dardanelles forts. On March 19, 1915, during the attack on the narrows, *Inflexible* struck a mine which blew a hole 9 m (30 ft) long by 8 m (26 ft) deep in the starboard bow. She retired from action and was eventually repaired at Gibraltar, having come close to sinking after shipping about 1600 tons of water.

In the meantime *Indomitable* had also been in action, having taken part in the battle at the Dogger Bank on January 24, 1915. She distinguished herself both by maintaining a high speed during the action and in towing to Rosyth the heavily damaged flagship *Lion.* By June 1915 the three sisters had been brought together to form the 3rd Battlecruiser Squadron of the Grand Fleet under Rear-Admiral Horace Hood, with his flag in *Invincible.* All three took part in the Battle of Jutland on May 31, 1916, and during the early stages of the battle seriously damaged the three German cruisers *Pillau, Frankfurt* and *Wiesbaden.* Later they formed up in the van of the British battlecruiser force and engaged the German battlecruiser squadron. At 1832 hours *Invincible* received a hit on Q turret, which was followed by the explosion of the midship magazines, throwing wreckage 120 m (400 ft) into the air. The ship broke in two, and the halves came to rest on the seabed with the extreme bow and stern sticking above the water. There were six survivors from her crew of 1133. The folly of placing lightly protected ships in the battle line was thus dramatically demonstrated; two other British battlecruisers, *Indefatigable* and *Queen Mary,* had already blown up that day.

After Jutland, *Inflexible* and *Indomitable* joined the 2nd Battlecruiser Squadron with which they remained until the end of the war. Both ships were sold for scrap in 1921.

See also *Indefatigable.*

Displacement: 17 300 tons (load), 20 000 tons (deep) *Length:* 172.8 m (567 ft) oa *Beam:* 23.9 m (78 ft 5 in) *Draught:* 7.9 m (26 ft) *Machinery:* 4-shaft direct-drive turbines, 41 000 shp=25 knots *Protection:* 152 mm (6 in) sides, 178 mm (7 in) turrets and barbettes, 76-19 mm (3-0.75 in) deck *Armament:* 8 12-in (305-mm) (4×2); 16 4-in (102-mm) (16×1); 5 18-in (46-cm) torpedo tubes (submerged; 4 broadside, 1 stern) *Crew:* 722 (peace time)

Invincible

British helicopter/STOL carrier class, built 1973. The cancellation in 1966 of the fleet carrier designated *CVA.01* left the Royal Navy with the dismal prospect of having to rely on shore-based air cover during the 1980s. The bitter lessons of the Second World War had shown that shore-based air support, however willing, tended to arrive too late. As an alternative to the enormous expense of fixed-wing aircraft carriers, there was a possibility that a 'mix' of antisubmarine helicopters and V/STOL aircraft could be accommodated in a much smaller hull. Once the traditional requirements of fixed-wing aircraft (arrester wires and a heavily strengthened landing deck) disappeared, it was possible to produce a utility carrier to provide local air superiority and strike.

The basis of such a design already existed in the form of a helicopter-carrying cruiser designated CCH, similar in concept to the French *Jeanne d'Arc,* with a cruiser bridge and guided weapons forward, and a flight deck aft. Despite initial political problems from a defence minister who was determined to prevent the revival of *CVA.01* in a new guise, common sense dictated that the CCH would be improved if its bridge and funnel were tidied up and put in a starboard island structure. As a precaution against political interference the clumsy designation 'through-deck cruiser' was coined. Later the design was referred to more correctly as a command cruiser, and then as an antisubmarine cruiser (CAH).

The rapid development of the Hawker Siddeley Harrier led to the design of a maritime version, the Sea Harrier, the first of which flew in 1978. The advent of this aircraft led to certain changes in the internal design of the CAH, for the workshops and magazines had to be tailored to carry spares and ordnance for the fixed-wing Sea Harriers as well as for Sea King helicopters. A slightly offset flight deck is provided to give more deck space, which was further increased with the cancellation of the Exocet surface-to-surface missiles, which were originally to be mounted alongside the twin Sea Dart launcher.

Internally the design is spacious, with accommodation for more than the planned air group of the nine Sea Kings and five Sea Harriers. It is believed that a maximum of 25 aircraft could be stowed without difficulty, and accommodation for 1000 Royal Marine Commandos can be provided. The hydraulic lifts are of new design, which can be loaded from three sides to reduce congestion in the hangar, which is of the closed type, narrow in the middle between the two lifts.

Originally a speed of only 24 knots was envisaged as the CCH was intended for escort duty, but the CAH is intended to work with the fleet, which means a minimum of 28 knots. *Invincible* is the largest ship so far designed for gas-turbine drive, with four Olympus units coupled in pairs to each shaft. Another unusual feature is the provision of spare gas-generators, which can be replaced by the ship's own crew. The massive amounts of air needed mean that two large funnels and a long superstructure are required.

One of the most important roles for the new vessels will be as flagships for task groups, and so there is a comprehensive outfit of long-range radar (Type 1022 air-warning array), Type 992R search and two Type 909 guidance radars for the Sea Dart, as well as a big hull-mounted sonar.

The lead ship *Invincible* (CAH.1) was launched on May 3, 1977, by Vickers at Barrow-in-Furness and was due to start sea trials at the beginning of 1979. Her sister *Illustrious* (CAH.2) was laid down in 1976 by Swan Hunter at Wallsend, on the River Tyne, and *Indomitable* (CAH.3) is probably also to be laid down by Swan Hunter. The lead ship and her sisters will have the revolutionary 'ski-jump' ramp fitted to the forward end of the flight deck. This simple device, invented by Lieutenant-Commander D R Taylor of the Royal Navy, permits a Sea Harrier to take off with 454 kg (1000 lb) more payload, and also improves safety during takeoff.

See also Sea Harrier, Sea King.

Displacement: 16 000 tons (standard), 19 500 tons (full load) *Length:* 206.3 m (677 ft) oa *Beam:* 27.4 m (90 ft) wl *Draught:* 7.3 m (24 ft)

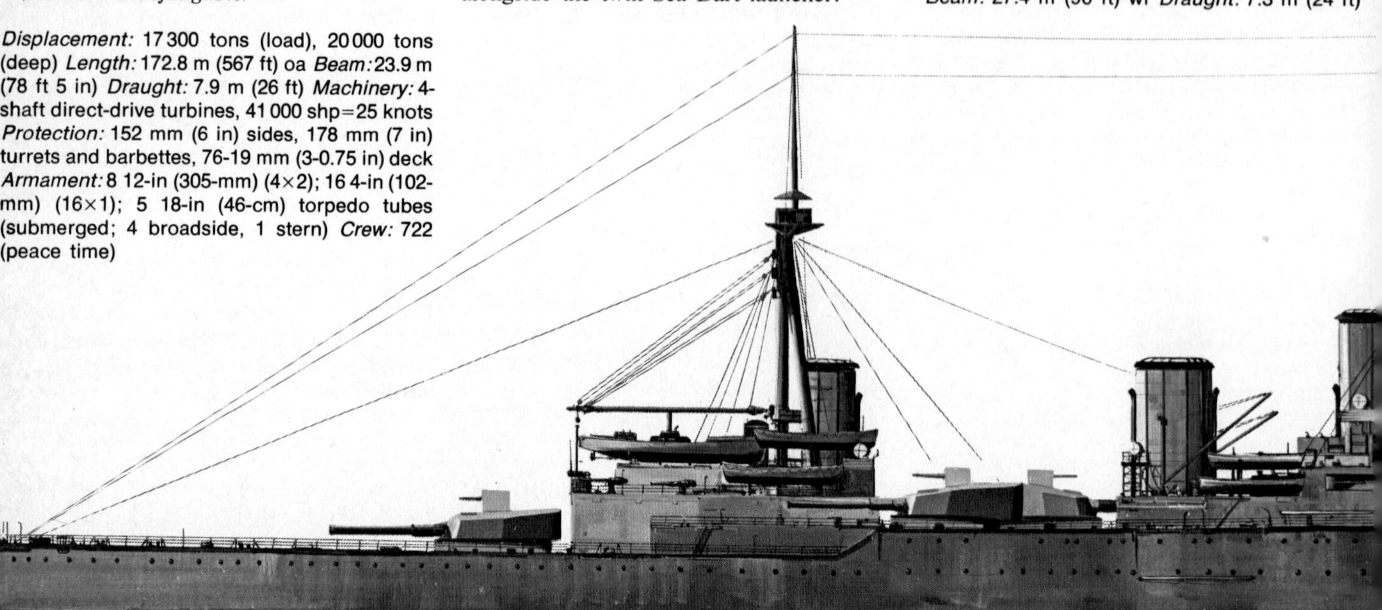

approx *Machinery:* 4 gas turbines, 2 shafts 112 000 shp=28 knots *Armament:* 1 twin Sea Dart SAM launcher *Aircraft:* 9 helicopters, 5 fixed-wing aircraft *Crew:* 900+air group

Iowa

US battleship, built 1892-97. Two years after the *Indiana* Class were authorized, Congress sanctioned a fourth 'coastline' battleship of improved design. Once again the contract went to the Cramp shipyard in Philadelphia; the USS *Iowa* (BB.4) was launched on March 28, 1896, and commissioned in June 1897.

Although the main features of the previous class were retained there were many improvements. The cumbersome 13-in (330-mm) guns were replaced by a lighter and more effective 12-in (305-mm), and this, combined with an increase of about 1000 tons in displacement allowed for higher freeboard, more coal and a better internal arrangement. The 8-in (203-mm) guns were moved to reduce the blast interference with the main battery, and 4-in (102-mm) quick-firers replaced the 6-in (152-mm).

Iowa served with the *Indianas* on blockade duty off Cuba during the Spanish-American war, and in 1911 she was modernized, as they were, with a cage mainmast. Four more 4-in (102-mm) guns were added, and the torpedo tubes were removed. She played no part in the First World War, and was renamed *Coast Battleship No 4* in April 1919 to release her name for a new battleship. In September 1920 she became unclassified hulk *IX-6*, and on March 23, 1923, was sunk as a target for the guns of the fleet off Panama.

Displacement: 11 340 tons *Length:* 110.5 m (362 ft 6 in) oa *Beam:* 22 m (72 ft 2 in) *Draught:* 7.3 m (24 ft) mean *Machinery:* 2-shaft reciprocating steam, 12 000 ihp=17 knots *Protection:* 381 m (15 in) belt, 381 mm (15 in) turrets, 254 mm (10 in) conning tower *Armament:* 4 12-in (305-mm)/35-cal (2×2); 8 8-in (203-mm)/35-cal (4×2); 6 4-in (102-mm)/40-cal (6×1); 20 57-mm (2.24-in) QF (20×1); 4 37-mm (1.46-in) QF (4×1); 4 0.30-in (7.62-mm) machine-guns (4×1); 4 14-in (35.6-cm) Howell torpedo tubes (beam, above water) *Crew:* 505

PPL

USS *Iowa* embodied a number of design improvements over the preceding *Indiana* Class

Iowa

US battleship class, built 1940-44. As early as 1937 the US Navy began studies on the design of a 45 000-ton battleship, as a contingency against a failure by the Japanese to ratify the 1936 London naval treaty, which retained the 35 000-ton limit laid down in 1922. The first ideas were for a heavily armoured ship with 12 16-in (406-mm) guns and a speed of only 27 knots (the so-called 'slow' designs), but in January 1938 emphasis switched to 'fast' designs capable of 30 knots. The reason for this seems to have been that the forthcoming series of 30-knot aircraft carriers would have been able to outstrip their battleship escorts, and a new type of fast capital ship was therefore needed.

Although never regarded as battlecruisers, the *Iowa* Class were just that, as they sacrificed armour for maximum speed while having the same weight of armament as the preceding *Washington* and *South Dakota* Classes of battleships. However, the scale of the protection was adequate for a front-rank capital ship, and the *Iowas* compared well with all their contemporaries except the giant Japanese *Yamato* Class. To conceal the thinning of the armour down to 310 mm (12.2 in) it was put about for many years that the class had 460-mm (18-in) belts and massive deck armour, though the 1937 studies had shown that it would have been impossible to reconcile such heavy protection with 30 knots' speed. Although US naval intelligence suspected that the Japanese were about to adopt 18-in guns, it was hoped that US ships would never need protection against such heavy guns. It was thought that the fast carrier's aircraft would force enemy battleships to keep their distance, and that the fast battleships would prevent any cruisers from getting close.

The 16-in (406-mm)/50-cal armament selected for the new class had suffered many birth pangs. A ludicrous breakdown of communications between the Bureau of Ordnance and the Bureau of Construction and Repair meant that from April to November 1938 the two bureaux worked on different dimensions and weights for the new triple 16 in turret. Briefly, this meant that the 11.35 m (37 ft 3 in) diameter barbettes designed for the new ships were too small to accommodate the existing 16-in/50-cal Mk II, which had been built in 1916-18 for the cancelled *South Dakota* and *Lexington* classes. The solution was to fit the new lightweight Mk VII 16-in/50-cal gun. The outcome of a long process of design by the Department of Ordnance, the Mk VII was small enough to fit into the barbettes originally designed. Its construction was rushed forward, and fortunately the manufacturers were equal to the challenge, and enough guns were produced to enable the first two ships to be laid down in the summer of 1940 and completed in the first half of 1943.

Six ships were planned—*Iowa* (BB.61), *New Jersey* (BB.62), *Missouri* (BB.63), *Wisconsin* (BB.64), *Illinois* (BB.65) and *Kentucky* (BB.66). BB.61 and 63 were to be built by New York navy yard; BB.62, 64 and 65 by Philadelphia navy yard; and BB.66 by Norfolk navy yard.

Iowa was launched on August 27, 1942, and in August the following year she sailed for Newfoundland to cover convoys against *Tirpitz*. After taking President Roosevelt to North Africa she went to the Pacific for service with the 5th Fleet. She sustained minor damage from hits by a Japanese shore battery in the Marshall Islands, and at the battle of Leyte Gulf she was part of Admiral Halsey's fast carrier force. She supported the final assault on Okinawa, bombarded Hokkaido and Honshu in July 1945, and was present at the surrender in Tokyo Bay. She decommissioned in 1949 but was reactivated for the Korean war in 1952, during which she carried out a number of bombardments. She has been mothballed since 1953.

HMS *Invincible* was lost at the Battle of Jutland when she took a hit on her Q turret which caused an explosion in the midships magazine. Wreckage was thrown 120 m (140 ft) into the air and the ship broke in half. She settled with her stern and bow projecting out of the water and only six survived from her crew of 1133. Her loss, with that of the *Indefatigable* and *Queen Mary*, proved the folly of using lightly armoured warships in the line with battleships

USS *Iowa* (BB-61) on October 15, 1952 during a bombardment of Kojo on the east coast of Korea in support of amphibious operations

New Jersey was launched on December 7, 1942, and went straight to the Pacific in January 1944 after working up for six months. As flagship of the 3rd Fleet she fought at Leyte Gulf, and logged more than 354 000 km (220 000 miles) as an escort to the fast carrier task forces. She decommissioned in June 1948, but like her sister, was reactivated for the Korean war from 1951 to 1953. In 1967 she was selected for recommissioning to provide much-needed fire support for the Vietnam war, and after an overhaul of communications and electronics she recommissioned in April 1968 for what must surely be the last operation involving battleships. She was a notable success on the 'gun line' until 1969, when a shortage of 16-in (406-mm) barrel liners forced her retirement. It is said that a forgotten field full of gun liners was rediscovered in the US, but this came too late

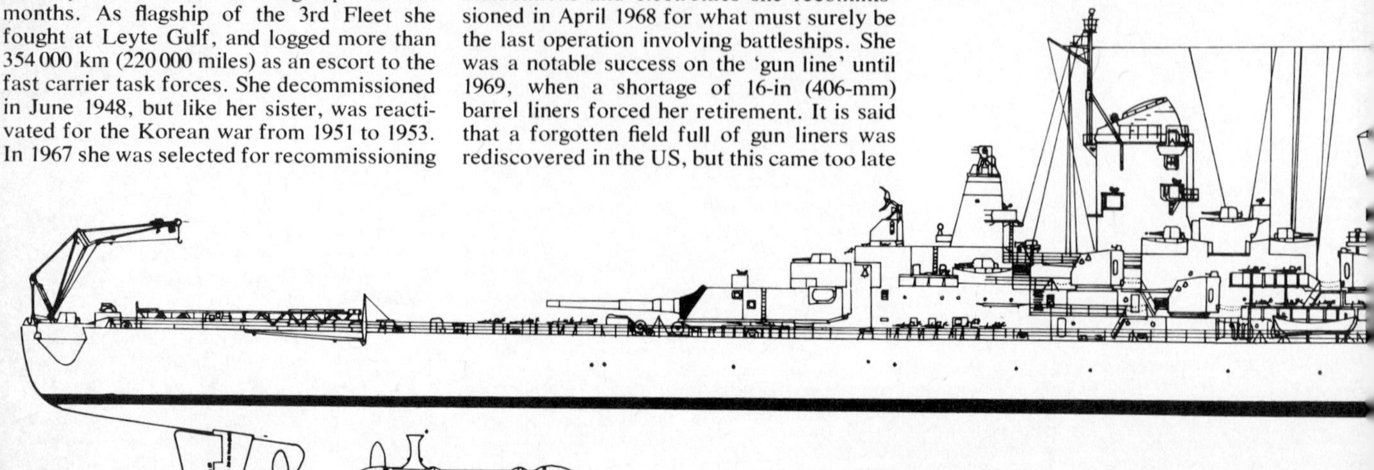

Mk II and Mk VII 16-in guns

	Mk II	Mk VII
Length oa (m/ft)	20.73/68	20.73/68
Diameter at breech (cm/in)	143.5/56.5	124.4/49
Diameter at muzzle (cm/in)	67.3/26.5	59.7/23.5
Weight of gun (kg/lb)	130 000/286 500	108 410/239 000
Weight of shell (kg/lb)	1016/2240	1225/2700
Propelling charge (kg/lb)	294/648	297/655
Muzzle velocity (m/sec/ft/sec)	808/2650	762/2500
Maximum range (m/yards)	41 240/45 100 at 46°	38 720/42 345 at 45°

The *Iowa* in 1954. After distinguished service in the Pacific she was decommissioned in 1958

Heal Photographs

Below: Iowa Class battleships did not possess heavy armour protection, but their combination of speed and fire power (nine 16-in [406-mm] guns) made them formidable warships

to reprieve *New Jersey*, and she decommissioned in December 1969.

Missouri, the 'Mighty Mo', was launched on January 29, 1944, and was commissioned less than six months later. She went to the Pacific at the end of that year and saw her first action off Iwo Jima. Her fame was assured when, on September 2, 1945, in Tokyo Bay the Japanese surrender was signed on her quarterdeck. She remained in commission after her sisters, but in January 1950 she ran hard aground in Chesapeake Bay, and suffered considerable hull damage. Despite this she served in Korea for three years, and was not decommissioned until 1955. She is earmarked for preservation as a memorial, in view of her association with the Japanese surrender.

Wisconsin was launched on December 7, 1943, and commissioned in April 1944, joining the 3rd Fleet at the end of that year. She was decommissioned in 1948 and served in the Korean war from 1951 to 1953. In May 1956 she rammed and sank the US destroyer escort *Eaton.* She was repaired with the bow of her incomplete sister *Kentucky*, and was decommissioned in 1958 for the last time.

Work on *Illinois* was held up by the steel shortage of 1943, and as she was only 22% complete by August 1945 she was cancelled and eventually scrapped. She and her sister *Kentucky* differed from the others, being designed for welding throughout. It was hoped to complete *Kentucky* with an armament of guided missiles, and work continued during 1948-50, by which time she was 73% complete with main machinery on board. However the project was recognized to be operationally and financially unrealistic, and she was stricken in June 1958; her four turbines were installed in the fast replenishment ships *Sacramento* and *Camden* in 1964-66.

As built, all four ships were very similar in appearance, with massive capped funnels and a pole mast stepped against the rear side of the after funnel. Before the Korean war the two catapults and floatplanes were removed, and the pole mainmast was replaced by a big lattice tripod to carry an air-warning and surveillance radar. Subsequently twin supports were added to strengthen the structure, and boat derricks were added as the former aircraft crane aft was not heavy enough to handle the boats. All ships had the 20-mm (0.79-in) AA guns removed and the quadruple 40-mm (1.57-in) Bofors AA guns were planned to be replaced by twin 3-in (76-mm)/50-cal guns. *New Jersey* had all light guns removed in 1968 and had a massive square structure built on top of her control tower, but was otherwise unaltered.

Although not the most heavily armoured battleships of the Second World War, the *Iowas*' combination of size and speed made them magnificent ships for the Pacific. Despite their length, the twin rudders made them manoeuvrable, and with maximum fuel stowage of more than 8000 tons they had greater range than any capital ship previously built. On the basis of trial figures they could, in theory, steam 29 000 km (18 000 miles) at 12

The Blackburn Iris first flew in June 1926 and when it entered service with the RAF in 1930 it was the largest flying boat in RAF use. Though only a limited number were produced they were up-engined and improved during their service careers with changed Mark designations

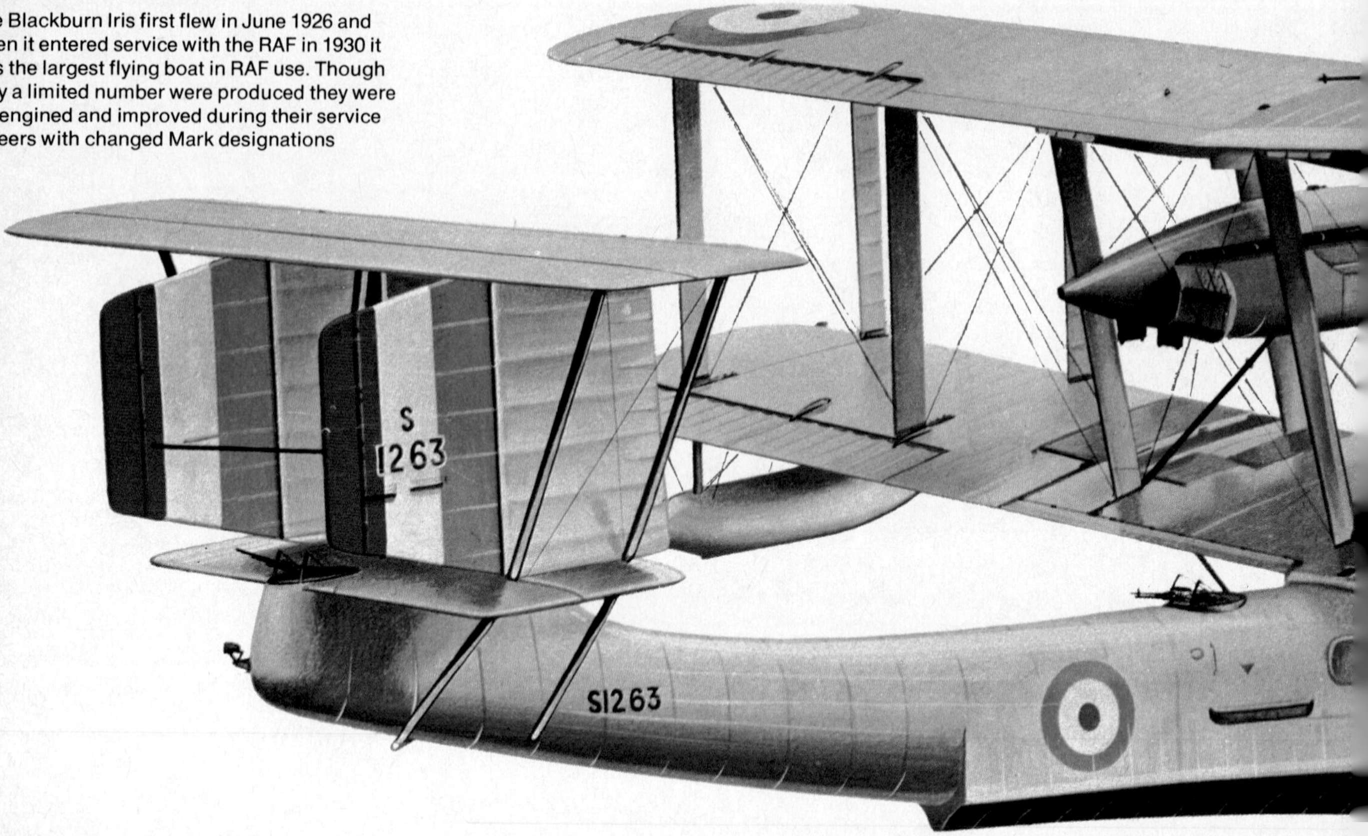

knots, 25 000 km (15 900 miles) at 17 knots and 8530 km (5300 miles) at 29.5 knots. During postwar NATO exercises they frequently refuelled the destroyer screen when an oiler was not available, and they had a high reputation for reliability.

See also *Montana.*

Displacement: 48 000 tons (standard), 57 000 tons (full load) *Length:* 270.43 m (887 ft 3 in) oa *Beam:* 32.97 m (108 ft 2 in) *Draught:* 11.58 m (38 ft) *Machinery:* 4-shaft geared steam turbines, 212 000 shp=33 knots *Protection:* 307 mm (12.1 in) belt, 121-38 mm (4.75-1.5 in) deck, 432-mm (17-in) turrets *Armament:* 9 16-in (406-mm)/50-cal (3×3); 20 5-in (127-mm)/38-cal DP (10×2); 60/80 40-mm (1.57-in) Bofors AA (15/20×4); 49/60 20-mm (0.79-in) Oerlikon AA (49/60×1) *Aircraft:* 3 Kingfisher floatplanes, 2 catapults *Crew:* 2788 (1626, *New Jersey* in 1968)

Iris, Blackburn

British flying boat. Originally designed to Air Ministry Specification R.14/24, the Blackburn R.B.1 Iris three-engined biplane of all-wood construction (RAF serial N185) made its first flight on June 19, 1926. N185 was modified to have a metal hull and more powerful engines, and was relaunched as the Iris II on August 2, 1927. Subsequent service testing led to an Air Ministry decision to equip one squadron with a developed variant, the Iris III, the prototype of which (N238) was launched at Brough on November 21, 1929. No 209 Squadron was reformed on January 15, 1930, to operate the type, and eventually received all four Iris IIIs built (N238, S1263, S1264, S1593).

During their service the Iris flying boats were the largest aircraft in RAF use, and undertook several excellent long-distance cruises. Later in 1931 the Air Ministry decided to modernize the Iris III, mainly by installing more powerful engines. The original engine was the Rolls-Royce Condor V-12 rated at 675 hp; the new engine was the 825-hp Buzzard. The modified aircraft were designated Iris V, the Mk IV being a conversion with AS Leopard radials (the centre engine a pusher). Only three were produced. S1593, sometimes referred to as the Iris VI, became the prototype of the later Blackburn Perth, the largest biplane flying boat ever used by the RAF, which mounted a 37-mm (1.46-in) Coventry Ordnance Works QF cannon in its nose cockpit. Only five Iris aircraft were ever built, some early aircraft being rebuilt to the specification of the later Marks.

The prototype Blackburn Iris flying boat, powered by three 825-hp Rolls-Royce Buzzard engines

(Mk I) *Span:* 29.11 m (95 ft 6 in) *Length:* 20.27 m (66 ft 6 in) *Gross weight:* 12 523 kg (27 608 lb) *Maximum speed:* 185 km/h (115 mph)

(Mk II) *Span:* 29.11 m (95 ft 6 in) *Length:* 20.27 m (66 ft 6 in) *Gross weight:* 12 409 kg (27 358 lb) *Maximum speed:* 179 km/h (111 mph)

(Mk III) *Span:* 29.57 m (97 ft) *Length:* 20.54 m (67 ft 5 in) *Gross weight:* 13 721 kg (30 250 lb) *Maximum speed:* 209 km/h (130 mph)

(Mk IV) *Span:* 29.11 m (95 ft 6 in) *Length:* 20.27 m (66 ft 6 in) *Gross weight:* 13 376 kg (29 489 lb) *Maximum speed:* 209 km/h (130 mph)

(Mk V) *Span:* 29.57 m (97 ft) *Length:* 20.54 m (67 ft 5 in) *Gross weight:* 14 651 kg (32 300 lb) *Maximum speed:* 208 km/h (129 mph)

Iron Duke

British battleship class. The *Iron Duke* Class of the 1911 Programme were the third and last group of British 13.5-in (343-mm) gun Dreadnoughts and the last British battleships to burn coal. They were basically repeats of the previous *King George V* Class, with the same arrangement of main armament and protection, but differed in adopting a 6-in (152-mm) gun secondary battery in place of 4-in (102-mm). This change was prompted by the fact that the 4-in (102-mm) gun lacked the stopping power required to counter the latest types of destroyer and the 6-in (152-mm) was the largest-calibre gun which could be hand-loaded. The change produced a 2000-ton increase in displacement which resulted from the added weight of the secondary battery and its 6-in (152-mm) armour, an increase of 0.3 m (1 ft) in the beam to maintain the level of stability, and an increase in machinery power and length in order to keep to the standard battleship speed of 21 knots.

In order to keep topweight to a minimum, the 6-in (152-mm) guns were positioned low down with five on each side in an upper-deck battery amidships and two in casemates on the main deck aft. In service this arrangement proved unsatisfactory because the guns were too close to the waterline. The 6-in (152-mm) gun ports were originally fitted with doors, but these were continually washed away in heavy seas and were eventually removed and replaced by rubber seals between the revolving gun-shields and the gun ports. The two guns aft, which were even closer to the waterline, proved completely unworkable in anything but a flat calm, and in heavy weather their casemates were often flooded out. Late in 1914 these guns were removed and the ports plated over. The guns were repositioned in new casemates on the forecastle deck abreast of the bridge where they had good arcs of fire. The *Iron Dukes* also differed from the *King George V* Class in having an after torpedo-flat as well as a forward one, giving them four broadside tubes instead of two. During construction, director control was added for the main armament, necessitating the fitting of a tripod foremast to provide a steady platform for the director. Two 3-in (76-mm) AA guns were

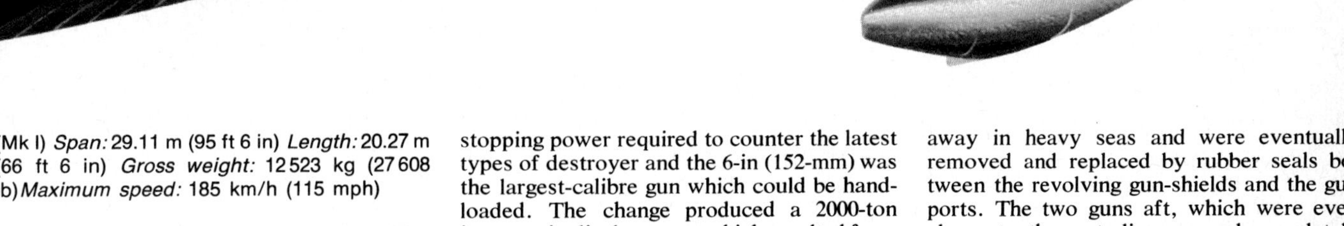

HMS *Iron Duke*, an improvement on the *King George V* Class with the same layout of guns but with more powerful secondary armament

added on the after superstructure, *Iron Duke* being the first British battleship to carry an AA armament.

The four ships of the class, *Iron Duke* (built by Portsmouth dockyard), *Marlborough* (built by Devonport dockyard), *Benbow* (built by Beardmore) and *Emperor of India* (built by Vickers) were laid down in 1912, launched during 1912-13 and completed in 1914. *Iron Duke* was completed with torpedo nets, but they were removed after her trials and were not fitted in her sister ships. Wartime alterations to the ships included the addition of extra protective plating over the magazines, enlarged foretop and bridgework, searchlight towers on the second funnel, and aircraft platforms on B and Q turrets. Mainmasts were added in the early 1920s.

Iron Duke became flagship of the Home Fleet in August 1914 and then flagship of Commander-in-Chief of the Grand Fleet, Admiral Sir John Jellicoe, on the outbreak of war. Her sisters were with the 1st and 4th Battle Squadrons until 1917, when all four ships joined the 1st Battle Squadron, *Iron Duke* having been relieved as fleet flagship by *Queen Elizabeth.* All four saw action at the Battle of Jutland (Skagerrak) on May 31, 1916, but the only one to be damaged was *Marlborough.* She was hit amidships by a torpedo which blew a hole 21 m (70 ft) long and 6 m (20 ft) deep in her side, but kept her place in the line and did not leave the battle fleet until the following morning. She spent three months in dockyard hands being repaired.

In 1919 the class transferred to the Mediterranean Fleet and spent several months in the Black Sea in support of the White Russians. In 1926 the class transferred to the Atlantic Fleet where they remained until 1929.

Under the terms of the first London naval treaty of 1930, *Benbow* and *Marlborough* were sold for scrap. *Emperor of India* was sunk as a target near Owers Bank off the Norfolk Coast and was later raised and scrapped. *Iron Duke* was saved from the breakers by conversion to a gunnery training ship. To meet the terms of the treaty she had to be demilitarized, B and Y turrets, the conning tower, side armour, torpedo tubes and some of her boilers were removed.

During the Second World War *Iron Duke* served as a depot ship. She was bombed and damaged at Scapa Flow in October 1939 and had to be beached, but continued in service until the end of the war. She was sold for scrap in 1946.

Displacement: 25 000 tons (load), 29 500 tons (deep) *Length:* 189.8 m (622 ft 9 in) oa *Beam:* 27.4 m (90 ft) *Draught:* 8.7 m (28 ft 6 in) *Machinery:* 4-shaft direct-drive steam turbines, 29 000 shp=21 knots *Protection:* 305 mm (12 in) belt, 280 mm (11 in) turrets, 64-25 mm (2.5-1 in) decks *Armament:* 10 13.5-in (343-mm) (5×2); 12 6-in (152-mm) (12×1); 2 3-in (76-mm) AA (2×1); 4 21-in (53-cm) torpedo tubes (submerged) *Crew:* 925

Iroquois

Canadian destroyer class. In December 1964 the Canadian minister of national defence announced that four helicopter-carrying destroyers (DDHs) would be built as part of a

National Maritime Museum

Above: **HMS *Iron Duke* entering harbour. *Below:* The *Iron Duke* bombarding Bolshevik positions in 1919 at Kaffa Bay on the Black Sea during the War of Intervention**

IWM

Above and Below: **HMCS *Huron*, an *Iroquois* Class destroyer. Her split funnels are designed to vent gas turbine fumes away from the radar array on the lattice foremast**

PPL

***Above:* HMCS *Iroquois* seen from one of her Sea King CHSS-2 helicopters, with the second flying astern to port. *Below:* The *Iroquois* fires a Sea Sparrow missile during a high-speed turn to starboard while on an exercise in the Caribbean in the summer of 1976**

Canadian Forces Photo

five-year programme to re-equip the Canadian forces. Although based on experience with the US *Annapolis* Class the new ships were to be much bigger, primarily in order to allow them to operate two Sea King CHSS-2 helicopters, and to have a surface-to-air missile defence. The decision to have a hangar and facilities for two Sea Kings was the most ambitious application of helicopters to small warships, which would give the new DDH-280 Class an unrivalled flexibility in anti-submarine operations. Experience in the *Annapolis* Class had shown that the big helicopter was invaluable to A/S work, and a second machine would reduce the number of occasions on which essential maintenance prevents flying.

The design grew in complexity, and rapidly outstripped the original *Annapolis* design. Gas turbines replaced the steam plant, and a special launching system for the Raytheon Mark 3 Sea Sparrow missiles had to be designed. The Italian OTO-Melara 127-mm (5-in)/54-cal gun was adopted, in a single mounting forward, with the Dutch M22 weapon-system control and radar, Canadian sonar, and US Navy torpedo tubes, Sea Sparrow missiles and gas turbines. The Sea Sparrow launching system in the forward superstructure is unique, as the missiles are swung out on extending arms, and then were reversed to face forward before firing.

Only four ships were built: *Iroquois* (DDH.280) and *Huron* (DDH.281), both by Marine Industries at Sorel, Quebec; *Athabaskan* (DDH.282) and *Algonquin* (DDH.283) by Davie Shipbuilding, Lauzon, Quebec. The names commemorate previous Canadian destroyers.

The ships are unusual in appearance, with a split, angled funnel to carry the gas-turbine exhaust away from the radar arrays on the lattice foremast. Being designed for ocean escort they have very high freeboard, with a full-width double hangar amidships to leave maximum space for the flight deck. The Canadian Beartrap hauldown device is fitted, an essential requirement for handling the big Sea Kings on what is still a small warship. Internally they are very spacious ships, and they are specially equipped to operate in Arctic conditions. They have passive flume-stabilizers in place of the fin type.

Displacement: 3550 tons (light), 4200 tons (full load) *Length:* 129.8 m (426 ft) oa *Beam:* 15.2 m (50 ft) *Draught:* 4.4 m (14 ft 6 in) *Machinery:* 2-shaft gas turbines, 50 000 shp=29 knots *Armament:* 1 127-mm (5-in)/54-cal; 2 quadruple Sea Sparrow Mk 3 SAMs; 1 Limbo Mk 10 mortar; 6 12.75-in (32.4-cm) torpedo tubes (2×3) *Aircraft:* 2 Sea King helicopters *Crew:* 254+40 for air unit

Iroquois, Bell UH-1

US multipurpose helicopter. Notwithstanding the production for the US services of several hundred armed helicopters whose official name is HueyCobra (and which share the basic H-1 designation), to most US servicemen the nickname Huey indicates the older, larger and far more numerous UH-1, the official name of which is Iroquois. To date, Bell has built a grand total of some 23 000 helicopters of all shapes and sizes, and it is a fairly safe estimate that more than 10 000 of these are members of the Iroquois family, a greater production total than any other military aircraft since the Second World War. The Iroquois has been in continuous production since 1959, after winning a June 1955 US Army competition for a utility/aeromedical/training helicopter as the Bell Model 204. The original three prototypes, designated XH-40, were ordered in 1955 and were powered by a 700-shp Lycoming T53-L-1 turboshaft engine. Later models have been developed with more than twice the power and carrying capacity, including more than 6000 of the Model 205.

The first XH-40 (55-4459) flew on October 22, 1956, but army and air force evaluation was conducted with six YH-40s which had 770-shp T53-L-1A engines and cabins which were 0.3 m (12 in) longer. Deliveries began on June 30, 1959, with the first of nine similarly powered HU-1s for the US Navy, and were followed by 183 examples of the HU-1A, including 14 equipped with dual controls and blind-flying panels for instrument training. (The HU designation, from which the Huey got its nickname, signified Helicopter, Utility. Under the triservice system introduced in 1962 it was reversed to become UH.) Deliveries of HU-1As were completed by March 1961, this version carrying six passengers and having a 770-shp T53-L-1A engine. It was used for casualty evacuation duties in Alaska, Europe and Korea, and 13 used in Vietnam were armed with two 0.30-in (7.62-mm) machine-guns and 16 2.75-in (7-cm) unguided air-to-surface rockets.

The HU-1A was followed by four YHU-1Bs with 13.41-m (44-ft) diameter redesigned rotor blades, 960-shp T53-L-5 engines, and an enlarged cabin for seven passengers, three stretchers (plus two sitting casualties and a medical attendant), or 1360 kg (3000 lb) of cargo, in addition to a two-man crew. Production of this model subsequently topped 1100, later batches having uprated 1100-shp T53-L-11 engines. In the late autumn of 1962, armed UH-1Bs (as they were now designated) became operational in Vietnam. Various weapon combinations were used, but the principal installation comprised a pair of movable 0.30-in (7.62-mm) M-60 machine-guns in each side of the cabin, firing out through the slide-back side doors, and a pack of 24 unguided 2.75-in (7-cm) HVAR rockets mounted externally on each side of the cabin. The US Army successor to the UH-1B, from September 1965, was the UH-1C, with extra fuel tankage and the T53-L-11 engine driving a new Bell 'door-hinge' rotor. Only a small batch was built, the UH-1C itself being overtaken by the AH-1G HueyCobra. (HueyCobra variants to date account for the designations AH-1G/J/Q/S/T in the H-1 series.)

Iroquois, Bell UH-1

A Bell UH-1H Iroquois helicopter comes in to land during training in the United States. The Iroquois, universally known as the Huey in the US Army, has proved a versatile, tough and popular helicopter in active service in Vietnam from 1962 to the close of US involvement and subsequently with South Vietnamese forces. It is capable of lifting seven loaded passengers and a four-man crew. Airmobile tactics in Vietnam produced an effective combination of troop-carrying 'Slicks' with armed 'Gunships' which gave fire support for infantry assaults

Bell Helicopters

Iroquois, Bell UH-1

Variants of the Bell Model 204 continued with the UH-1E assault model for the US Marine Corps, similar to the B and C but with an external rescue hoist in addition to the gun and rocket armament. Deliveries, to Marine Air Group 26, began in February 1964, and totalled 250, plus 20 examples of a TH-1E model for training.

The US Air Force ordered 146 examples of the UH-1F in 1963, with 14.63-m (48-ft) rotors and a change of engine to the 1100-shp General Electric T58-GE-3. The first UH-1F flew on February 20, 1964, and deliveries started in the following September for support duties at Air Force missile sites in the US. Some UH-1Fs were converted to, or built as, UH-1Ps, and deployed in Vietnam for 'sky-shouting' psychological warfare missions. A small number of TH-1F instrument and hoist trainers were also completed.

Other Bell Model 204 variants included three for the US Navy. The 27 HH-1Ks were built for air-sea rescue duties; 90 were completed as TH-1L Seawolf training helicopters; and eight others as UH-1L utility models.

The UH-1M was an Army variant, more than 80 of which were converted from UH-1Cs or built as new, and was operational in Vietnam from late 1969. It carried an INFANT (Iroquois night fighter and night tracker) system, comprising low-light TV and a searchlight, plus an XM-21 gun, all of Hughes manufacture.

Meanwhile Bell had developed the Model 205, with 1100-shp Lycoming T53-L-11 engine, 14.63-m (48-ft) rotor, and an enlarged cabin for 12-14 people. As the UH-1D (well over 1800 built), this became the real workhorse Army helicopter in Vietnam from 1963 onwards, partly for armed patrol and escort but chiefly as a troop carrier or as a casualty evacuation helicopter, carrying up to six stretchers. It was followed into production from September 1967 by the most prolific Iroquois model of all, the UH-1H, of which well over 4000 have been built to date. It is generally similar to the D, but is powered by a 1400-shp T53-L-13 turboshaft. The USAF has 30 similar HH-1Hs, with external hoist, for local base rescue duties.

Military exports of the Bell 204/205 series from US production have been relatively few, including small batches of UH-1Bs and Ds for Australia (Air Force and Navy) and Norway, and UH-1Hs for Canada and New Zealand. Foreign licence production, however, has been considerable. Since 1962, Fuji has built 90 UH-1Bs and about 50 UH-1Hs for the Japanese defence force, in addition to civil production; Dornier built 352 UH-1Ds for the West German army; and the AIDC in Taiwan has produced 118 UH-1Hs for the Nationalist Chinese army. The Agusta group in Italy has built a special AB 204AS antisubmarine version for the Italian navy and many hundreds of standard military 204/205s (some with Rolls-Royce Gnome engines) for Austria, Ethiopia, Greece, Iran, Kuwait, Morocco, the Netherlands, Oman, Saudi Arabia, Spain, Sweden, Turkey, the United Arab Emirates, and Zambia.

Nor is this the end of the Iroquois story. To meet, initially, a Canadian armed forces requirement, Bell combined the UH-1H airframe with a Pratt & Whitney (Canada) T400-CP-400 twin-turboshaft 1530-shp powerpack to produce the UH-1N (Bell Model 212), of which the CAF ordered 50 (their designation is CH-135). Three hundred were ordered by the US Air Force (79) and Navy/Marine Corps (221) initially; further US orders followed, and Agusta is building both the 212 and its own antisubmarine AB 212ASW for the Italian, Turkish and several South American navies. Latest development is the Bell 214A, a larger and more powerful 212 with a single 2930-shp Lycoming LTC4B-8D turboshaft. Iran has ordered more than 300 214As, under the name Isfahan, and is planning to build under licence 350 more of a special 214ST hot-climate version with twin 1625-shp T700-GE-TIC engines during the late 1970s-early 1980s.

(UH-1B) *Rotor diameter:* 13.41 m (44 ft) *Fuselage length:* 12.08 m (39 ft 8 in) *Gross weight:* 3855 kg (8500 lb) *Maximum speed:* 237 km/h (147 mph)

(UH-1D) *Rotor diameter:* 14.63 m (48 ft) *Fuselage length:* 12.77 m (41 ft 11 in) *Gross weight:* 4310 kg (9500 lb) *Maximum speed:* 222 km/h (138 mph)

(UH-1H) *Rotor diameter:* 14.63 m (48 ft) *Fuselage length:* 12.77 m (41 ft 11 in) *Gross weight:* 4310 kg (9500 lb) *Maximum speed:* 204 km/h (127 mph)

(AB 212ASW) *Rotor diameter:* 14.63 m (48 ft) *Fuselage length:* 14.02 m (46 ft) *Gross weight:* 5081 kg (11 202 lb) *Maximum cruising speed:* 204 km/h (127 mph)

(Iranian 214ST) *Rotor diameter:* 15.85 m (52 ft) *Fuselage length:* approx 14.94 m (49 ft) *Gross weight:* 7030 kg (15 500 lb) *Maximum cruising speed:* approx 241 km/h (150 mph)

Irving Allied code-name for Nakajima J1N Japanese reconnaissance and attack See **J1N**

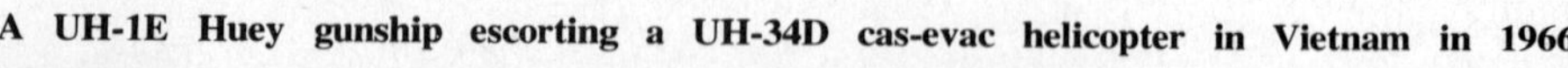

A UH-1E Huey gunship escorting a UH-34D cas-evac helicopter in Vietnam in 1966

US Marine Corps

The Iroquois has been widely exported in many variants. Customers include Austria, Germany, Ethiopia, Greece, Iran, the Netherlands, Saudi Arabia, Spain, Sweden, Turkey, the United Arab Emirates and Zambia, where the Iroquois has been deployed in both civil and military roles

Isaac Peral

Spanish submarine, built 1916. Very similar to but larger than the British *H.1* Class, *Isaac Peral* was built by Bethlehem Steel's Fore River yard to their standard design. After an undistinguished career she was reduced to a hulk in the 1920s, and remained for many years at Cartagena under the name *A0*, where she was used for training mechanics.

Displacement: 488/750 tons (surfaced/submerged) *Length:* 60 m (197 ft) pp *Beam:* 5.8 m (19 ft) *Draught:* 3.4 m (11 ft) *Machinery:* 2-shaft diesel/electric, 600 bhp/1200 shp=15/10 knots (surfaced/submerged) *Armament:* 4 18-in (46-cm) torpedo tubes (bow); 1 3-in (76-mm) AA *Crew:* 32

The Spanish submarine *Isaac Peral*, built in 1916 and used mainly as a training vessel

IWM

Ise

Japanese battleship class. With the European powers and the US rapidly expanding their battle fleets with modern Dreadnoughts it was only natural that Japan, the other major naval power in the Far East, should do likewise. So under the 1912 Emergency Expansion Programme, planned in response to the possibility of a war in Europe spreading to the Far East, Japan laid down two new Dreadnoughts, the *Ise* and *Hyuga*.

The design was basically an improved *Fuso* type with the siting of the main armament and machinery rearranged. The machinery was concentrated amidships so that the two centre turrets (C and D) and their magazines could be grouped together aft of the machinery spaces with C turret superimposed on D. (In *Fuso* C and D turrets were split fore and aft of the after boiler and engine room.) By concentrating the armament in this way the restricted arc of fire of C and D turrets in *Fuso* was increased in *Ise* to bear forward to within 30° of the keel line (it was 36° in *Fuso*); C turret could bear aft to within 15° of the keel line and D to within 30° (both turrets could only bear aft to within 31° on *Fuso*). Even more important than the improvement in the arc of fire was the resulting improvement in the fire control. The secondary guns were sited further forward than in *Fuso* and the calibre reduced from 6-in (152-mm) to 5.5-in (140-mm) and the number of casemated guns raised from 16 to 20.

During a refit carried out during the early 1930s a new towering bridge structure was built in place of the original tripod foremast, a new searchlight platform added around the after funnel and a distinctive cowl smoke deflector capped the forefunnel. A floatplane was housed aft and launched from atop X turret. During the refit two of the casemate guns were removed and the 3-in (76-mm) AA replaced by four twin 5-in (127-mm) AA mounts.

Along with many other units of the Japanese navy these two battleships were completely modernized during the middle to late 1930s, being fully reboilered (eight oil-fired boilers replacing the original 24 mixed-firing boilers) and re-engined. The reduction in the number of boiler rooms enabled the forefunnel to be removed. The stern was rebuilt to a new design. The armament was also modernized, the maximum elevation of the 14-in (356-mm) guns being increased from 15° to 43° and that of the 5.5-in (140-mm) from 20° to 30°. Two more 5.5-in (140-mm) were removed and 20 light 25-mm (1-in) AA added on *Ise* and 40-mm (1.57-in) and 13-mm (0.51-in) AA added on *Hyuga*, which were subsequently replaced by 20 25-mm (1-in) in 1940. A new catapult was added on the quarterdeck and more modern seaplanes carried. All the extra equipment and more modern armament required improved command facilities and modern gunnery fire-control equipment, which resulted in the bridge structure being enlarged. The modernization resulted in an increase in the displacement by 7000 tons and in the overall length by 7.6 m (25 ft).

Following the heavy carrier losses at Midway the ships were converted to carriers.

See also *Hyuga*.

Name	laid down	launched	completed
Ise	5/15	11/16	12/17
Hyuga	5/15	1/17	4/18

(As completed) *Displacement:* 29 990 tons (normal), 36 500 tons (full load) *Length:* 208.2 m (683 ft) oa *Beam:* 28.7 m (94 ft) *Draught:* 8.8 m (29 ft) *Machinery:* 4-shaft geared turbines 45 000 shp=23 knots *Protection:* 305-102 mm (12-4 in) main belt, 64-32 mm (2.5-1.5 in) deck, 305-203 mm (12-8 in) turrets, 305 mm (12 in) barbettes, 305-152 mm (12-6 in) conning tower, 152 mm (6 in) casemates *Armament:* 12 14-in (356-mm) (6×2); 20 5.5-in (140-mm) (20×1); 4 3-in (76-mm) AA; 6 21-in (53-cm) torpedo tubes (submerged) *Crew:* 1360

(As modernized 1934-37) *Displacement:* 36 000 tons (standard) *Length:* 215.8 m (708 ft) oa *Beam:* 33.8 m (111 ft) *Draught:* 9.1 m (30 ft) *Machinery:* 4-shaft geared turbines, 80 825 shp=25.3 knots *Protection:* As completed *Armament:* 12 14-in (356-mm); 16 5.5-in (140-mm); 8 5-in (127-mm) AA (4×2); 20 25-mm (1-in) AA; 3 aircraft *Crew:* 1376

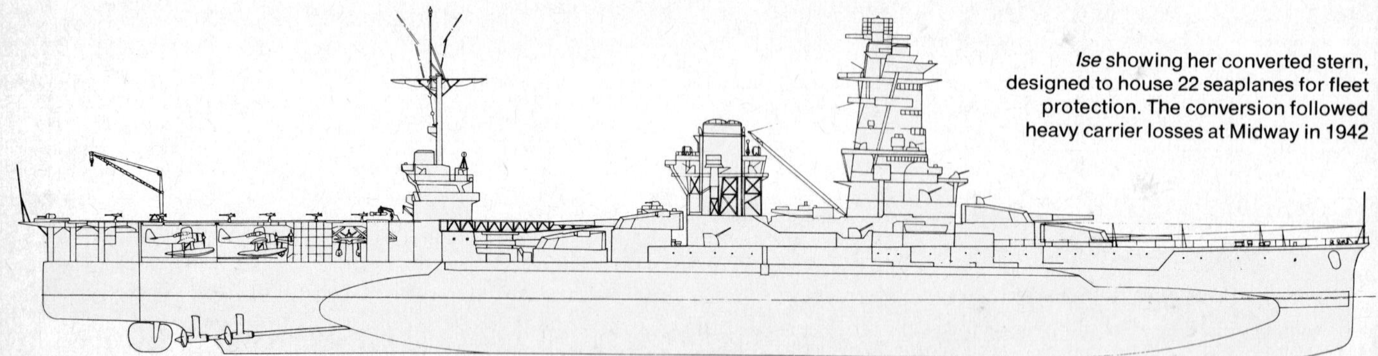

Ise showing her converted stern, designed to house 22 seaplanes for fleet protection. The conversion followed heavy carrier losses at Midway in 1942

Ise **after her conversion to a carrier battleship, underway on August 24, 1943 off Sata Point, Japan. She was sunk by US aircraft on July 28, 1945**

US Navy

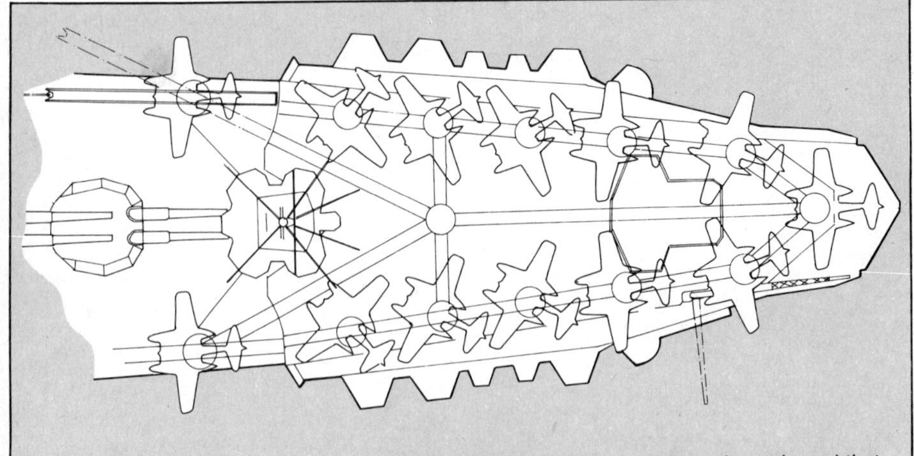
The layout of the stern deck of *Ise* showing part of the seaplane stowage. It was hoped that all 22 aircraft could be launched in 20 minutes from catapults and recovered by crane when they landed alongside their parent ship. In the end no aircraft were used in combat because there were insufficient pilots. The catapults were subsequently removed

Iskra, PZL-Mielec TS-11

Polish trainer/light ground-attack aircraft. Design work on this two-seat all-metal cantilever mid-wing monoplane with retractable undercarriage was completed by late 1958. It flew for the first time on February 5, 1960, powered by an 800-kg (1764-lb) st HO-10 Polish-designed turbojet engine mounted in the fuselage, aft of the cockpit. The fuel capacity is 1200 litres (264 Imp gal).

Production commenced in November 1962 with ten preproduction aircraft, and deliveries to the Polskie Lotnictwo Wojskowe (Polish air force) began in March 1963. It entered series production later that year and by the end of 1965 was in service with most Polish training units. The powerplant was changed on later models to the 1000-kg (2205-lb) st SO-3 turbojet. The cockpit carries the crew of two in tandem, and is fully pressurized and fitted with ejector seats.

Designated Iskra 100, the single-seat version for ground-attack duties was introduced in 1972. This carries an armament of one forward-firing 23-mm (0.90-in) cannon in the nose on the starboard side, an S-13 gun camera, and four underwing attachments for 100-kg (220-lb) bombs, eight-rocket pods or 7.62-mm (0.30-in) gun pods. The Iskra 200 or 200SB armament trainer appeared in 1975.

Several hundred TS-11s have been built, and production of all three variants was still in progress in 1978. Fifty Iskra 100s went to the Indian government in 1975-76.

(TS-11) *Span:* 10.06 m (33 ft) *Length:* 11.10 m (36 ft 5 in) *Gross weight:* 3840 kg (8466 lb) *Maximum speed:* 720 km/h (447 mph)

Israel Aircraft Industries Israeli aircraft
See **Arava, Kfir, Nesher, Westwind**

Israel Aircraft Industries Israeli missiles
See **Gabriel**

Italia

Italian coast defence ship, built 1876-85. She and her sister *Lepanto* had been two of the most outstanding capital ships of their day, but both were obsolete by 1914. *Lepanto* was struck off the Navy List in January 1914, and her sister followed her four months later. However, *Italia* was reprieved by the outbreak of the war in April 1915 and was towed by the battleship *Ammiraglio di St Bon* to Brindisi, where she served as a floating battery in the outer harbour. She was formally reinstated on the Navy List in May 1915 and served at Brindisi until the end of 1917. She then left for La Spezia, where she was converted to a grain carrier with only a light armament of two 4.7-in (120-mm) guns. She was laid up in January 1921 and was stricken later that year and scrapped.

Displacement: 13 898 tonnes (normal) *Length:* 124.7 m (409 ft 2 in) oa *Beam:* 24.42 m (80 ft 1 in) *Draught:* 9.12 m (29 ft 11 in) *Machinery:* 2-shaft compound reciprocating steam, 11 900 ihp=9 knots (by 1915) *Protection:* 120 mm (4.7 in) deck, 480 mm (18.9 in) citadel *Armament:* (As guardship) 3 17-in (432-mm)/26-cal Model C; 1 17-in (432-mm)/27-cal Model B (2×2); 7 150-mm (5.9-in)/26-cal (7×1); 4 4.7-in (120-mm)/23-cal (4×1); 12 57-mm (2.24-in)/40-cal QF (12×1); 2 37-mm (1.46-in)/25-cal QF (2×1); 4 machine-guns; 4 14-in (36-cm) torpedo tubes (beam) *Crew:* 701

Itsukushima

Japanese minelayer. *Itsukushima* was ordered under the 1923 Programme for long-range minelaying operations with a radius of 5000 nautical miles at 16 knots and a bunkerage of 300 tons of oil. The design was for a medium-sized vessel, with a fairly heavy defensive armament of three 5.5-in (140-mm) guns.

To conserve oil consumption and extend the radius of action the design specification stipulated the fitting of diesel engines.

Ise and *Hyuga* in the background with sisters *Nagato* and *Kirishima* before the Second World War. Only *Nagato* survived the war, and she was sunk at Bikini in 1946

She was laid down on February 2, 1928, launched on May 22, 1929, and completed on December 26, 1929. This was the first time that a ship of the Japanese navy had relied solely on diesel engines for propulsion, and in this respect *Itsukushima* was treated very largely as an experimental vessel. The exhaustive trials she carried out provided valuable data from which the Japanese drew conclusions concerning their plans for future large naval units powered solely by diesel engines.

Being designed for independent minelaying operations at long range, *Itsukushima* was provided with extensive mine-storage facilities, four mine rails extending from just aft of the bridge to two trapdoors at the stern. For practice minelaying operations, dummy mines could be retrieved over the bows and run back to the mine hold on rails sited to starboard on the forecastle.

She was rearmed in 1944, the 3-in (76-mm) AA being replaced by three 25-mm (1-in) AA and six 13-mm (0.51-in) AA. A new standard mine had been designed by the Japanese and 400 of these new mines could be stored in the large mine hold. *Itsukushima* was torpedoed and sunk by the Dutch submarine *Zwaardvisch* in the Java Sea on October 17, 1944.

Displacement: 1970 tons (standard), 2408 tons (full load) *Length:* 104 m (341 ft 3 in).wl *Beam:* 11.8 m (38 ft 9 in). *Draught:* 3.2 m (10 ft 6 in) *Machinery:* 3-shaft diesels, 3000 bhp=17 knots *Armament:* 3 5.5-in (140-mm); 2 3-in (76-mm) AA; 250-500 mines *Crew:* 235

Iver Hvitfeldt

Danish coast-defence ship. *Iver Hvitfeldt* was built at the Royal Dockyard, Copenhagen and was completed in 1887. She was the first Danish ship to have guns mounted in barbettes, rather than the old-fashioned turrets. She was a typical low-freeboard ship of the type favoured by Scandinavian navies, with two Krupp 260-mm (10.2-in) guns in single mountings, and four 120-mm (4.7-in) guns on each side of the flush deck amidships. She was fitted with antitorpedo nets.

She was partially modernized in 1898-99, but was badly damaged by fire in 1904. During repairs in 1905-07 the 120-mm (4.7-in) guns were replaced by 57-mm (2.24-in) QF guns. She was immediately put into reserve, where she remained until 1919 when she was stricken and scrapped.

Displacement: 3290 tons (normal) *Length:* 73.9 m (242 ft 5 in) pp *Beam:* 15 m (49 ft 3 in) *Draught:* 5.6 m (18 ft 4 in) *Machinery:* 2-shaft reciprocating steam, 5100 ihp=15.5 knots *Protection:* 292 mm (11.5 in) belt, 216 mm (8.5 in) turrets, 53 mm (2.1 in) deck, 115 mm (4.5 in) conning tower *Armament:* 2 260-mm (10.2-in) (2×1); 4 120-mm (4.7-in) (4×1); 2 57-mm (2.24-in) QF (2×1); 8 37-mm (1.46-in) QF (8×1); 3 38-cm (15-in) torpedo tubes (1 submerged, 2 above water) *Crew:* 265

IVL Finnish aircraft See **Myrsky**

Iwami Japanese battleship See ***Borodino***

Iwo Jima

US amphibious assault ship class, built 1960-68. *Iwo Jima*, authorized in FY 1958 was the first ship in the world to be designed and built specifically for helicopter operations. The design was prepared following the ill-fated Suez operation of 1956, during which a helicopter-borne commando assault was carried out from two small carriers lying offshore.

The amphibious capability of the *Iwo Jima* Class is based around a Marine battalion landing team and its supporting arms of guns, vehicles, equipment and supporting personnel, with sufficient helicopter capacity to provide complete mobility for the force. Being designed to carry out an amphibious assault, the ships are equipped with extensive medical facilities, including a fully equipped hospital.

The flight-deck area provides sufficient space for either seven Sea Knight or four Sea Stallion helicopters to carry out all forms of helicopter operation, while the hangar area below can house either 19 Sea Knight or 11 Sea Stallion helicopters. Being designed solely for helicopter operations there are no catapults or arrestor wires on the deck, and there is no angled deck and no landing markings for fixed-wing aircraft. Two deck-edge lifts feed the hangar, one to port amidships opposite the bridge and one to starboard aft of the island. When not in use these lifts fold up against the hull, and act as hangar doors. In addition two small elevators are provided to transport cargo from the hold or hangar to the flight deck.

Between 1970-74 the ships in the class were progressively rearmed, the port quarter and flight-deck level twin 3-in (76-mm) mountings being replaced by two BPDMS Sea Sparrow launchers. Late in 1971 *Guam* was refitted to carry out tests as an interim design for the sea control ship (SCS) concept. For this she carried 12 Harrier V/STOL aircraft and a number of Sea King antisubmarine helicopters for convoy escort duties. She reverted to her amphibious role in 1974, but retained the Harriers.

Displacement: 17 000 tons (light), 17 515-18 000 tons (full load) *Length:* 180.4 m (592 ft) oa *Beam:* 25.6 m (84 ft) *Draught:* 7.9 m (26 ft) *Machinery:* 1-shaft geared turbines, 22 000 shp=23 knots *Aircraft:* 20 helicopters *Armament:* 8 3-in (76-mm) (4×2) *Crew:* 652+1724 troops

No and name	completed
LPH-2 *Iwo Jima*	6/61
LPH-3 *Okinawa*	4/62
LPH-7 *Guadalcanal*	7/63
LPH-9 *Guam*	1/65
LPH-10 *Tripoli*	8/66
LPH-11 *New Orleans*	11/68
LPH-12 *Inchon*	6/70

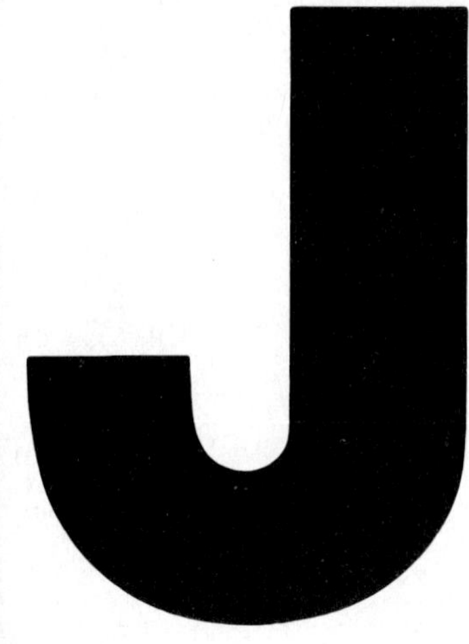

HM Submarine *J.1* after her presentation to the Royal Australian Navy in March 1919. She was sold for scrap in 1924

PPL

J.1

British submarine class. The 'J' Class were double-hull submarines developed from the 'G' Class but some 500 tons larger in order to accommodate a heavier machinery plant for high speed. They were designed primarily to counter the incorrectly reported construction by Germany of 18-knot submarines and as, at the time, the diesel engine had reached its limit in size they were provided with three 1200-hp Vickers 12-cylinder diesels instead of the more usual two.

Their designed surface speed was 19.5 knots and at the time of their completion during 1916-17 they were the fastest submarines in the world. It was hoped that this high speed would enable them to operate with the main fleet but they were never so employed which, considering the later experience with the 'K' Class, was fortunate. They also had high endurance (6400 km [4000 miles] at 12 knots) and were equipped with long-range wireless for reconnaissance in enemy waters. As completed the casing was stopped short of the bow but several had this extended forward while the gun, originally mounted on the casing, was moved to a platform in front of the conning tower.

The original *J.1-J.8* were ordered in January 1915 but *J.3* and *J.4* were later cancelled and their numbers re-allocated to *J.7* and *J.8*. An additional unit, *J.7*, was ordered in May 1916 and differed from the earlier group in being 50 tons heavier and having her conning tower further aft.

On completion they joined the 11th Submarine Flotilla at Blyth and off this port, on October 15, 1918, the *J.6* was sunk in error by the decoy ship *Cymric*. The remaining boats were presented to the Royal Australian Navy in March 1919. They were sold for scrap in 1924 except *J.3* and *J.7* which were not sold until 1926 and 1929 respectively.

J.1, J.2—built by Portsmouth dockyard. *J.3, J.4*—built by Pembroke dockyard. *J.5, J.6* and *J.7*—built by Devonport dockyard.

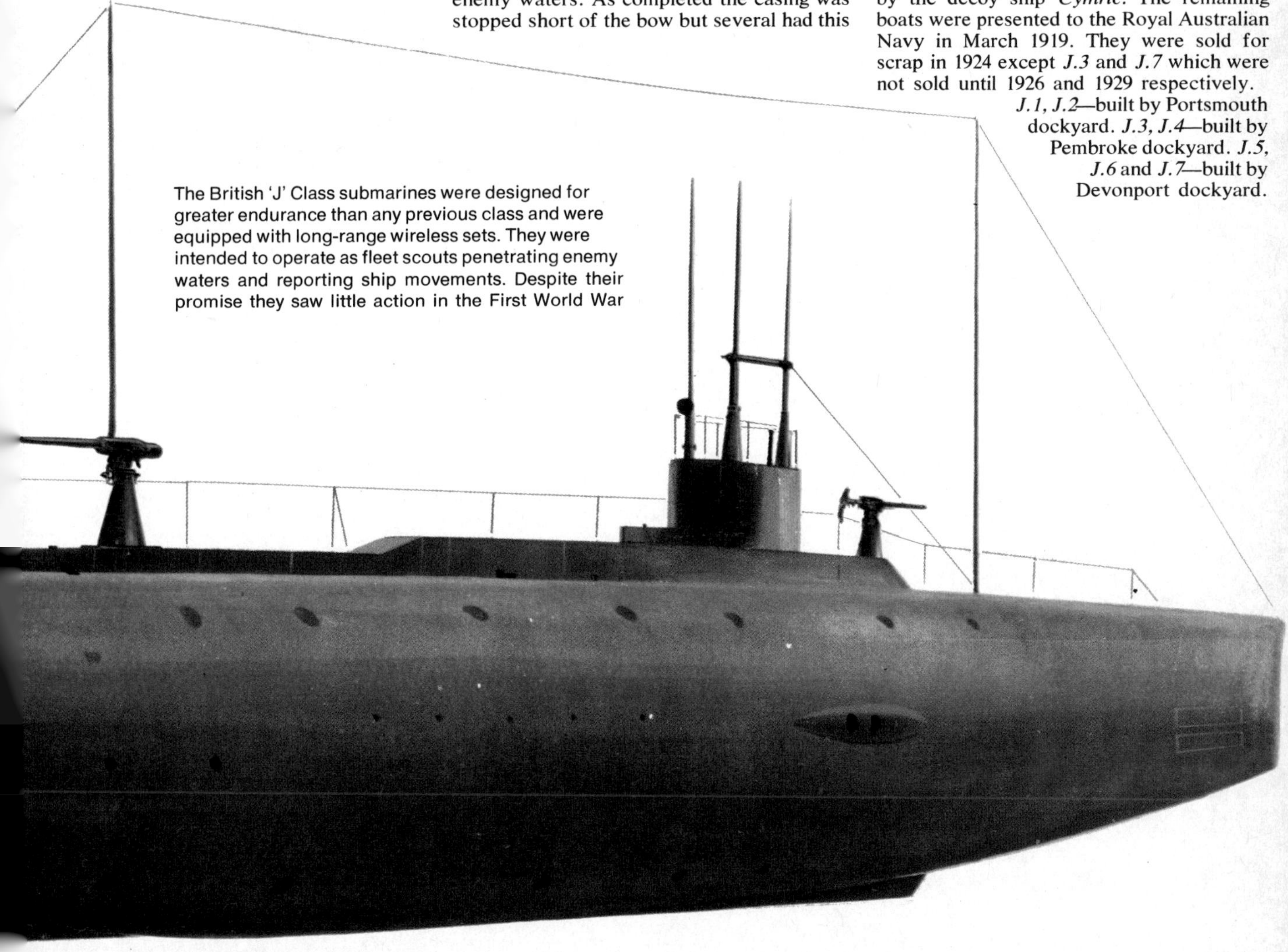

The British 'J' Class submarines were designed for greater endurance than any previous class and were equipped with long-range wireless sets. They were intended to operate as fleet scouts penetrating enemy waters and reporting ship movements. Despite their promise they saw little action in the First World War

Displacement: 1210 tons/1760 tons (surfaced/submerged) *Length:* 83.81 m (275 ft) oa *Beam:* 7.16 m (23 ft 6 in) *Draught:* 4.27 m (14 ft) *Machinery:* 3-shaft diesel/electric drive, 3600 bhp/1400 hp=19/9.5 knots (surfaced/submerged) *Armament:* 1 3-in (76-mm) AA; 6 18-in (46-cm) torpedo tubes *Crew:* 44

The British 'J' Class submarines had three-shaft diesel/electric engines which produced 3600 bhp/1400 hp. This gave them a surface running speed of 19 knots and a submerged speed of 9.5 knots—the fastest submarine class in the world at that time. The bulk of the vessels were presented to the Royal Australian Navy in March 1919

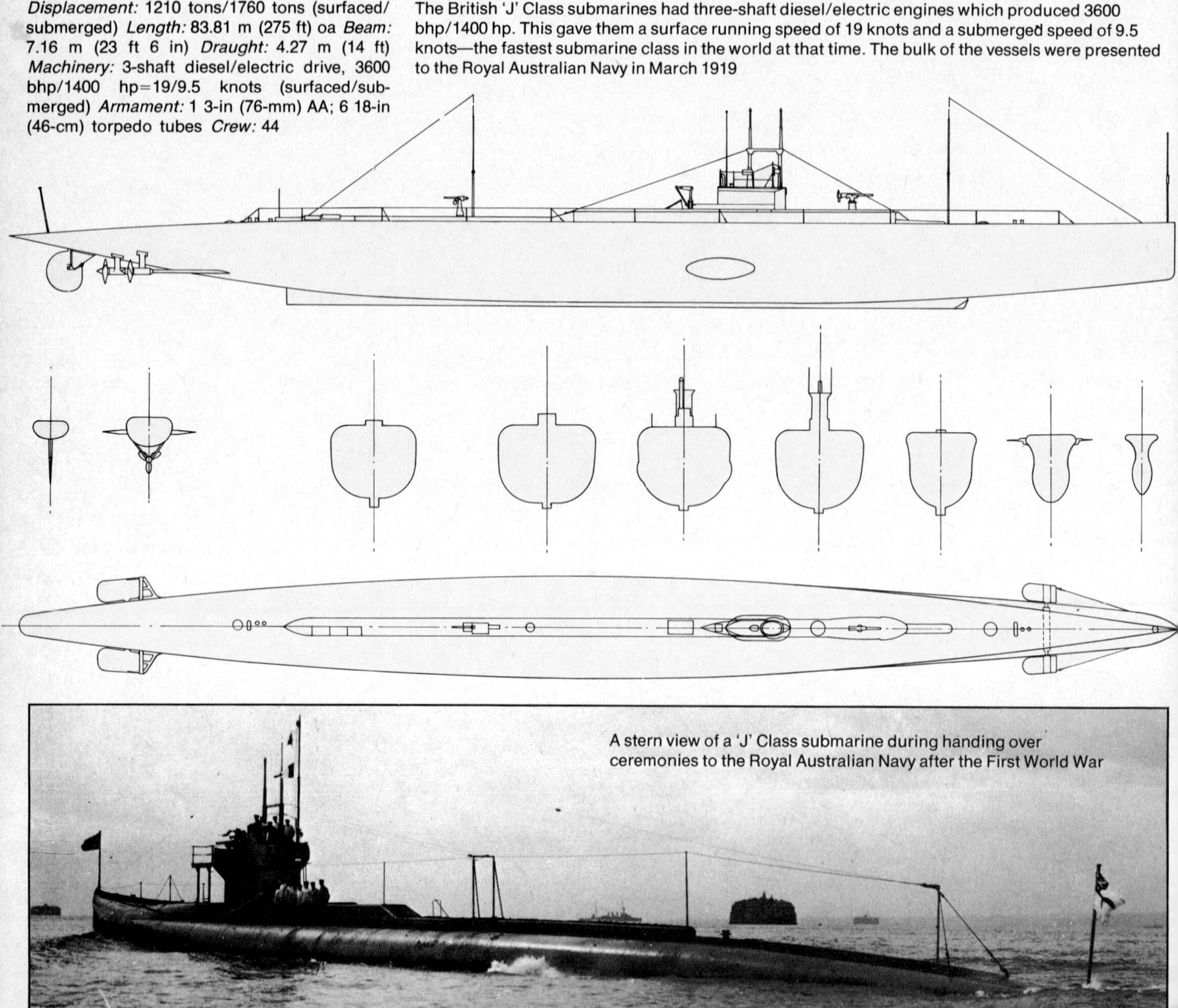

A stern view of a 'J' Class submarine during handing over ceremonies to the Royal Australian Navy after the First World War

'J' Class British destroyers See ***Javelin***

J.1, Junkers

German reconnaissance aircraft. Evolved as a close-support aircraft for the German front-line infantry, the Junkers J.1 was designed by Dr Hugo Junkers in 1917 to embody his personal belief in the use of metal instead of fabric as the best form of structural skin for aeroplanes. In 1915 Junkers had produced the original J.1 (the factory designation for the officially titled E.1), a neat, all-metal monoplane scout of cantilever-wing design.

Impressed with Junkers' constructional standards and ideas, the German authorities asked him in 1917 to design an armoured biplane to replace the more traditionally built two-seaters then in use as tactical reconnaissance machines. The resulting J.1 (its factory title was J.4) emerged in October 1917 as an angular, yet highly functional design. Employing large cantilever wings, the J.1's fuselage was hexagonal in cross-section, and incorporated a completely armoured nose capsule of 5-mm (0.2-in) chrome-nickel sheet steel to protect the crew cockpits and engine. Both wings were constructed of Dural framework covered by 2-mm (0.08-in) Dural skin, and interplane struts were neatly placed close to the fuselage. It was powered by a 200-hp Benz Bz IV six-cylinder in-line water-cooled engine.

Inevitably the finished design was relatively heavy—the nose capsule alone weighed 470 kg (1036 lb)—and needed a lengthy takeoff run and strong control once airborne. But against these disadvantages was set the near-immunity from ground fire enjoyed by the crew when flying at the necessary low level required to accomplish the aircraft's prime role.

Normal armament comprised two synchronized 7.92-mm (0.312-in) Spandau LMG/08 machine-guns, together with a ring-mounted 7.92-mm (0.312-in) Parabellum machine-gun operated by the observer. In addition, J.1s often carried radio equipment for direct contact with the infantry commanders. It was, however, not uncommon for J.1s to fly pure supply sorties, dropping food and ammunition to isolated forward positions. Two additional downward-firing machine-guns for trench-strafing were considered at one stage, but were never incorporated due to the impracticability of accurate sighting.

In all a total of 227 Junkers J.1s were built before the Armistice, entering front-line service from late 1917. By August 1918 a total of 189 machines were recorded as being with the first-line Infanterieflieger units along the Western Front in France and Belgium. Nicknamed *Möbelwagen* (furniture van) by its crews, the J.1 was nevertheless well liked and appreciated in operational service, in spite of the difficulties involved in landing and taking off on rough ground.

Span: (upper wing) 16 m (52 ft 6 in) *Length:* 9.1 m (29 ft 10 in) *Gross weight:* 2175 kg (4795 lb) *Maximum speed:* 156 km/h (97 mph)

The Junkers J.1 reconnaissance aircraft, nicknamed the *Möbelwagen* (furniture van) by its crews

J1N1, Nakajima Gekko

Japanese reconnaissance aircraft and night fighter. Although a failure in its original role of escort fighter, the J1N1 became one of the major Japanese combat aircraft of the Second World War. In 1938 the Imperial navy asked Mitsubishi and Nakajima to submit proposals for a long-range escort fighter able to fly at 280 knots to a range of 1300 nautical miles, or up to 2000 nautical miles with extra fuel. Mitsubishi gave up, but Nakajima's design staff under K Nakamura created an aircraft which incorporated every possible feature to overcome the inevitable handicaps of large size and poor manoeuvrability.

First flown in May 1941, the three-seat J1N1 prototype was noteworthy for its armament, which comprised two 7.7-mm (0.303-in) Type 97 machine-guns and a 20-mm (0.79-in) Type 99 cannon firing ahead, and two remotely sighted rear barbettes, aimed by the navigator, each with two Type 97s. Constructed entirely of metal, apart from fabric-covered control surfaces, the new fighter had long leading-edge slats and slotted flaps that opened to 15° for combat, giving excellent manoeuvrability. This was, however, marred by annoying aileron buffeting, and airframe vibration at high angles of attack (as in tight manoeuvres). The rear barbettes were a very advanced scheme, more complex than those of the contemporary Me 210, but they too suffered from mechanical problems which, together with the buffeting and vibration difficulties, led the navy to abandon any immediate plans for the J1N1.

In July 1942, however, after continued flight development, the navy ordered the J1N1-C as a three-seat reconnaissance aircraft. By this time the vibration problem had been solved, and the troublesome rear armament was removed. Unlike the prototype, which had 'handed' engines, the -C had two identical 1130-hp Nakajima Sakae 21 radials, both turning clockwise (seen from behind). As the Type 2 Model 11 reconnaissance aircraft it went into combat service in the Solomons and other Pacific theatres, receiving the Allied codename Irving. It was strange that a reconnaissance aircraft should have powerful nose armament but be without defence to the rear, but it was nevertheless well-liked.

In any case it was soon to find a new role. The navy urgently needed a high-performance night fighter capable of intercepting such Allied bombers as the B-17 and B-24, and one J1N1 fighter model was flying in Japan by the winter of 1942-43. This was the J1N1-F, with one of the three crew members operating as a full-time gunner in a large manually aimed dorsal turret with a single Type 99 cannon. Credit for the most successful of the many Japanese night fighters is assigned to Commander Yasuna Kozono of the 251st Kokutai (air corps) in the New Britain area. Independently of similar armament schemes first tested at Tarnewitz in Germany, he proposed oblique cannon to fire up or down in a no-deflection shot while the fighter was formating with the hostile bomber. Eventually the J1N1-S Gekko (moonlight) night fighter Model 11 went into production at the Nakajima plant, following the principles proved in actual fighting with a number of aircraft modified in the field by the 251st Kokutai, and known as the J1N1-C-Kai.

The C-Kai was still a lumpy three-seater, with steps in the rear fuselage steps inherited from the abandoned barbettes. Above and below the fuselage, in line with the trailing edge, were two pairs of Type 99 Model II cannon, with higher rate of fire and various other improvements compared with the Model I gun. Each pair was set at an inclination of 30° (the Germans used much steeper inclinations) and either could be sighted and fired by the pilot using special periscopic sights. In some aircraft primitive radar was fitted, with a Yagi nose aerial plus two pairs of dipoles on each side of the rear fuselage. The third crew member was provided with the displays and radar-control boxes. Only a handful of C-Kai conversions were flown, but in late May 1943 two of them each destroyed a B-24 over Rabaul at night, to the surprise of the US Army.

In contrast, the J1N1-S Gekko was an optimized design, with a new streamlined fuselage seating pilot and observer only. The upper and lower pairs of cannon were installed in a neater way, weight was reduced and performance increased, despite different engine installations having exhaust-flame dampers. As far as is known, all 1-S aircraft had AI radar, an improved type with four Yagi aerials projecting from the nose and no dipoles on the rear fuselage.

Total production of the J1N1 amounted to 477, of which at least 400 probably were Gekkos. Unlike most Japanese night fighters this one was effective, and up to altitudes of around 9000 m (29 500 ft) it provided a formidable challenge to most Allied night-flying aircraft. Combat records are not readily available, but the Gekko certainly shot down many Allied bombers in a number of theatres, especially in the Pacific island campaigns. Over Japan itself, however, the Gekko proved no better than other would-be home defenders, as it could not climb to the operating altitude of the B-29, whilst beating the big bomber's speed. Gekkos were assigned to Atsugi, near Yokohama, for the defence of Kanto and Chubu prefectures, and at least two other home airfields. It remains a mystery why the inadequate performance was not improved by fitting more powerful engines.

A torpedo-carrying version of the J1N1 was proposed, but only one prototype was built and there is no record of flight trials.

One J1N1-S Gekko is preserved by the National Air and Space Museum in Washington.

Span: 16.98 m (55 ft 8 in) *Length:* 12.18 m (40 ft) *Gross weight:* 7527 kg (16594 lb) *Maximum speed:* 507 km/h (315 mph)

J2M Raiden, Mitsubishi

Japanese fighter aircraft. Until 1938 the Japanese invariably designed their fighters to have the best possible manoeuvrability and pilot view, accepting compromises in such other factors as speed, climb and firepower to achieve this objective. But in that year both the Imperial army and navy did a complete about face, and authorized work on fighters designed for the highest possible performance and, increasingly, the greatest practical firepower, even at the expense of manoeuvrability. The navy fighter was the J2M, designed by a team led by Jiro Horikoshi, creator of the Zero. Though he never regarded the J2M as a replacement for that classic fighter, or even a successor to it, he welcomed the opportunity to design an interceptor. All such aircraft had previously been the preserve of the army, as the navy fighters all had to have long range.

First flown on March 20, 1942, the J2M1 obviously sacrificed much at the altar of streamlining. The 1460-hp Mitsubishi MK4C Kasei 13 two-row engine had an extension shaft driving the VDM-licensed German propeller, to allow a finely profiled cowling with fan cooling. The remarkably small wing had laminar section and needed small combat manoeuvre flaps. The pilot's canopy, unlike the vast transparent area of the Zero, was as shallow as a racer's, and test pilots complained that forward vision was extremely limited, and distorted by the blown-plastic windscreen. Despite these measures the J2M1 did not achieve the required flight performance, and when the J2M2 flew in September 1942 it incorporated many changes including an 1820-hp Kasei 23a (MK4R-A) driving a different type of propeller with four blades, and with ejector exhaust stacks as on later Zeros. The cockpit canopy was also completely redesigned incorporating

The Mitsubishi J2M Raiden (thunderbolt) was a departure from earlier Japanese fighter specifications for manoeuvrability and pilot visibility. Like European intercepters it had a very fast steep climb and a powerful cannon armament for engaging enemy bombers

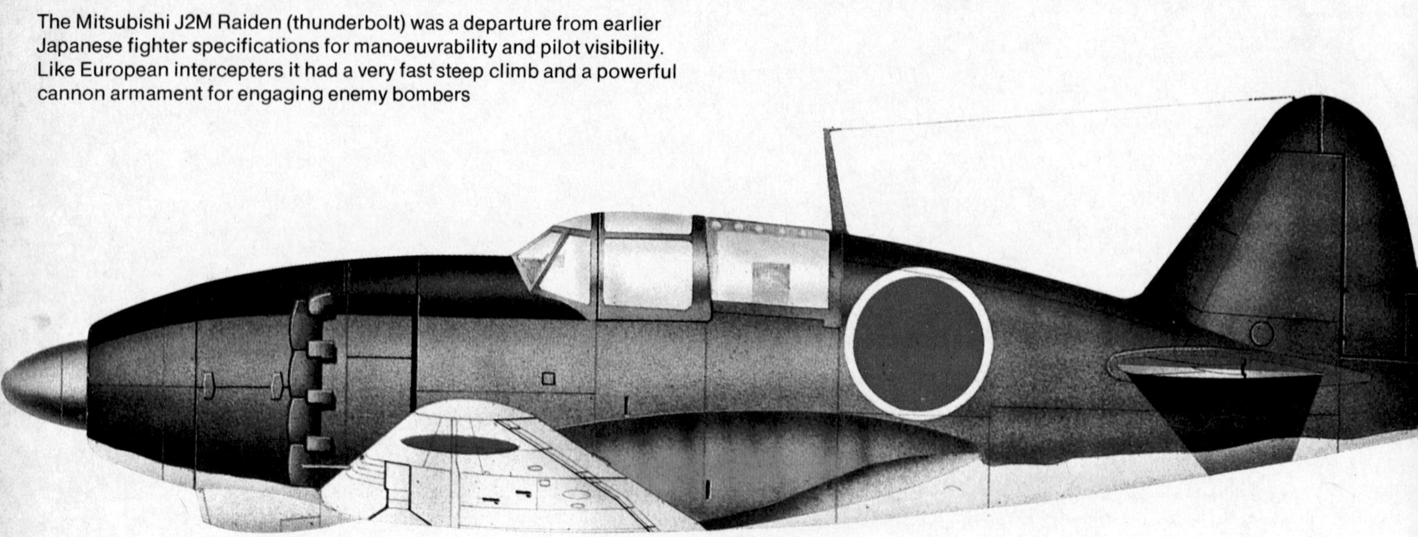

a proper windscreen some 30 cm (1 ft) higher, with flat panels of bulletproof glass.

In October 1942 the J2M2 was named Raiden (thunderbolt) and put into production. Initially 3600 were planned for delivery inside 18 months, but trouble with the design persisted. The engine and propeller vibrated badly at high power, exhaust smoke was excessive, and several aircraft broke up in the air. At least one aircraft dived into the ground after takeoff when the retracting tailwheel fouled the elevator cables. Production at the navy base at Suzuka built up slowly. and it was December 1943 before the 381st Kokutai at Toyohashi received Raidens for conversion training. Only 155 of the J2M2 Raiden 11 series were built, with armament of two 20-mm (0.79-in) Type 99-I wing cannon and two 7.7-mm (0.303-in) machine-guns above the fuselage. In June 1943 production switched to the J2M3 Raiden 21 with four wing cannon (two Type 99-I and two Type 99-II with increased rate of fire) and no fuselage guns. The J2M3a followed in January 1944 with four Type 99-II, and in June 1944 the continuing complaints about field of view were met by the J2M6 and 6a (the 6 being a modified 3 with different guns) with a bulged canopy giving a better view to the rear. Several Raidens engaged in home-defence duties were discovered in 1945 modified with one cannon firing obliquely upwards from the rear fuselage, but there is no evidence that this was for night fighting.

In August 1944 flight testing began on the J2M4 Raiden 32 with no fewer than six cannon (two in the fuselage decking) and the turbocharged MK4ru series engine, but this installation proved very troublesome and effort was soon concentrated on the more straightforward J2M5 Raiden 33, with an MK4U-A Kasei 26a which was equipped with an improved gear-driven supercharger. Armed with two cannon only, the 33 could at least intercept the B-29, but by late 1944 the Japanese aircraft industry had virtually disintegrated into chaos and very few of this type were delivered. A few of the 26a-series engines were also installed in existing Raiden 21/21a/31/31a fighters, these being redesignated J2M7 or 7a Raiden 23 or 23a. But as the engine supply was the critical factor in limiting production of new Raiden 33s the number of conversions was very small.

The navy managed to have only 480 of all models built by VJ-Day, less than the planned output for a single month, and this despite a second assembly line at Koza naval air arsenal. This exceptionally poor performance was in no way due to faults in the Raiden itself, imperfect as it was.

In service the J2M Raiden was still criticized in certain respects by its pilots, most of whom did not like so 'hot' an aircraft especially when based on rough island airstrips. But gradually the fact that the Raiden could climb about as fast as any Allied fighter, and more steeply, came to be greatly appreciated, and the firepower was usually more than adequate. This small-winged fighter first saw action at the battle of the Marianas in September 1944, receiving the Allied codename Jack. In January 1945 two Raiden 21a fighters were captured in a flyable condition by British Commonwealth air forces, and a famous photograph exists of both airborne together in ATAIU (Allied Tactical Air Intelligence Unit) markings.

In general, Allied pilots evaluated Jack as one of the best Japanese fighters, especially when used in the simple up/down day interception role. Handling was rated 'exceptional' at all speeds up to 525 km/h (326 mph), with good all-round stability, rapid roll and surprisingly good radius of turn. Despite the small wing there was no problem with high-speed stalls, and though there was little or no warning of an impending stall it was possible to recover almost instantly with little loss of height. At high speeds, however, aileron control became increasingly heavy.

Span: 10.8 m (35 ft 5 in) *Length:* 9.70 m (31 ft 10 in), (J2M5) 9.95 m (32 ft 8 in) *Gross weight:* (J2M3) 3435 kg (7573 lb) *Maximum speed:* (J2M2) 596 km/h (370 mph), (J2M3) 612 km/h (380 mph)

J8M Shusui, Mitsubishi

Japanese rocket intercepter aircraft. In 1943 the German Messerschmitt Me 163B aroused great interest in Japan, both the army and navy having no aircraft of remotely comparable performance, nor any intercepter capable of climbing to the level of the B-29 Superfortress which was known to be intended primarily for attacks on Japan. Delegations of technical staff visited the Messerschmitt AG plant at Regensburg, and the test airfields at Peenemünde and Zwischenhahn, and concluded a licence agreement for the Me 163B and its Walter HWK 109-509C-1 bifuel rocket rated at 2000 kg (4410 lb) sea-level thrust.

Mitsubishi Jukogyo KK were assigned the main production task, and a U-Boat was despatched with a dismantled Me 163B and all engineering drawings. It was sunk by the Allies en route, and all the Japanese received for an expenditure of over 50 million Reichsmark was a rocket engine and a simple instruction manual. Nevertheless, work went ahead on a copy, with army designation Ki-200 and navy designation J8M1, both receiving the name Shusui (translated variously as 'swinging sword', or 'rigorous sword'). While both services and Mitsubishi strove to create the aircraft and its Toko Ro.2 (KR-10) rocket motor, trials went ahead successfully with MXY8 Akigusa (autumn grass) gliders, first flown in December 1944. Several other unpowered or turbojet versions were under construction in 1945.

On July 7, 1945, the first Navy J8M1 took off from Yokosuka in the hands of the project pilot Toyohiko Inuzuka. The motor failed at about 400 m (1300 ft) in a steep climb and Inuzuka lost control, crashed and was killed. No other J8M or Ki-200 flew, though production was in hand by VJ-Day. Mitsubishi, Nissan and Fuji had tooled to build the J8M1 with two 30-mm (1.18-in) Type 5 cannon, and J8M2 with one cannon and extra fuel. The Ki-200 was to have had two 30-mm cannon.

(J8M1) *Span:* 9.5 m (31 ft 2 in) *Length:* 6.05 m (19 ft 10 in) *Gross weight:* 3885 kg (8565 lb) *Maximum speed:* 900 km/h (559 mph)

J9, Junkers German fighter aircraft
See **Junkers D**

J10, Junkers German fighter aircraft
See **Junkers CL**

The Saab J21, the only combat aircraft to enter service in both piston- and jet-engined versions

J21, Saab

Swedish fighter and ground-attack aircraft. This unusual pusher aircraft was probably the first to show the world-class capability of the engineers of Saab and the Royal Swedish Air Board. It was also the only production combat aircraft in history to go into service in both piston-engined and jet versions.

The Air Board issued the specification in March 1941, and design staff under Frid Wänström soon proposed a twin-boom layout using the only engine then available, the 1200-hp Twin Wasp radial. In 1942 it became clear that German Daimler-Benz DB 605B engines of 1475 hp could soon be imported, making the J21A an outstanding machine, the first prototype of which flew on July 30, 1943. One of its unique features was a Saab ejection seat, the first in the world on a production aircraft, to overcome the danger of bailing out at high speed just ahead of the propeller. Other unusual features included twin fins, slight sweepback on the wings (to give a satisfactory centre of gravity), internal wing radiators and tricycle landing gear.

The first 54 production aircraft were J21A-1 fighters with one 20-mm (0.79-in) and two 13.2-mm (0.52-in) guns in the nose, all except the first few having a licence-built (Svenska Flygmotor) DB 605 engine. F9 Wing at Gothenburg was equipped with J21A-1s in 1945. The next 124 to be built were of the J21A-2 type, followed by the 120 A-3 aircraft. The latter had wingtip tanks, underwing bomb or rocket racks and provision for a ventral pod containing a horizontal row of eight 13.2-mm (0.52-in) guns giving devastating firepower. Most A-2 and A-3 subtypes were modified into A21A attack machines, with air-to-surface weapons.

In 1945, plans for a J21B type with a 2000-hp Rolls-Royce Griffon engine were swiftly superseded by the 21R with the de Havilland Goblin turbojet. After a considerable amount of unexpected trouble, the first of four converted prototypes flew at Norrköping on March 10, 1947. With the superior J29 already on the drawing board, Saab built only 30 of the J21RA (1360-kg [3000-lb] Goblin 2) and 30 of the J21RB (1500-kg [3300-lb] Svenska-built Goblin 3). After brief service with F10 (Skånska Flygflottilj) these pioneer Swedish jets were converted for ground-attack work as the A21RA or RB and operated until 1954 by F7 (Skånska Flygflottilj). Usual armament was one 20-mm (0.79-in) and four 13.2-mm (0.52-in) in the nose, the eight-gun pod, bombs and rockets.

Span: (J21R) 11.38 m (37 ft 4 in) *Length:* 10.13 m (34 ft 3 in) *Gross weight:* (J21A) 4132 kg (9110 lb), (J21R) 4990 kg (11 000 lb) *Maximum speed:* (J21A) 640 km/h (398 mph), (J21R) 800 km/h (497 mph)

J 22, FFVS

Swedish fighter aircraft. In the autumn of 1940, with Saab fully occupied in producing bombers and reconnaissance aircraft, the Royal Swedish Air Board organised a design team led by Bo Lundberg to produce an interim single-seat fighter, since it could no longer shop abroad for such aircraft. Work began in January 1941, and the first of two prototypes flew for the first time on September 20, 1942. It was of wood and steel construction, powered by a Swedish-built 1100-hp Pratt & Whitney Twin Wasp radial engine.

Designated J 22, an initial order for 60 aircraft 'off the drawing board' had been placed in March 1942. Component construction was undertaken by about 500 small companies not normally connected with the aviation industry. Final assembly and flight testing was done by FFVS (Flygförvaltningens Verkstad—government aircraft works) near Stockholm, and a few aircraft were completed at the workshops of the Flygvåpnet (Swedish air force) at Arboga. Deliveries began to the F9 Wing at Gothenburg in November 1943, two versions being produced: the J 22A with two 13.2-mm (0.52-in) M/39A plus two 8-mm (0.315-in) M/22F machine-guns; and the J 22B with four M/39A guns. In both cases, all armament was carried in the wings.

A total of 198 aircraft were produced (141 J 22A, and 57 J 22B), and some were still in service in 1952, although by that time the type was being phased out in favour of the more modern Saab-21R and de Havilland Vampire jet fighters.

Span: 10 m (32 ft 10 in) *Length:* 7.8 m (25 ft 7 in) *Gross weight:* 2835 kg (6250 lb) *Maximum speed:* 575 km/h (357 mph)

J29, Saab

Swedish fighter, reconnaissance and ground-attack aircraft. Popularly known as the Tunnan (barrel), the portly Saab-29 did more than merely confirm the reputation the Swedish engineers gained with the J21. Compared with contemporary British aircraft, such as the Meteor and Venom (which had the same de Havilland Ghost engine) the Saab-29 was notably more advanced in aerodynamics, structure and configuration. It was the first swept-wing fighter in service in Western Europe, preceded worldwide only by the MiG-15 and F-86A.

The original design featured a fat body, slim tailboom and unswept wing. Subsequently availability of the Ghost engine made sweepback worthwhile, the new wing being

The Saab J29 'Tunan' (barrel) was the first swept wing fighter in Western Europe preceded only by the MiG-15 and F-86A

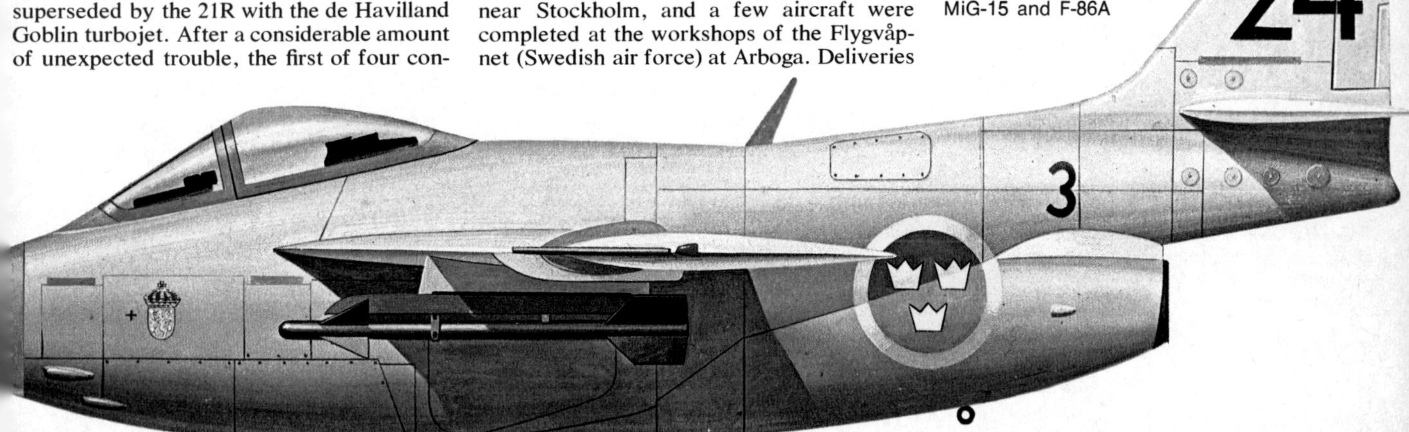

tested on a Safir. The prototype flew on September 1, 1948, and the first production version, called J29A in service with the Flygvåpnet, entered service with F13 Wing at Norrköping in May 1951. Powered by a Ghost rated at 2270 kg (5000 lb) built by Svenska Flygmotor as the RM2, it had an efficient nose inlet and short jetpipe, narrow-track main gears which caused few problems, a Saab ejection seat, four 20-mm (0.79-in) Hispano guns under the nose, a removable rear fuselage for engine access, and plain flaps and boosted ailerons. Two 400-litre (88-Imp gal) drop tanks could be carried. When wired for such underwing ordnance loads as two 250-kg (550-lb) bombs, various groups of Bofors rockets or two Sidewinder AAMs the aircraft was redesignated A29A (attack).

Most A29s were of the B subtype, first flown on March 11, 1953. This, the most numerous variant (361 were built), had increased internal fuel and improved multi-role capability. The S29C was an unarmed reconnaissance model with six cameras in the bulged underside of the forward fuselage, 76 entering service from late 1953. Only a few J29Ds were built, these being used mainly for development of the RM2B engine with SFA (Svenska) afterburner and two-position eyelid nozzle raising thrust to 2800 kg (6170 lb). In the 29E, Saab followed contemporary practice in extending and drooping the outboard leading edge, adding a dogtooth discontinuity and a small fence (an axial strip to keep the air flowing back across the wing). This raised the critical Mach number from 0.86 to 0.9, though supersonic dives were not attempted. All surviving S29C models were modified with the new wing, which no longer had a slatted leading edge.

The Saab-29F was the final production type, a combination of the wing of the E with an afterburning engine. It was fully equipped for air fighting or ground attack, but was normally designated J29F rather than A29F in service. A good all-round combat aircraft, the F first flew on March 20, 1954. It was later armed with the Rb324, the Swedish-built model of the Sidewinder AAM. The last F was completed in April 1956, but Saab and the Flygvåpnet subsequently spent three years rebuilding B (and a few D and E) models to F standard.

The J29B equipped F22 volunteer air wing in the United Nations peacekeeping force in the Congo in 1961, and F models continued in combat duty until 1965. In 1961 Austria's 1st Jagdbomber Staffel was equipped with 15 ex-Flygvåpnet J29Fs, and a year later a second batch of 15 were supplied. On the second series the left pair of guns could be replaced by a Vinten reconnaissance-camera pack.

Total production of the Tunnan amounted to 661, of which 656 were delivered for combat duty. In the Austrian air force the last was retired in 1973, and a few in both countries remained in use into the late 1970s as target tugs.

Span: 11 m (36 ft 1 in) *Length:* 10.13 m (33 ft 3 in) *Gross weight:* (J29F) 8000 kg (17 637 lb) *Maximum speed:* 1060 km/h (659 mph)

J32B, Saab Swedish all-weather jet fighter aircraft See **Lansen**

'Jack' Allied codename for Mitsubishi J2M Raiden Japanese intercepter See **J2M**

Jägaren

Swedish fast patrol boat class, built 1972-78. For many years the Swedish navy had planned to build a successor to the *Spica* Class torpedo boats, with a heavier gun armament. However, the growing threat from surface-to-surface missiles led to a change of policy. To foster interdependence with the rest of Scandinavia, and at the same time avoid the cost of developing a new missile, the decision was made to collaborate with Norway. The Norwegian *Hauk* Class was chosen as the basis, with the Kongsberg Våpenfabrikk Penguin surface-to-surface missile, while Sweden provided the electronics and the Bofors 57-mm (2.24-in) gun.

A prototype was built, the *Jägaren* (P.151), by Bätservice, Mandal and delivered in 1972. After extensive trials a further 16 boats (P.152-167) were ordered in May 1975 from Bergens Mekaniste Verksteder (11 boats) and Westermöen (five boats). The following names have been allocated: *Hügin, Kaparen, Magne, Mjolner, Mode, Munin, Mysing,*

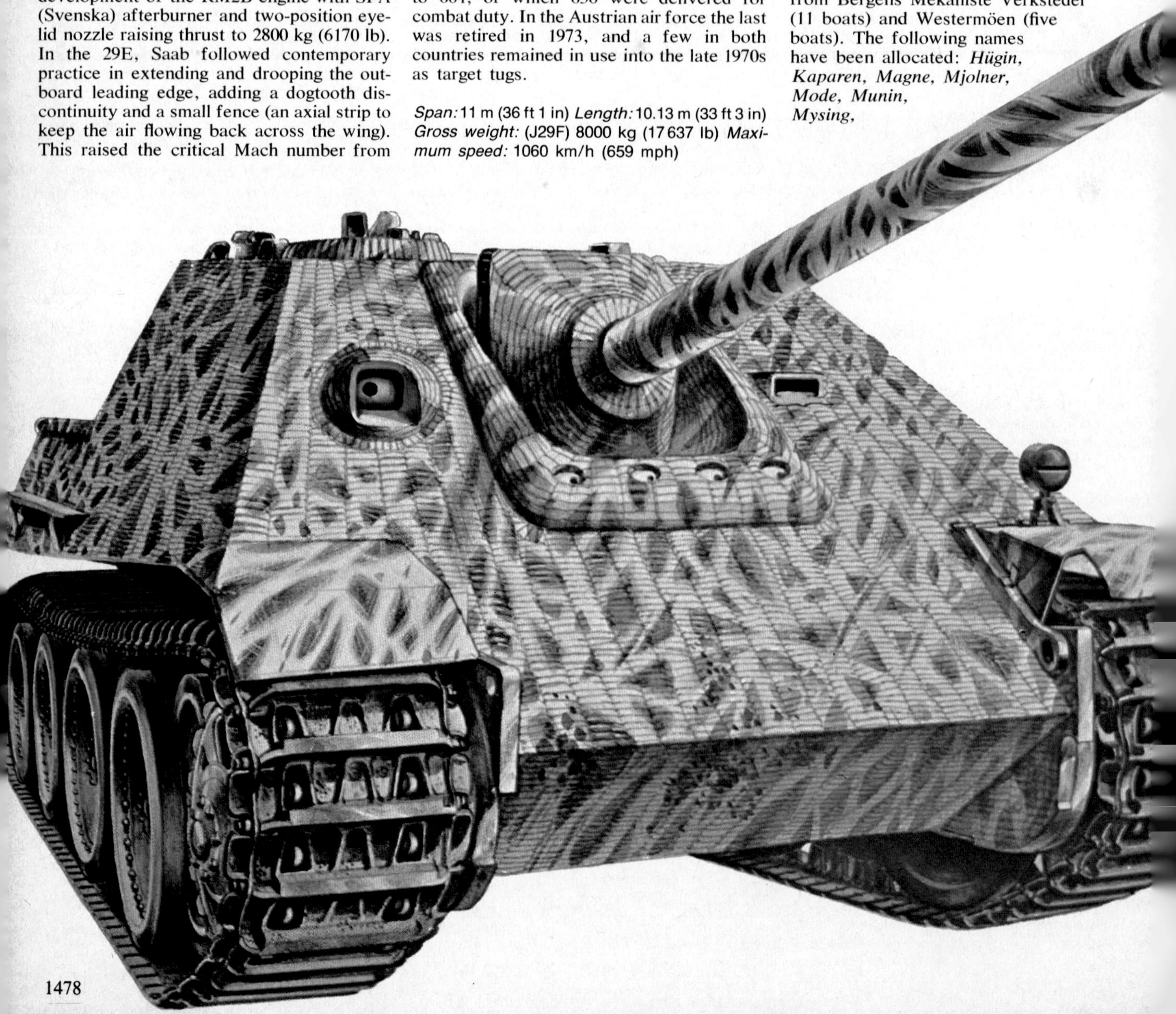

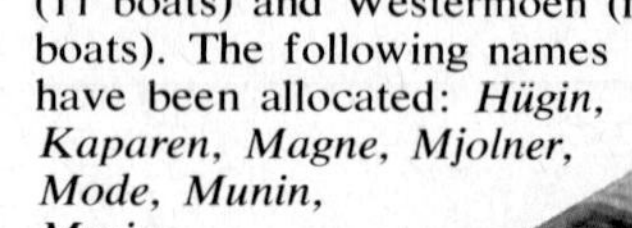

Snapphann, Spejaren, Stärkodder, Syrbjornen, Tirfing, Tordon, Vaktaren, Vale and *Vidar. Hügin* was launched in June 1977.

The boats are fitted with minelaying rails, and as they have an additional gun position amidships they can be converted to gunboats if needed.

See also *Hauk*, Penguin.

Displacement: 140 tons (standard), 170 tons (full load) *Length:* 36 m (118 ft 1 in) oa *Beam:* 6.2 m (20 ft 4 in) *Draught:* 1.5 m (4 ft 11 in) *Machinery:* 2-shaft diesel, 7000 bhp=34 knots *Armament:* 1 57-mm (2.24-in)/70-cal; 6 Penguin SSMs (6×1) *Crew:* 20

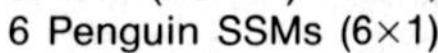

The Jagdpanther (hunting panther) SdKfz 173 was one of the finest SP antitank guns of the war. It mounted a powerful 88-mm (3.5-in) PAK 43/3 L/71 gun on a Panther tank chassis. The absence of a turret allowed a lower silhouette with well-angled frontal armour. The 88-mm gun could penetrate 226 mm (8.9 in) at an angle of 30° at 460 m (500 yards) and was capable of destroying even the heavy Soviet JS-1 and 2 tanks—other Allied armour had little hope

Jagdpanther

German tank destroyer, in service 1944-45. In mid-1943 the lack of a powerful and reliable tank destroyer was keenly felt by the German forces on the Eastern Front, and it was decided to use the Panther tank chassis as the basis for a new design. The prototype was demonstrated before Hitler in October 1943, approved, and put into production in February 1944. Production of 150 a month was planned, but due to production delays and the bombing of factories, this figure was never reached and only 382 were built before the war ended.

The Jagdpanther (hunting panther) consisted of the Panther Ausf 'G' chassis with the superstructure built up to form a closed compartment with a steeply-sloped front plate. Into this plate was fitted an 88-mm (3.5-in) PAK 43 gun so as to have a traverse of 11° to each side. The frontal armour was 80 mm (3.1-in) thick and the side armour 60 mm (2.36 in). Inside the fighting compartment was a crew of five men and 60 rounds of ammunition. It was an excellent weapon in its class, low and fast and with a powerful gun, but like all limited traverse weapons it was extremely vulnerable to attack from the flanks and rear.

An improved model mounting a 128-mm (5-in) PAK 44 gun was planned, but did not get beyond the mock-up stage.

For data and information on the basic chassis design, see under Panther.

Weight: 45 500 kg (44.78 tons) *Length:* 7.2 m (23 ft 7 in) *Width:* 3.27 m (10 ft 9 in) *Height:* 2.73 m (9 ft) *Powerplant:* Maybach gasoline, V-12, 700 bhp at 3000 rpm *Protection:* 60-80 mm (2.36-3.14 in) *Armament:* 1 88-mm (3.5-in) PAK 43/3 L/71 gun; 1 7.92-mm (0.312-in) MG 34 machine-gun *Crew:* 5

Jagdpanzer

German tank destroyer. The Jagdpanzer IV (SdKfz 162) was developed early in 1943 and was based on the chassis of the PzKpfw IV Ausf 'F' tank, then in volume production. The vehicles were built by Vomag of Plauen and went into service early in 1944. The hull was built up into a box-like superstructure with a sloped front plate, into which was fitted the 75-mm (2.95-in) gun. The sides were also slightly sloped, and later versions were fitted with skirting plates of mild-steel sheet over the suspension and track to act as burster plates against hollow-charge munitions. The original specification called for the fitting of the 75-mm Stu K 42 L/70 gun, a high-velocity weapon derived from that used in the Panther tank. These guns were not available at first, and the less powerful PAK L/48 gun was therefore installed.

Vehicles equipped with the L/70 gun in late 1944 were designated SdKfz 162/1.

A combined total of 1531 Jagdpanzer IV vehicles were built before the war ended.

See also Elefant, Hetzer, Jagdpanther, Jagdtiger.

Weight: 24 000 kg (23.62 tons) *Length:* 5.41 m (17 ft 9 in) *Width:* 2.88 m (9 ft 5 in) *Height:* 2.54 m (8 ft 4 in) *Armour thickness:* 50-20 mm (1.97-0.79 in) *Armament:* 1 75-mm (2.95-in) PAK 39 L/48 (SdKfz 162 only); 1 75-mm StuK 42 L/70 (SdKfz 161/1 only); 1 7.92-mm (0.312-in) MG 34 machine-gun *Powerplant:* Maybach V-12 gasoline 300 bhp at 3000 rpm *Crew:* 4

Jagdpanzer Kanone

West German self-propelled tank destroyer. This vehicle was developed in the late 1950s by Hanomag and Henschel of Germany and MOWOG of Switzerland, prototypes being completed and tested in 1960. Production commenced in 1965, and 750 vehicles were produced by 1967.

The chassis design is that used in the Marder MICV (mechanized infantry combat vehicle) and consists of a tracked unit with five road wheels and using torsion-bar suspension. The hull is sloped on all faces and the front plate mounts the US 90-mm (3.5-in) gun M36, as used in the M47 tank. The gun is fitted with a fume extractor and muzzle brake, and 57 rounds of ammunition are carried. An infrared searchlight is fitted, together with infrared sighting and driving aids.

In addition to its use by the Bundeswehr, the Belgian army have purchased 80 vehicles, assembling them in Belgium. Whilst basically the same as the German equipment, these use a Belgian laser rangefinder and fit the FN-MAG machine-gun instead of the MG-3 used by the Germans.

It has recently been proposed to up-gun the Bundeswehr models, replacing the 90-mm guns with the British 105-mm (4.1-in) L7 gun, but no firm decision on this has yet been announced.

Weight: 27 500 kg (27.06 tons) *Length:* 6.24 m (20 ft 6 in) *Width:* 2.98 m (9 ft 9 in) *Height:* 2.08 m (6 ft 10 in) *Protection:* 12-50 mm (0.47-1.96 in) *Armament:* 1 90-mm (3.5-in) gun M36; 1 7.62-mm (0.30-in) MG-3, co-axial; 1 7.62-mm MG-3, AA *Powerplant:* Daimler-Benz diesel, 8-cylinder, 500 bhp at 2200 rpm *Speed:* 70 km/h (43 mph) *Range:* 400 km (250 miles) *Crew:* 4

Jagdpanzer Rakete

West German self-propelled antitank missile carrier. This is the same basic vehicle as the Jagdpanzer Kanone. The hull is built up in the same way as the JPzK, but instead of mounting a gun the vehicle carries two launchers for SS 11 missiles mounted on the roof plate. A total of 14 missiles are carried inside the hull, and the launchers can be reloaded from the inside of the vehicle. The launchers are side by side and each can traverse outwards to cover from straight ahead to 90° on the flank.

In 1975 the Bundeswehr announced that the SS 11 missile was to be phased out of service and replaced by the Hot missile, the vehicles being modified accordingly. This installation used a single launcher in the roof, and 19 missiles are carried inside. The

The Jagdpanzer Kanone mounts a US 90-mm (3.5-in) Gun M36 with two 7.62-mm machine-guns

Rheinstahl GmbH

changeover from SS 11 to Hot is expected to be completed by 1980.

Weight: 23 000 kg (22.6 tons) *Length:* 6.24 m (20 ft 6 in) *Width:* 2.98 m (9 ft 9 in) *Height:* (With missiles) 2.6 m (8 ft 6 in) *Protection:* 12-50 mm (0.47-1.96 in) *Armament:* 1 90-mm (3.5-in) gun M36, 1 7.62-mm (0.30-in) MG-3, co-axial; 1 7.62-mm MG-3, AA; 2 launchers for SS 11 missiles; *Powerplant:* Daimler-Benz diesel, 8-cylinder, 500 bhp at 2200 rpm *Speed:* 70 km/h (43 mph) *Range:* 400 km (250 miles) *Crew:* 4

Jagdtiger

German heavy self-propelled tank destroyer, in service 1944-45. During the Second World War all German tanks were considered candidates for conversion into self-propelled equipments, and the 'King Tiger' tank was no exception. The only question was how to arm it, since the basic tank had the most powerful 88-mm (3.5-in) gun then in existence. Fortunately, at the time the question came up, a new design of antitank gun, the 128-mm (5-in) PAK 44, was being perfected and a modified version was adopted for the Jagdtiger.

As with other Jagdpanzer types, the basic tank hull was built up into a box-like superstructure with sloping front and sides, and the gun was mounted in the front plate in a ball mantlet giving limited traverse. The front plate was 250 mm (9.8 in) thick cast armour plate, while the sides were 80 mm (3.1 in) thick, giving excellent protection to the crew. Due to the extra weight of armour and gun the chassis was lengthened. The 128-mm gun fired a 28.3-kg (62 lb 6 oz) piercing shell at 1000 m/sec (3280 ft/sec) and could penetrate 173 mm (6.8 in) of armour at 3000 m (3300 yards) range, a formidable performance. Thirty-eight rounds of ammunition were carried in the vehicle.

A total of 150 Jagdtigers were ordered, but only 70 were built, due to delays in production. A small number were armed with the 88-mm gun of the Jagdpanther due to difficulties in supply of the 128-mm gun.

Due to its weight and size, the tactical movement of the Jagdtiger was somewhat circumscribed by the strength of bridges, but it was an extremely powerful equipment and served well in the final months of the war.

Weight: 71 735 kg (70.6 tons) *Length:* 7.8 m (25 ft 7 in) *Width:* 3.6 m (11 ft 10 in) *Height:* 2.83 m (9 ft 3 in) *Armament:* 1 128-mm (5-in) PAK 44; 1 7.92-mm (0.312-in) MG 34 or 42 machine-gun *Powerplant:* Maybach petrol, V-12, 700 bhp at 3000 rpm. *Speed:* 35 km/h (22 mph) *Range:* 160 km/h (100 miles) *Crew:* 6

Jägerfaust

German recoilless aircraft gun. Jägerfaust was one of a number of similar weapons tried in Germany in 1944-45 but was the only one considered to be worth developing. It was an upward-firing recoilless gun of 50-mm (1.96-in) calibre mounted in the wings or fuselage of a fighter aircraft. It consisted of a steel tube, closed at the bottom end, into which was loaded a 50-mm high-capacity, high-explosive shell with an impact and self-destruction fuze. The tube was rifled and the shell was fitted with a prerifled driving band. It weighed 1 kg (2 lb 3 oz) and carried 450 gm (1 lb) of high explosive, which was considered sufficient to do fatal damage to a four-engined bomber with one shot. Beneath the shell was a 60-gm (2.1-oz) propelling charge and an electric igniter.

This loaded unit was fitted into a carrier tube built vertically into the aircraft and the electric igniter connected to a firing circuit. To operate the weapon, the fighter attacked the bomber from head-on, since the high crossing speed was considered the most difficult case for the machine-gunners in the bomber. As the fighter swooped beneath the bomber, the pilot fired the Jägerfaust. An electric switch fired each tube at a 2 millisecond interval so that the salvo was spaced along the line of flight, and the tubes were aligned so as to spread the salvo over a 20-m (66-ft) front at 100-m (328 ft) range. As contact was made to the electric igniter, the propelling charge exploded and fired the shell upwards at 400 m/sec (1300 ft/sec) and, at the same time, fired the steel tube downwards with the same momentum, so that no recoil was felt by the aircraft.

As an improvement, an automatic photo-electric sight was developed which sensed the change in light as the fighter passed beneath the bomber and automatically fired the weapon. In this case, since the automatic reaction was more accurate than the human reaction of the pilot, only two tubes were fired, and thus the fighter could make three passes before returning to base.

Jägerfaust was developed at the Hugo Schneider AG of Leipzig, by Dr Heinrich Langweiler, the inventor of the Panzerfaust. Work began in April 1944 and by the end of the war a flight of 12 Messerschmitt Me 163 fighters had been equipped with the weapon and were stationed at Brandeis airfield near Leipzig. According to some reports, one Allied bomber was shot down with this device, but this has never been confirmed.

Calibre: 50 mm (1.96 in) *Weight of shell:* 1 kg (2 lb 3 oz) *Muzzle velocity:* 400 m/sec (1300 ft/sec) *Range:* 100 m (110 yards)

Jaguar

French super-destroyer class, built 1922-27. Under a law passed in 1922 six *contre-torpilleurs* or super-destroyers were authorized. Based on the Italian *esploratori* they had a designed displacement of 2160 tonnes and a speed of 35 knots, and were intended to be a hybrid type of warship between a light cruiser and a destroyer.

A new gun was designed, the 130-mm (5.1-in)/40-cal. The shell weighed 32 kg (71 lb) and it had a range of 18 560 m (20 300 yards). The main drawback was its slow rate of fire of 5-6 rds/min. French gun-designers still favoured a hand-worked rotating breech-mechanism as opposed to the sliding block which was popular with the Germans.

The original intention was to provide 36 units by 1940, and the first six were laid down in 1922-23: *Jaguar* and *Panthère* by Lorient arsenal, *Leopard* and *Lynx* by Chantiers de la Loire, Nantes, *Chacal* by Penhoët and *Tigre* by Chantiers de la Bretagne. They proved fast and reliable steamers, and on trials *Tigre* averaged 35.93 knots for eight hours, with 55 000 shp on 2540 tonnes, and for one hour maintained 36.7 knots with 57 200 shp.

In September 1939 the ships were a little slower. P gun had been removed and the two 75-mm (2.95-in) AA guns had been replaced by four twin 13.2-mm (0.52-in) machine-guns. There were plans to rearm them with 100-mm (3.9-in) AA guns to serve as AA ships but this was abandoned after the outbreak of war in 1939.

Two ships were early casualties; *Jaguar* was torpedoed by the German *Schnellboote* (motor torpedo boats) *S.21* and *S.23* off Dunkerque on May 23, 1940, while *Chacal* was bombed and sunk off Cape d'Alprecht the following day. *Leopard* escaped to Portsmouth, but on July 3 she was taken over by force by the Royal Navy; she was handed over to the Free French navy at the end of August with the addition of a British-pattern 4-in (102-mm) gun and other light AA. The

The French super-destroyer *Tigre*, a *Jaguar* Class vessel which served until 1954

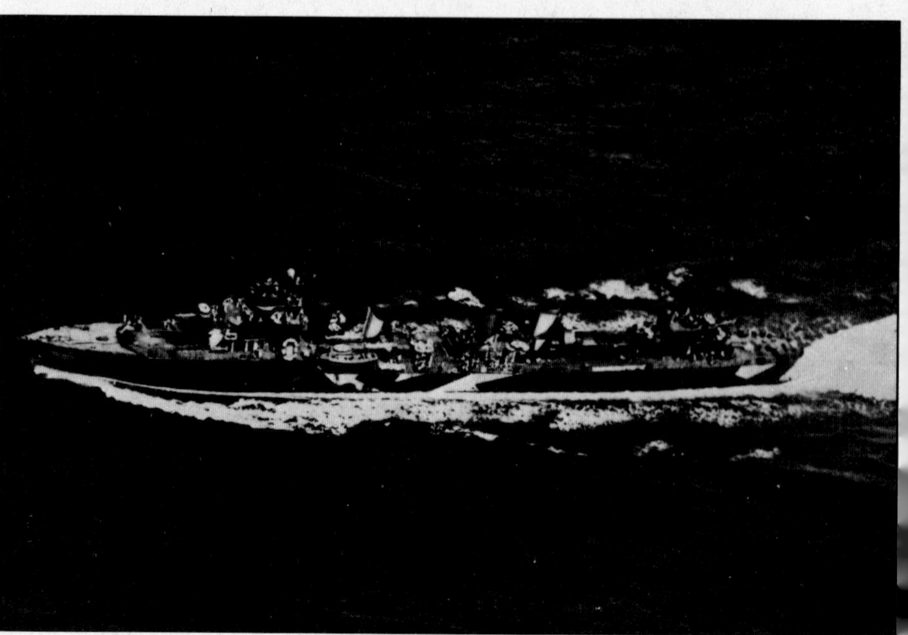

decision was taken to convert her to a long-range escort, with the forward boiler-room replaced by a fuel tank. During this refit the AA armament was strengthened by the addition of two 2-pdr (40-mm) pom-poms, seven Oerlikon 20-mm (0.79-in) AA and two twin 13.2-mm (0.52-in) machine-guns.

She did not recommission until March 1942, but in July 1942 she helped HMS *Spey* and *Pelican* to sink *U 136*. On May 27, 1943, she ran aground off Tobruk and was damaged beyond repair.

Panthère and *Lynx* were scuttled at Toulon on November 27, 1942; *Panthère* was towed to La Spezia as *FR.22* but was later scuttled there when the Italians surrendered in September 1943. *Tigre* was lying disarmed at Toulon in June 1940, and was captured by the Italians. She was incorporated into the Marina Militare as *FR.23*, but was handed back to the French in October 1943. In April 1944 she was damaged by glider-bombs off Corsica. Later while undergoing the first stage of a conversion to a fast troop-transport, the forward boiler was replaced by a fuel tank as in *Leopard.*

After the removal of the forward boiler she displaced 3500 tonnes (full load) and could make 29 knots. She served in the postwar Marine Nationale until 1954.

Displacement: 2400 tonnes (normal), 2950 tonnes (full load) *Length:* 126.8 m (416 ft) oa *Beam:* 11.3 m (37 ft 1 in) *Draught:* 4.1 m (13 ft 6 in) *Machinery:* 2-shaft geared steam turbines, 50 000 shp=35 knots *Armament:* 5 130-mm (5.1-in)/40-cal (5×1); 2 75-mm (3-in) AA (2×1); 6 55-cm (21.7-in) torpedo tubes (2×3) *Crew:* 195

Jaguar

West German fast patrol boat class, built 1957-64. A total of 40 torpedo boats was ordered for Federal Germany, 32 built in 1957-62 by Lürssenwerft, Bremen-Vegesack and eight built in 1958-64 by Krögerwerft, Rendsburg: *Iltis* (P.6058); *Jaguar* (P.6059); *Leopard* (P.6060); *Luchs* (P.6061); *Wolf* (P.6062); *Tiger* (P.6063); *Panther* (P.6064); *Löwe* (P.6065); *Fuchs* (P.6066); *Marder* (P.6067); *Seeadler** (P.6068); *Albatros** (P.6069); *Kondor** (P.6070); *Greif** (P.6071); *Falke** (P.6072); *Geier** (P.6073); *Bussard** (P.6074); *Habicht** (P.6075); *Sperber** (P.6076); *Kormoran** (P.6077); *Weihe* (P.6082); *Kranich* (P.6083); *Alk* (P.6084); *Storch* (P.6085); *Pelikan* (P.6086); *Häher* (P.6087); *Elster* (P.6088); *Reiher* (P.6089); *Pinguin* (P.6090); *Dommel* (P.6091); *Zobel* (P.6092); *Wiesel* (P.6093); *Dachs* (P.6094); *Hermelin* (P.6095); *Nerz* (P.6096); *Puma* (P.6097); *Gepard* (P.6098); *Hyäne* (P.6099); *Frettchen* (P.6100); *Ozelot* (P.6101).

The Type 140 design, to which most of the class conform, was developed from the successful *Schnellboote* (motor torpedo boats) produced by Lürssen in the Second World War, with steel framing, diagonal mahogany planking and alloy bulkheads and superstructure. Armament comprised four single deck tubes and two single 40-mm (1.57-in) Bofors guns. Ten units marked * were Type 141, with Maybach diesels, instead of Mercedes-Benz.

The *Zobel* Group (P.6092-6101) had a different bridge, with a sloping front instead of the stepped type. They underwent modernization in 1970-72 and were then known as Type 142, or the *Zobel* Class. The conversion provided them with Dutch M20 fire control and the new Seal wire-guided torpedoes for use against surface targets. These are mounted on the stern firing aft, and the tactics are to steam away rapidly from the enemy once the torpedoes have been fired. The gun armament remained the same.

All were for disposal at the end of 1975 with the entry of the new Type 148 missile boats. Seven were sold to Greece, and seven to Turkey, with three each to cannibalize for spares.

Greek boats: P.196 *Esperos* (ex-*Seeadler*); P.197 *Kataiqis* (ex-*Falke*); P.198 *Kentauros* (ex-*Habicht*); P. 199 *Kyklon* (ex-*Greif*); P.228 *Laiaps* (ex-*Kondor*); P.229 *Scorpios* (ex-*Kormoran*); P.230 *Tyfon* (ex-*Geier*)

Turkish boats: P.330 *Firtina* (ex-*Pelikan*); P.331 *Tufan* (ex-*Storch*); P.332 *Kilic*; P.333 *Mizrak* (ex-*Löwe*); P.334 *Yildiz* (ex-*Alk*); P.335 *Kalkan* (ex-*Wolf*); P.336 *Karayel* (ex-*Tiger*)

Displacement: 160 tons (standard), 190 tons (full load) *Length:* 42.5 m (139 ft 5 in) wl *Beam:* 7.2 m (23 ft 7 in) *Draught:* 2.4 m (7 ft 10 in) *Machinery:* 4-shaft diesels, 12 000 bhp=42 knots *Armament:* 2 40-mm (1.57-in)/70-cal Bofors (2×1); (Type 140, 141) 4 53-cm (21-in) torpedo tubes (4×1), (Type 142) 2 tubes (2×1); (Type 142) 4 mines *Crew:* 39

Die Bildstelle der Marine

***Above: Frettchen* (P.6100), a German *Jaguar* Class fast patrol boat. Both *Frettchen* and *Ozelot* (below) were part of the *Zobel*, or Type 142, Group modernized in 1970-72**

PPL

A two-seat Jaguar International in desert camouflage during a proving flight prior to being handed over for service in the Sultan of Oman's air force in March 1977

BAC

Jaguar, SEPECAT

Anglo-French attack aircraft and trainer. In the years following the 1957 British defence white paper the belief expressed therein that the Royal Air Force was 'unlikely to require' any more manned combat aircraft was increasingly seen to be ludicrous. There was, however, no reference to a trainer, and by 1963 the RAF had drawn up the AST.362 (Air Staff Target) covering a trainer capable of flying useful tactical attack missions. The British Aircraft Corporation at Preston carried out the project studies, arriving at a design designated P.45, with two afterburning Rolls-Royce RB.172 engines and a dash capability of Mach 1.7.

The government continued to show little interest, until a collaborative aircraft programme with France suddenly seemed a good way to improve Anglo-French relations and get Britain into the Common Market. France formulated a trainer specification called ECAT (école de combat et appui tactique) in 1964, which was intended to replace the Magister and T-33 and also, in the tactical role, the SMB.2, F-84F and F-100. There were, however, problems in this collaboration since Britain wanted all the power and speed it could get, and had a wholly unwar-

ranted fixation on supersonic performance, while the French wanted simplicity, cheapness and low-cost reliability. After numerous extremely difficult meetings at the political level the chosen industrial partners were allowed to meet in May 1965. They were BAC (Preston) and Breguet on the airframe, and Rolls-Royce and Turboméca on the engine.

For political reasons, the airframe was not based on the P.45, which was the right size and power, but on the Breguet Br.121, which was tailored to engines of less than half the thrust, and carried a weapon load of 590 kg (1300 lb). The project was launched in the same month by a memorandum which promised 300 'ECAT strike trainers', France buying 75 single-seat strike aircraft and 75 tandem-seat trainers, and Britain 150 trainers. At this time the RAF wanted ever greater capability, including 4180-km (2600-mile) ferry range, while the French were prepared for less and less capability in order to get a cheaper ECAT at the earliest possible date. French leadership was a political necessity, but most of the work was done at Preston, and the aircraft which eventually appeared, named Jaguar in June 1965, was based on the British specification. The French air force resigned themselves to delay and higher cost, but appreciated the very much greater capability. Thrust with full afterburner of the Adour turbofan began at 3000 kg (6600 lb) in the prototype Jaguar, first flown at Istres on September 8, 1968. Thrust was subsequently increased to 3313 kg (7305 lb) in production aircraft, and to 3630 kg (8000 lb) in the Jaguar International export version. RAF Jaguars are being uprated and will eventually have Adour-58 engines of 3810-kg (8400-lb) thrust. This power has been combined with a small but outstandingly efficient slatted and flapped wing to give the Jaguar the capability to lift an external weapon load of 4540 kg (10 000 lb). Internal armament comprises a single 30-mm (1.18-in) DEFA or Aden gun in tandem-seat conversion trainers, and two similar guns in tactical models.

French Jaguar A (*appui*, tactical) aircraft have simple navaids including a twin-gyro platform and doppler. The RAF Jaguar GR.1 is a much more advanced aircraft with inertial navigation, HUD (head-up display), projected-map display, integrated navigation attack subsystem and laser ranger and marked-target seeker in a chisel nose. The Jaguar M (*marin*, marine) for the French navy, identified by its single mainwheels, was cancelled in 1973 and replaced by the Etendard of reduced capability.

Squadron delivery began in May 1972 for the French versions and June 1973 for the British, but the rate of delivery to the RAF had resulted in completion of that service's order of 202 (165 single-seat GR.1 and 37 two-seat T.2) by 1978. The French air force had in 1978 received all its Jaguar E trainers but only 100 of 160 single-seaters, and it was expected that a further order would be placed to increase the French order beyond 200. In addition 12 Internationals had been delivered to Oman and 12 to Ecuador, most of them equipped to fire Matra Magic close-range antiaircraft missiles from overwing pylons that do not affect the underwing weapon load. Further changes since first delivery include a multisensor reconnaissance pod carried on the centreline by RAF Jaguars and a modified pod for French A-models with an Atlis laser in the nose. An option for export customers is the Agave nose radar with a Ferranti 1058 LRMTS (laser ranger and marked-target seeker) in a small fairing to the rear. All tactical versions are equipped with a folding flight-refuelling probe on the right side of the nose, but this is absent from the standard two-seaters. The Martin-Baker seats are cleared for use at zero height, zero airspeed in RAF aircraft, or down to 167 km/h (104 mph) in French aircraft, whose seats are licence-made by SAMM.

The Anglo-French Jaguar attack aircraft is capable of lifting external loads of up to 4540 kg (10 000 lb) which makes it a useful ground-attack fighter. In this role French Jaguars have seen action against Polisario insurgents, where one has been lost to AA fire. French crews have found that the Jaguar can operate and be maintained under front-line conditions in Africa, operating from airstrips crude by European standards. Besides serving the RAF and French air force 12 Jaguars have been exported to Oman and 12 to Ecuador

XZ111

An RAF Jaguar GR1 of No 2 Squadron Laarbruch on a reconnaissance mission near the Dutch border in August 1976. The SEPECAT Jaguar is a multirole aircraft jointly built by the British Aircraft Company and Avions Marcel Dassault/Breguet Aviation under the company name of Société Européan de Production de l'Avion E.C.A.T. It is built as a trainer which can be used as a two-seat operational aircraft and as a single-seat tactical support fighter. In this role French Jaguars have been in action in Africa and proved reliable and easy to maintain in front-line conditions. They can carry nuclear weapons or a variety of payloads slung from wing and fuselage pylons. The BAC-designed, flush-fitting reconnaissance pod for RAF Jaguars mounted on the centreline contains optical cameras for horizon-to-horizon coverage and Hawker Siddeley Type 401 infrared linescan (IRLS) for additional daylight, poor weather and night capability. The cameras are installed in two rotatable drums within the pod with the IRLS to the rear

MOD-RAF

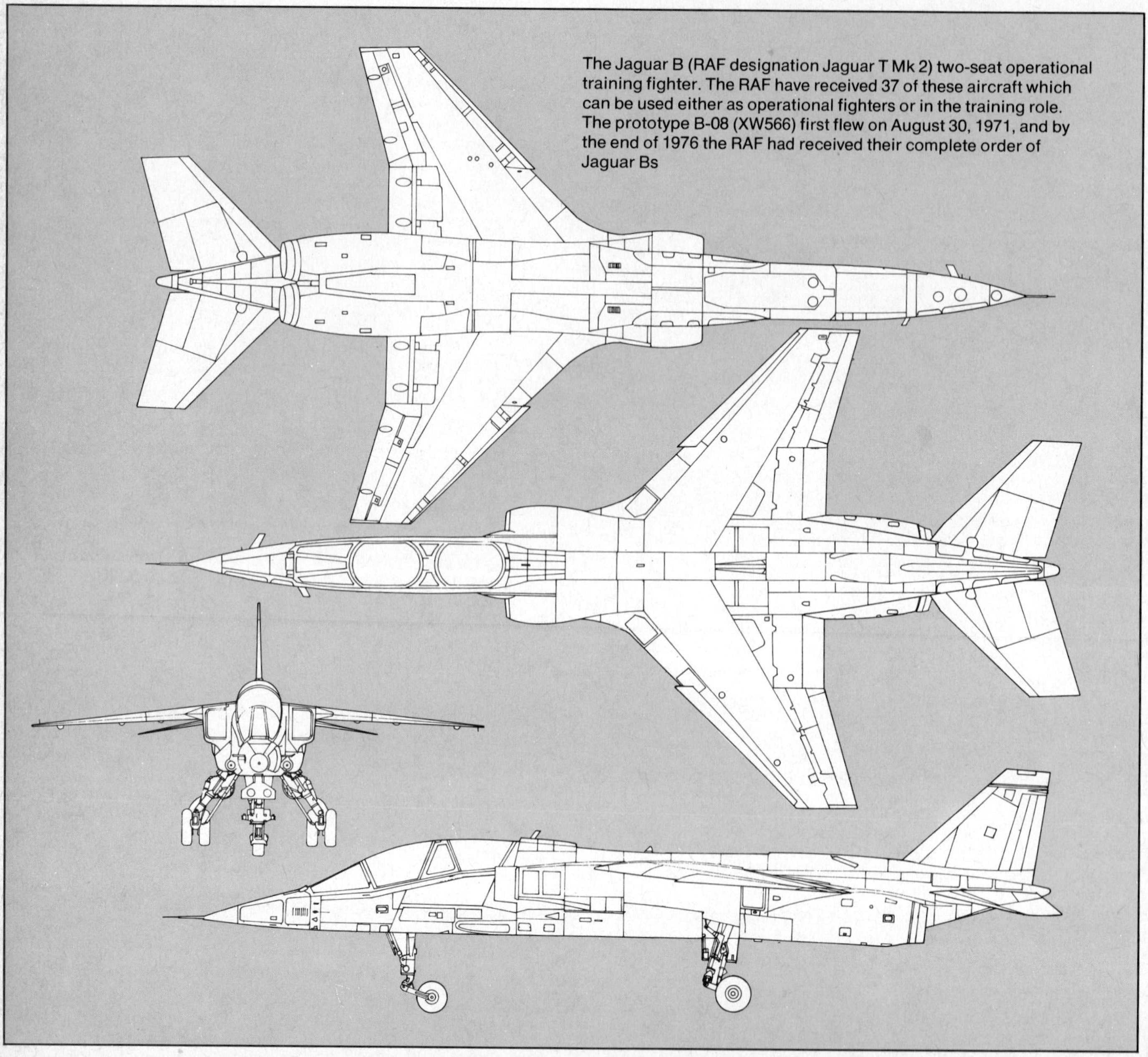

The Jaguar B (RAF designation Jaguar T Mk 2) two-seat operational training fighter. The RAF have received 37 of these aircraft which can be used either as operational fighters or in the training role. The prototype B-08 (XW566) first flew on August 30, 1971, and by the end of 1976 the RAF had received their complete order of Jaguar Bs

Below: **One of the two British-built Jaguar prototypes (XW563) SO7 drops a bomb from its wing pylon during stores release trials in the late 1960s**

BAC

This aircraft has proved outstandingly popular with flight and ground crews, by virtue of its effortless reliability, long range and endurance, absence of any shortcomings at low-medium altitudes, and good engineering. It has demonstrated its ability to operate away from paved runways, simulated attack missions with bombloads being flown from motorways and from grass (though this has not been made part of routine squadron training). Possibly the only adverse comment to be made is that it is almost too potent an aircraft for use as a trainer, leading both countries to create new trainer types, namely the Hawk and Alpha Jet.

Span: 8.69 m (28 ft 6 in) *Length:* (Single-seat) 16.83 m (55 ft 3 in), (two-seat) 17.53 m (57 ft 6 in) *Gross weight:* 15 400 kg (34 000 lb) *Maximum speed:* 1700 km/h (1055 mph), Mach 1.6

Jakob Hobein

Dutch torpedo boat class, built 1890-91. Three very small boats were built by Yarrow Thornycroft at Chiswick on the River Thames for the Royal Netherlands Navy. Originally numbered *3, 21* and *22,* they were later renamed *Jakob Hobein, Jan Harign* and *Jasper Lijnsen,* and were similar to 19 older boats numbered *1, 2* and *4-20,* also built by Thornycroft in 1878-86.

These tiny torpedo boats were useless and were scrapped during the First World War.

Displacement: 83.6 tons (normal) *Length:* 13.87 m (45 ft 6 in) pp *Beam:* 2.92 m (9 ft 7 in) *Draught:* 1.55 m (5 ft 1 in) *Machinery:* 1-shaft reciprocating steam, 460 ihp=18 knots *Armament:* 1 37-mm (1.46-in) QF; 1 14-in (36-cm) torpedo tube *Crew:* 15

Jaktfalk, Svenska/ASJA J6

Swedish fighter aircraft. In January 1930 the Flygvåpnet (Swedish air force) purchased the prototype of a small, single-seat biplane fighter first flown the previous October by the Svenska Aero AB. The fighter was a somewhat stubby design, with a fixed undercarriage incorporating wheel spats. It was powered by a 456-hp Armstrong Siddeley Jaguar VIc radial engine, and bore the service designation J 5.

After further flight testing, two more prototypes were ordered in March 1930; these were designated J 6 and were powered by 450-hp Bristol Jupiter VIF engines. Five production J 6s, named Jaktfalk I (gerfalcon) were ordered in June 1930. During June-July 1931 the two J 6 prototypes were flown in competitive trials against British Bristol Bulldog IIs, as a result of which three J 6As with 500-hp Bristol Jupiter VIIF engines were ordered. They were delivered in late 1933, just before Svenska Aero AB went into liquidation. A further seven aircraft with the same powerplant were built by ASJA (AB Svenska Järnvägsverkstäderna), which had acquired the old company's assets. Although basically similar, the new aircraft were designated J 6B. Armament on all models comprised two 8-mm (0.315-in) machine-guns in the upper front fuselage.

Of the 18 produced, exports were made to Norway (one J 6A) and Finland (one J 6A, two J 6Bs). The others remained in Swedish fighter service until 1940, and on second-line duties until 1941.

(J 6A) *Span:* 8.80 m (28 ft 10 in) *Length:* 7.50 m (24 ft 7 in) *Gross weight:* 1470 kg (3240 lb) *Maximum speed:* 310 km/h (193 mph)

Jastreb, Soko J-1

Yugoslav reconnaissance and light attack aircraft. The Jastreb (hawk) is basically an attack version of the G2-A Galeb two-seat armed trainer, which began development in 1957. The Jastreb J-1, which entered series production in 1968, is a single-seat variant utilizing the more powerful 1360-kg (3000-lb) st Rolls-Royce Viper 531 turbojet engine, with provision for two 454-kg (1000-lb) under-fuselage JATO rockets. Other modifications include a metal fairing over the rear cockpit, improved day and night reconnaissance equipment, plus electronic navigation and communication instruments. In 1978 approximately 100 J-1s were in service with the Yugoslav air force and four of the J-1-E export variant were in service with the Zambian air force.

The fixed armament comprises three 0.5-in (12.7-mm) Colt-Browning machine-guns in the nose; in addition, there are eight underwing attachment points for weapons such as two 250-kg (550-lb) bombs; two groups of smaller stores; two 200-litre (44-Imp gal) napalm tanks; or rocket projectiles of varying numbers and sizes between 5.7-12.7 cm (2.24-5 in). A semiautomatic camera gun and gyrogunsight are standard equipment. The aircraft are fitted with ejector seats.

Tactical reconnaissance counterparts are designated RJ-1 and RJ-1-E. The TJ-1, production of which began in January 1975, is a two-seat operational conversion and pilot proficiency training model, with the same capabilities as the J-1. The two-man crew sit in tandem in ejector seats and the cockpit canopies are separate and jettisonable. Two cameras are carried in the wingtip tank nosecones. The TJ-1 is used by the Yugoslav air force and has reportedly been exported.

(J-1) *Span:* 11.68 m (38 ft 4 in) over tip-tanks *Length:* 10.88 m (35 ft 8 in) *Gross weight:* 5100 kg (11 245 lb) *Maximum speed:* 820 km/h (510 mph)

Jaureguiberry

French battleship, built 1891-96. *Jaureguiberry* was launched at La Seyne, Toulon, on October 27, 1893, at a time when the French navy was making a big effort to challenge the Royal Navy. Although she had a reputation as a reliable steamer and good seaboat she did not compare well with her British contemporaries. The massive unarmoured sides, the great weight of funnels and masts and the four single turrets combined to produce a ship which would not be able to fight in heavy weather or stand up to contemporary British ships such as *Majestic* and *Canopus.*

In August 1914 she was the oldest battle unit in the French fleet, and the years of neglect of the fleet had taken their toll. When she appeared at Gallipoli in March 1915 to replace *Bouvet,* Admiral Gueprattte reported that *Jaureguiberry* was full of inflammable material, her magazines were unprotected by the belt armour, the belt was in any case submerged, and the stokehold bulkheads had rusted through. With defective magazine flooding as well, he concluded that the ship could be expected to burn, blow up or founder without much difficulty.

She nevertheless survived some hits from Turkish guns and returned to Port Said in July 1915, from where she joined the French division off the coast of Syria. After a spell as guardship in the Suez Canal at Ismailia and carrying artillery to Suez she was laid up at Port Said in 1918.

On her return to Toulon in February 1919 she was disarmed, and a year later she was stricken, remaining in existence as a hulk until 1934.

Displacement: 11 818 tons (normal), 12 229 tons (full load) *Length:* 109.7 m (359 ft 11 in) pp *Beam:* 22.15 m (72 ft 8 in) *Draught:* 7.75 m (25 ft

The French battleship *Jaureguiberry* in 1905. Despite her age she survived the First World War

IWM

5 in) *Machinery:* 2-shaft reciprocating steam, 14300 ihp=17.5 knots *Protection:* 450-250 mm (17.7-9.8 in) belt, 370 mm (14.6 in) turrets, 230 mm (9 in) conning tower *Armament:* 2 305-mm (12-in)/40-cal (2×1); 2 274-mm (10.8-in)/40-cal (2×1); 8 140-mm (5.5-in) (8×1); 14 47-mm (1.85-in) (14×1); 2 45-cm (17.7-in) torpedo tubes (beam, submerged) *Crew:* 597

Javelin

British destroyer class. Ordered in March 1937 the *Javelin* or 'J' Class destroyers were provided under the 1936 Estimates. Their design represented an attempt to combine the features of the large *Afridi* Class destroyers with those of the smaller fleet destroyers of the 'A' to 'I' Classes. The ultimate aim was to reduce the size and cost compared with the *Afridis*, but as a complex armament and fire-control system were demanded this reduction was comparatively small.

The main weight-saving feature was the adoption of two boilers in place of three which, although individually heavier and of greater power, occupied less space and allowed for a 6-m (20-ft) reduction in length and the use of one funnel instead of two. The overall machinery weight was also increased to provide for greater power and higher speed, and this weight low down in the ship improved stability and allowed the beam to be reduced by 23 cm (9 in). Thus most of the 200-ton reduction in weight over the *Afridi* design resulted from savings in the hull weight. The armament was very similar to that of the *Afridi* Class, the main difference being the omission of the fourth twin 4.7-in (120-mm) gun mounting to allow for the fitting of two quintuple torpedo-tube mountings in place of one quadruple. The close-range AA armament was the same, but was positioned differently with the pom-pom mounting abaft the funnel and the two 0.5-in (12.7-mm) mountings in the bridge wings. To improve seakeeping the new ships were given more sheer forward than in the *Afridi* Class. Unlike earlier British destroyers they were longitudinally framed for ease of construction.

Originally nine 'J' Class ships were ordered following the earlier practice of having eight destroyers and one flotilla leader. But since they were, like the *Afridi* group, large enough to allow for the leader to be one of the class instead of an enlarged vessel, the ninth ship was cancelled. *Jervis* was chosen to be fitted out as leader and was identical in appearance to the other ships of the class except for a slightly longer after superstructure which provided additional accommodation. All the vessels of the class were laid down in 1937, launched in 1938 and completed in 1939. A second flotilla of the same design, the 'K' or *Kelly* Class, were ordered in March 1937 under the 1937 Estimates and a third flotilla, the 'N' or *Napier* Class, in April 1939 under the 1939 Estimates. The 'K' Class were laid down during 1937-38, launched during 1938-39 and completed during 1939-40. The 'N' Class were laid down during 1939-40, launched during 1940-41 and completed during 1940-42. The leaders for these two flotillas were *Kelly* and *Napier.*

Wartime alterations were generally standard through the class. During 1940-41 the after bank of torpedo tubes was replaced by a 4-in (102-mm) AA gun, and two 20-mm (0.79-in) AA guns were mounted abreast the searchlight platform amidships. During 1941-42 the 0.5-in (12.7-mm) mounting in the bridge wings was replaced by two more 20-mm and air-warning, surface-warning and gunnery radar were fitted. The 'N' Class were completed incorporating many or all of these alterations. Those that survived to 1943-44 had the 4-in AA gun removed and the after torpedo tubes replaced, and the majority had their single 20-mm guns replaced by twin 20-mm mountings. Some of the 'N' Class also had two single 20-mm added on the quarterdeck. Lattice foremasts replaced the tripods in *Javelin, Jervis, Kelvin, Kimberley, Napier, Nepal* and *Norman,* and in 1945 some of the 'N' Class were fitted with 40-mm (1.57-in) AA guns.

The three flotillas saw considerable war service and much action and of the 16 ships of the 'J' and 'K' groups no less than 12 were lost. On completion the 'J' Class were formed into the 7th Destroyer Flotilla and the 'K' Class into the 5th Destroyer Flotilla, both joining the Home Fleet. The most famous ship of the class and one of the most famous destroyers of the Second World War was the leader of the 5th Flotilla, HMS *Kelly,* commanded by Captain Lord Louis Mountbatten.

One of the class's first actions occurred on December 7, 1939, when *Jersey,* patrolling off Cromer with *Juno,* was hit aft by a torpedo. This was one of a salvo fired by the German destroyers *Hans Lody* and *Erich Giese,* which were engaged in laying mines and withdrew from the scene undetected. The badly damaged *Jersey* was towed home by *Juno* and was repaired between January-September 1940. Several of the class took part in the Norwegian Campaign and on May 9, 1940, *Kelly* and *Kandahar* were carrying out a sweep for enemy minelayers in the North Sea when *Kelly* was hit by a torpedo from the E-Boat *S31.* The torpedo detonated abreast the forward boiler room and blew a hole in the port side which extended from the upper deck to the keel. Despite this extensive damage and further attacks by German E-Boats and aircraft she was towed to the Tyne, a journey which took over three days, where she was under repair until December 1940.

HMS *Jupiter* (foreground) and HMS *Kashmir, Javelin* and *Kelly* Class destroyers, during operations early in the Second World War

Meanwhile another ship of the class had survived extensive damage. On the night of November 24-25, 1940, *Jackal, Javelin, Jersey, Jupiter* and *Kashmir* fought a short action with the German destroyers *Karl Galster, Hans Lody* and *Erich Steinbrinck* in the English Channel. During the action *Javelin* was torpedoed by *Hans Lody* and had both her bow and stern blown off. She was towed to Plymouth and repaired in Devonport dockyard by December 1941.

In the latter half of 1940 *Jaguar, Janus, Jervis, Juno, Kandahar, Kimberley, Kingston* and *Khartoum* were transferred to the Mediterranean to form the 14th Destroyer Flotilla. On June 23, 1940, while in the Red Sea, *Khartoum, Kandahar, Kingston* and the sloop *Shoreham* attacked and sank the Italian submarine *Torricelli* with gunfire. Later that day an air cylinder on the after torpedo tubes of *Khartoum* accidentally exploded blowing a torpedo warhead into the superstructure and starting a fire. The ship was beached off Perim Harbour where her after magazines exploded, wrecking the after part of the ship. She was subsequently stripped of useful equipment and abandoned.

In April 1940 the 5th Flotilla, now consisting of *Kelly, Kelvin, Kashmir, Kipling, Jersey* and *Jackal,* also transferred to the Mediterranean where they relieved the 14th Flotilla at Malta for antishipping patrols. On May 2, 1941, *Jersey* was mined and sunk in the entrance to Malta harbour when returning from such a patrol. Shortly after this, Malta became untenable and the 5th Flotilla left to join the 14th in the Eastern Mediterranean. Here both flotillas became involved in the battle for Crete and three more of the class were lost. On May 21, *Juno* sank when one of her magazines exploded following a bomb hit. Two days later *Kashmir* and *Kelly* were attacked by 24 Ju 87 dive-bombers. *Kashmir* was sunk in two minutes and *Kelly* was hit aft by a 454-kg (1000-lb) bomb while turning at 30 knots and capsized. She later sank leaving 279 survivors from the two ships, including Lord Mountbatten, to be picked up by *Kipling.* On December 19, 1941, *Kandahar* ran into a minefield off Tripoli and had her stern blown off. She drifted clear the following day and after the survivors had been picked up she was sunk by *Jaguar.*

On March 22, 1942, *Kipling, Kelvin, Kingston* and *Jervis* took part in the second battle of Sirte. During the action *Kingston* was damaged by a 381-mm (15-in) shell from the Italian battleship *Littorio.* The following month she was bombed while under repair in dry dock at Malta and became a constructive total loss; she was subsequently used as a blockship at Malta but was raised and broken up in 1947. A few days after Sirte, on March 26, *Jaguar* was sunk by two torpedoes from *U 652* north-east of Salūm.

On May 11, 1942, *Jackal, Jervis, Kipling* and *Lively* were attacked by aircraft north-west of Mersa Matruh while on their way to intercept an enemy convoy. In the ensuing battle *Kipling* and *Lively* were sunk and *Jackal* badly damaged. *Jervis* took *Jackal* in tow on the following day, but an oil fire in her boiler room burned out of control and she had to be abandoned and sunk. One more ship of the class was lost in 1942, *Jupiter,* which unlike the rest did not serve in the Mediterranean. In January 1942 she joined the Eastern Fleet and on February 27 was sunk during the Battle of the Java Sea.

The last ship of the 'J' and 'K' group to be lost was *Janus* which was sunk by a glider bomb off the Anzio beachhead on January 23, 1944. Of the four survivors *Javelin, Jervis* and *Kelvin* returned home in 1944 for the Normandy invasion while *Kimberley* served in the Mediterranean until the end of the war. All four were sold for scrap in 1949.

The 'N' Class ships also joined the Home Fleet on completion but *Nepal* was the only vessel to be manned by the Royal Navy. *Napier, Nestor, Nizam* and *Norman* were manned by the Royal Australian Navy, *Nerissa* was transferred to the Polish navy and renamed *Piorun* and *Noble* and *Nonpareil* were sold to the Royal Netherlands Navy and renamed *Van Galen* and *Tjerk Hiddes* respectively. *Piorun* served for two short periods in the Mediterranean in 1941 and 1943, but otherwise served with the Home Fleet until the end of the war. She was returned to the Royal Navy in 1946 and sold for scrap in 1955.

The four Australian ships were transferred to the Mediterranean Fleet and then to the Eastern Fleet in 1941 where they were joined by the two Dutch vessels and *Nepal* in 1942. In June 1942 the Australian vessels, and *Poirun* from the Home Fleet, were temporarily transferred to the Mediterranean for the Malta convoy 'Vigorous'. During this convoy *Nestor* was badly damaged in an air attack, and after being abandoned had to be sunk by *Javelin.* In May 1945 the Eastern Fleet ships transferred to the British Pacific Fleet, where they took part in the operations against Okinawa and the final assault on Japan. Most of the class was sold for scrap during 1955-58 but *Tjerk Hiddes* was sold to Indonesia and renamed *Gadjah Mada* in 1951 and was not scrapped until 1961.

'J' Class
Jackal, Javelin—built by John Brown
Janus—built by Swan Hunter
Jaguar—built by Denny
Jervis—built by Hawthorn Leslie
Jersey—built by White
Juno—built by Fairchild
Jupiter—built by Yarrow

'K' Class
Kandahar—built by Denny
Kashmir, Kimberley—built by Thornycroft
Kelly—built by Hawthorn Leslie
Kelvin—built by Fairfield
Khartoum—built by Swan Hunter
Kingston—built by White
Kipling—built by Yarrow

'N' Class
Napier, Nestor—built by Fairfield
Nerissa, Nizam—built by John Brown
Noble, Nonpareil—built by Denny
Norman, Nepal—built by Thornycroft

Displacement: 1760 tons (standard), 2330 tons (full load) *Length:* 108.7 m (356 ft 6 in) oa *Beam:* 10.9 m (35 ft 9 in) *Draught:* 2.7 m (9 ft) *Machinery:* 2-shaft geared steam turbines, 40 000 shp=36 knots *Armament:* 6 4.7-in (120-mm) (3×2); 4 2-pdr AA (1×4); 8 0.5-in (12.7-mm) AA (2×4); 10 21-in (53-cm) torpedo tubes (2×5) *Crew:* 183

HMS *Jaguar* leads a patrol into harbour. She was sunk on March 26, 1942, by two torpedoes from *U 652* north-east of Salūm off Africa

The destroyer HMS *Nepal* followed by the battleship HMS *Valiant*, part of the Eastern Fleet operating against Sabang in Northern Sumatra in 1944. *Nepal* was one of eight *Napier* Class, repeats of the *Javelin* Class, destroyers ordered in the 1939 programme. She was laid down under the name *Norseman* but renamed *Nepal* and allocated to the Dutch for service in the Dutch East Indies. While under construction at Thornycroft's yard at Woolston the *Norseman* narrowly escaped destruction when a German bomber dropped a stick of six bombs across the yard. As a result of this damage the Dutch chose to buy *Noble* and *Nonpareil*, and *Nepal* was not sent to the Far East until later in the war

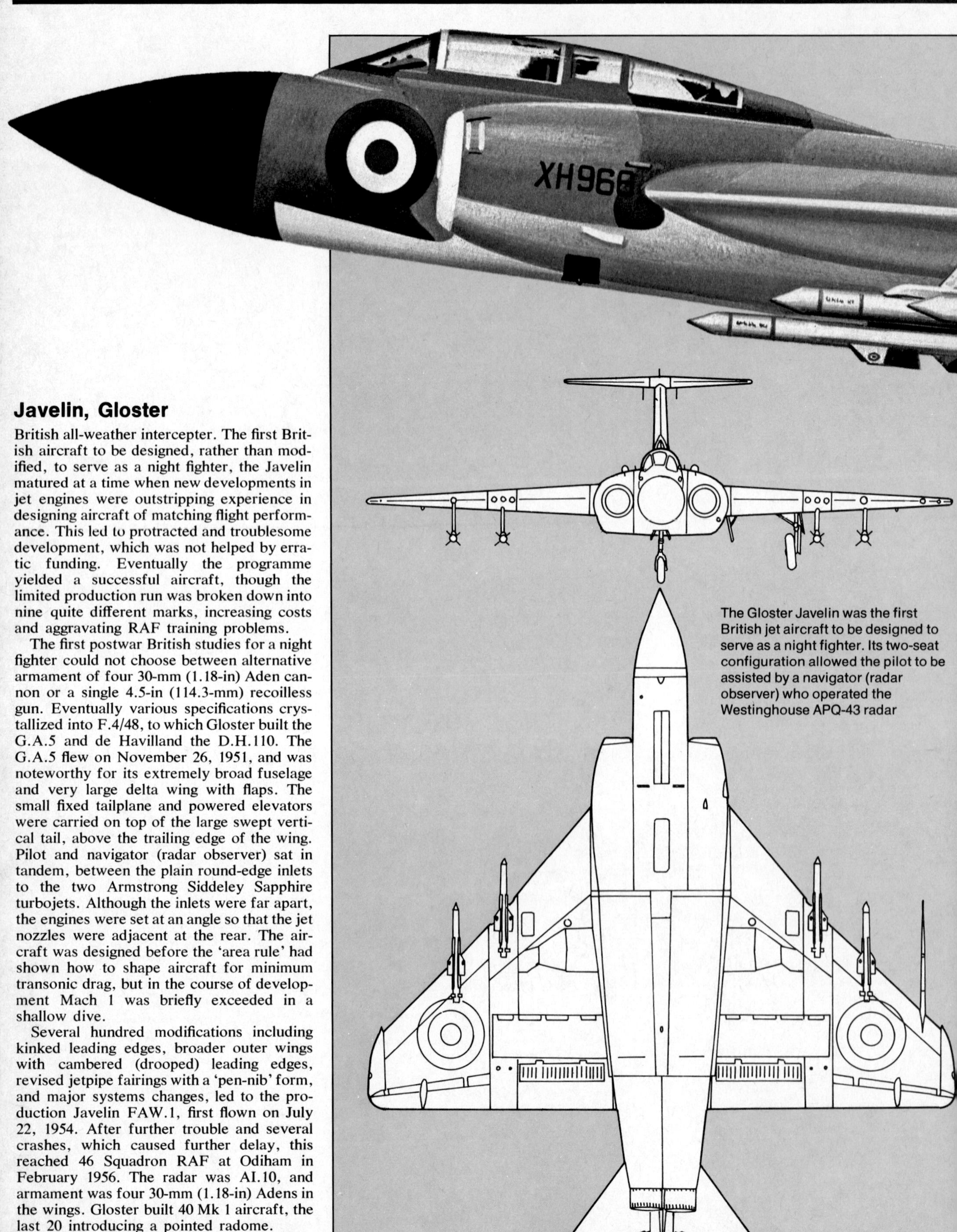

The Gloster Javelin was the first British jet aircraft to be designed to serve as a night fighter. Its two-seat configuration allowed the pilot to be assisted by a navigator (radar observer) who operated the Westinghouse APQ-43 radar

Javelin, Gloster

British all-weather intercepter. The first British aircraft to be designed, rather than modified, to serve as a night fighter, the Javelin matured at a time when new developments in jet engines were outstripping experience in designing aircraft of matching flight performance. This led to protracted and troublesome development, which was not helped by erratic funding. Eventually the programme yielded a successful aircraft, though the limited production run was broken down into nine quite different marks, increasing costs and aggravating RAF training problems.

The first postwar British studies for a night fighter could not choose between alternative armament of four 30-mm (1.18-in) Aden cannon or a single 4.5-in (114.3-mm) recoilless gun. Eventually various specifications crystallized into F.4/48, to which Gloster built the G.A.5 and de Havilland the D.H.110. The G.A.5 flew on November 26, 1951, and was noteworthy for its extremely broad fuselage and very large delta wing with flaps. The small fixed tailplane and powered elevators were carried on top of the large swept vertical tail, above the trailing edge of the wing. Pilot and navigator (radar observer) sat in tandem, between the plain round-edge inlets to the two Armstrong Siddeley Sapphire turbojets. Although the inlets were far apart, the engines were set at an angle so that the jet nozzles were adjacent at the rear. The aircraft was designed before the 'area rule' had shown how to shape aircraft for minimum transonic drag, but in the course of development Mach 1 was briefly exceeded in a shallow dive.

Several hundred modifications including kinked leading edges, broader outer wings with cambered (drooped) leading edges, revised jetpipe fairings with a 'pen-nib' form, and major systems changes, led to the production Javelin FAW.1, first flown on July 22, 1954. After further trouble and several crashes, which caused further delay, this reached 46 Squadron RAF at Odiham in February 1956. The radar was AI.10, and armament was four 30-mm (1.18-in) Adens in the wings. Gloster built 40 Mk 1 aircraft, the last 20 introducing a pointed radome.

Production then continued with 30 FAW.2 aircraft equipped with the American Westinghouse APQ-43 radar (called AI.22 in Bri-

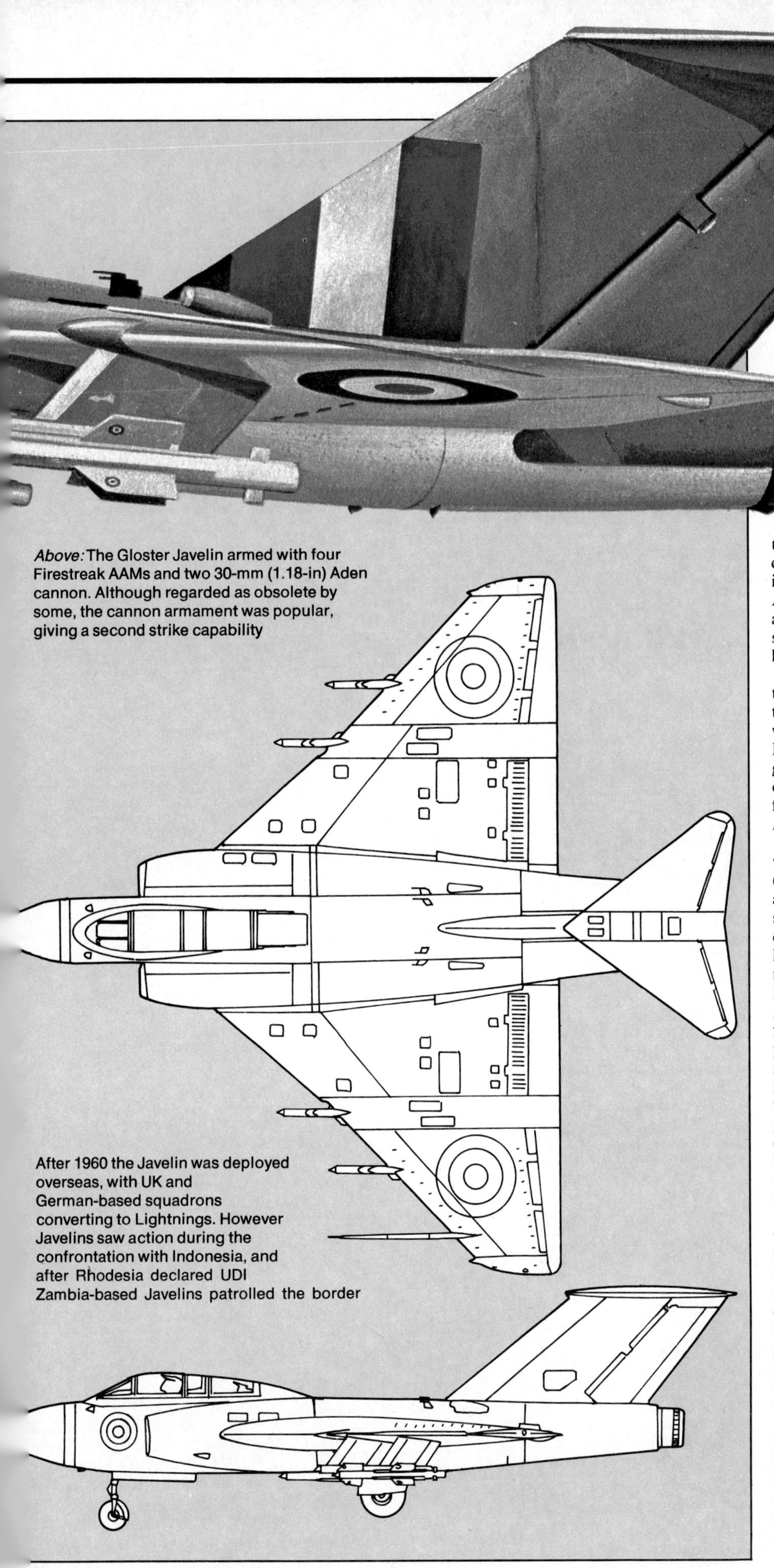

Above: The Gloster Javelin armed with four Firestreak AAMs and two 30-mm (1.18-in) Aden cannon. Although regarded as obsolete by some, the cannon armament was popular, giving a second strike capability

After 1960 the Javelin was deployed overseas, with UK and German-based squadrons converting to Lightnings. However Javelins saw action during the confrontation with Indonesia, and after Rhodesia declared UDI Zambia-based Javelins patrolled the border

tain), supplied under the MDAP (mutual defense assistance program), which resulted in a shorter nose. The T.3 was developed by Air Service Training as a dual trainer. It had an elevated rear seat with a periscope gunsight, and a simple gunsight-ranging radar in a longer nose. Twenty-one T.3s were built.

The FAW.4 Javelins had an all-flying tail, the elevators now acting as antibalance tabs, to give better longitudinal control. Equipped with AI.10 radar, 50 FAW.4s were built. The FAW.5 (64 built) carried 1136 litres (250 Imp gal) additional fuel in flexible cells in the outer wings. The 33 FAW.6 aircraft which followed were fitted with the Westinghouse AI.22 radar.

The standard engine in these first six marks was the Sapphire 102 or 103, rated at 3765-kg (8300-lb) thrust. Provision was made for two auxiliary fuel tanks to be mounted side by side flush against the wide belly, from Mk 2 onwards. By 1956 the 200-series Sapphire had become available, and the Sapphire 203 rated at 5000 kg (11 000 lb) was used in the FAW.7, which was a largely new aircraft. An AI.17 radar was matched with armament of four Firestreak AAMs carried on underwing pylons, two of the original guns being retained. The wings were again changed to house even more fuel, and in the ferry mode four drop tanks could be carried on the AAM pylons. The ailerons were given blunt trailing edges, two rows of vortex generators were fitted upstream of them, and the rear fuselage was lengthened. A total of 96 FAW.7s were built, more than any other Javelin mark.

The final new-built variant was the FAW.8, with Sapphire 203/204 engines with simple low-augmentation afterburning giving a thrust of 6074 kg (13 390 lb). This again had the short-nosed US radar, and also introduced a Sperry autopilot and further modified outer leading edges, a third row of vortex generators, pitch and yaw dampers, and local structural reinforcement. The 47 of this type brought total production, excluding prototypes, to 381.

The final mark was the FAW.9, all rebuilt by Gloster from the Mk 7, which retained the long-nosed British radar but otherwise had all the features of the Mk 8 plus provision for a crude flight-refuelling probe high on the right side of the nose. The 46 of this type entered service in 1959-61.

This large but quite docile aircraft was

A cannon-armed Javelin Mk 1 takes off. The Javelin was a docile, rather slow fighter, and considering its poor performance reasonably popular with its pilots. The last Javelins were withdrawn from front-line service in Hong Kong in early 1968

reasonably popular in service, considering its rather poor performance. From 1960 most of its service was overseas, the last home unit to convert from Javelins to Lightnings doing so in 1964. Javelins continued in Germany to 1966, in Cyprus to 1967, and in Hong Kong until early 1968. Had they been retained they might have become candidates for rebuilding yet again with modern radar and weapons.

Span: 15.87 m (52 ft 1 in) *Length:* (FAW.2, 6 and 8) 17.14 m (56 ft 3 in), (FAW.8, 9) 17.30 m (56 ft 9 in) *Gross weight:* (FAW.1) 15 420 kg (34 000 lb), (FAW.9) 19 470 kg (42 930 lb) *Maximum speed:* 1094 km/h (680 mph) (sea level)

Jeanne d'Arc

French armoured cruiser, built 1896-1903. Following the success of *Dupuy de Lôme,* Admiral Fournier proposed a new design which was executed by Emile Bertin with many improvements.

The waterline was protected by a narrow belt of 150-75 mm (6-3 in) armour. Two thin steel decks closed in the upper and bottom edges of the belt to form a long box, inside which the hull was subdivided into cofferdams, ammunition passages and coal bunkers. This form of protection was designed to keep out medium-calibre shells: the upper deck was intended to burst the shells not kept out by the belt, while the lower or splinter-deck stopped the fragments. It was adopted for other large cruisers and even battleships.

The armament was heavy, two 193-mm (7.6-in) Model 1893 in single turrets at either end, 14 138.6-mm (5.46-in) on the broadside at two levels and two submerged torpedo tubes. The engines were located amidships, with the boilers in two groups forward and aft. The designed horsepower was greatly exceeded on trials, but *Jeanne d'Arc* still only reached 22 knots with 33 000 hp. The stokeholds became so hot that the trials had to be suspended while improvements were made to the ventilation. She never reached the contract speed of 23 knots, and consumed prodigious quantities of coal, but was nevertheless the precursor of many similar cruisers.

From 1912-14 she served as a training ship, but after the outbreak of war she joined the 2nd Light Squadron in the Channel, and later served under British control in the Western Approaches. In 1915 she went to the Eastern Mediterranean and with the battleship *Jaureguiberry* and the cruiser *Amiral Charner* captured Ruad Island and Castelorizo. In September she evacuated Armenian refugees from Antioch, and she remained off the Syrian coast until the end of 1917. During the last year of the war she escorted troop convoys from the US. After the Armistice in 1918 she returned to training duties, and in 1929 she went into reserve. She was stricken in 1933 and sold for scrap.

Displacement: 11 270 tonnes (normal) *Length:* 145 m (475 ft 9 in) oa *Beam:* 19.4 m (63 ft 8 in) *Draught:* 8.1 m (26 ft 7 in) *Machinery:* 3-shaft reciprocating steam, 28 000 ihp=23 knots (designed) *Protection:* 150-75 mm (6-3 in) belt, 50-40 mm (2-1.6 in) decks, 200 mm (8 in) turrets *Armament:* 2 194-mm (7.6-in)/45-cal (2×1); 14 138.6-mm (5.46-in)/45-cal (14×1); 16 47-mm (1.85-in) QF (16×1); 2 45-cm (17.7-in) torpedo tubes (beam, submerged) *Crew:* 626

Jeanne d'Arc

French training cruiser, built 1928-30. Under the 1927 Programme, the French navy ordered a training cruiser, with the armament of a light cruiser, light protection and accommodation and classrooms for 156 midshipmen and 20 instructors. Her sea speed was a modest 22-23 knots, but this was enough to give her a useful wartime role in the protection of commerce.

The 155-mm (6.1-in) guns were the same type as those in the *Duguay Trouin* Class. She was given a full outfit of equipment found in regular cruisers, including torpedo tubes, a catapult and two Loire-Nieuport 130 floatplanes, to enable the midshipmen to train realistically.

At the French armistice in 1940 *Jeanne d'Arc* was in the West Indies hunting for German raiders, and she remained at Martinique until the end of 1942. Then, after being docked at Puerto Rico, she sailed for Algiers. There she was hastily rearmed with six 40-mm (1.57-in) Bofors guns by the US repair ship *Vulcan* the day before she embarked 1200 troops and 110 tons of material for the invasion of Corsica. Shortly afterwards the floatplanes and catapult were removed, and the AA armament was increased to two quadruple Bofors mountings and 20 single 20-mm (0.79-in) Oerlikons.

After 35 years of service this much-loved ship was replaced by a new helicopter-carrier/training cruiser with the same name, and she was scrapped in 1966.

Displacement: 7921 tons (normal), 8950 tons (full load) *Length:* 170 m (557 ft 9 in) oa *Beam:* 17.7 m (58 ft 1 in) *Draught:* 6.4 m (21 ft) *Machinery:* 2-shaft geared steam turbines, 32 500 shp=25 knots *Protection:* 20 mm (0.79 in) box citadel over magazines, 30 mm (1.18 in) deck *Armament:* 8 155-mm (6.1-in)/55-cal (4×2); 4 75-mm (2.95-in)/60-cal AA (4×1); 4 37-mm (1.46-in) AA (2×2); 12 13.2-mm (0.52-in) AA; 2 55-cm (21.7-in) torpedo tubes (above water, beam) *Crew:* 615

Musées de la Marine

Jeanne d'Arc, French training cruiser, in US two-tone camouflage pattern in the mid-1940s

Jeanne d'Arc

French helicopter/training ship. The world's first ship to be ordered as a helicopter carrier was the French navy's *Jeanne d'Arc*. Intended to replace the 1931 vintage training cruiser of the same name, she was to be used for the seagoing instruction of junior officers in peacetime and as an antisubmarine or 'Commando' carrier in war. As the cruiser was to remain in commission until the new ship was ready to take over her duties, the latter was ordered as *La Résolue* and was known as such for a year after commissioning.

Ordered in March 1957, the carrier was not laid down, at Brest naval dockyard, until July 1960, completing for trials three years later, on July 1, 1963. By this time, two US Navy purpose-built assault helicopter carriers of the *Iwo Jima* Class were in service, the first of which had been ordered a year later than the French ship.

The layout adopted was similar to that seen 20 years before in the Japanese *Chiyoda* and *Chitose*, where the forward portion of the hull was given over to armament and command and control, and the after half-length accommodated the aviation facilities. In *La Résolue/Jeanne d'Arc*, these consisted of a hangar 'box', measuring approximately 50 m (164 ft) in length and 18 m (59 ft) in width, with a depth of two decks, located at quarterdeck level abaft the bridge structure; the roof of the hangar formed the 62×21 m (203×69 ft) flight deck. A single lift, measuring 12×6 m (39×20 ft) was situated on the centreline at the extreme after end of the 'box', opening on to the hangar and the quarterdeck. This siting, which has most of the advantages of the deck-edge lift position but none of its major disadvantages of exposure to heavy seas, was first seen in the US Navy's *Thetis Bay*, a 1945 escort carrier which completed conversion to the assault helicopter carrier role nine months before the French ship was ordered. A single crane on the port deck edge was installed to transfer helicopters from the quay-side or lighters straight to the lift.

Aircraft complement in wartime would be eight Sud 3210 Super Frelon helicopters, equipped either for submarine detection and attack or as troop carriers. In peacetime, part of the hangar is used for classrooms, the bulkheads and decks being designed for quick removal in order to clear the hangar when required. Only four aircraft can be stowed with the ship fitted for training.

Armament was intended to consist of six 100-mm (3.9-in) dual-purpose automatic guns in single turrets, but only four were installed, one on either side of the bridge and two on the quarterdeck. Also planned for installation was a quadruple 30.5-cm (12-in) antisubmarine mortar which could also fire 100-kg (220-lb) projectiles to a range of 5950 m (6500 yards) in the shore bombardment role. This was never fitted, nor was a proposed Masurca surface-to-air missile system because the plans were changed when she was under construction. Fitted with a full kit of air warning, height-finding and aircraft direction radars, she was capable of controlling fighters as well as long-range maritime patrol aircraft.

Of cruiser size (10 000 tons, 182 m [597 ft] length), *La Résolue/Jeanne d'Arc* was designed with economy of operation in mind. Her two-shaft steam turbine machinery produced 40 000 shp, giving the respectable speed of 26.5 knots and a range of 6000 nautical miles, on only 1360 tonnes of fuel. The 1924 British carrier *Hermes*, with virtually identical dimensions and power, could achieve only half the range on 50% more fuel.

After a year of trials and modifications, which included the raising of the funnel, previously set almost flush with the upper bridge level, *La Résolue* commissioned for service on June 30, 1964. On July 16, she formally relieved the old cruiser of the training task and her name. Since then, she has seen world-wide service on midshipmen's training cruises.

Displacement: 10 000 tons (standard), 12 365 tons (full load) *Length:* 182 m (597 ft) oa *Beam:* 22 m (72 ft 2 in) wl, 24 m (78 ft 9 in) max *Draught:* 7.32 m (24 ft) *Machinery:* 2 sets geared steam turbines, 2 shafts, 40 000 shp=26.5 knots *Aircraft:* 4 (as training ship) 8 (as ASW or assault ship) *Armament:* 4 100-mm (3.9-in) DP *Crew:* 906 including cadets and midshipmen (capacity for 700 marines as assault ship)

Jeanne d'Arc, the world's first helicopter carrier, with Super Frelon helicopters on deck

Marius Bar

Marius Bar

The French helicopter training cruiser *Jeanne d'Arc*. She is intended for a peacetime training role for naval cadets, but with a minimum of modification can be turned into a helicopter assault ship. She can carry four heavy helicopters and has a crew of 809, consisting of 30 officers, 587 ratings and 192 cadets. In wartime the helicopters are increased to eight and she can carry a battalion of 700 men. Laid down at Brest in 1960, she was launched in 1961 and commissioned two years later. After sea trials she was given a taller funnel to keep smoke and exhaust fumes clear of the bridge. She has a range of 9650 km (6000 miles)

Above: Jeep-mounted SAS patrol in the North African desert

Jeep

US Army utility vehicle. In 1940 the US Ordnance Technical Committee issued a specification for a light utility car with four-wheel drive, to carry a 270-kg (600-lb) payload, and to have an overall weight of 590 kg (1300 lb) or less: 175 automobile and engineering companies were invited to submit models within 75 days. Only two companies attempted to meet this tight deadline, the American Bantam Car Company and Willys-Overland Motors. Only Bantam managed to produce their model on time, and they consequently received the first contract. Experience soon showed, however, that their vehicle was under-powered and not sufficiently robust.

The chief engineer at Willys-Overland, Barney Roos, considered the military specification to be unrealistic, particularly the weight limit, and he set about designing a vehicle which would meet the physical demands of military service, without worrying too much about the weight. In conjunction with engineers of the US Army Quartermaster Corps, Roos developed a sturdy and powerful vehicle which, when tested in November 1940, proved to be a complete success.

By this time the need for a light vehicle was pressing, and the US government now raised the weight limit to 980 kg (2160 lb) and invited

Rijksinstitut Voor Ologsdocumentatie

A Willy's Jeep in north-west Europe. Jeeps accompanied US troops from North Africa to Europe during 1939-45 and modernized versions were still in service in the late 1970s

Above: The Jeep as the Allies' military runabout. Used by Soviet forces as well as the western Allies, captured Jeeps were pressed into service with the Germans. *Left:* The Jeep as a fighting vehicle. SAS and reconnaissance troops used Jeeps fitted with Vickers and Browning machine-guns for deep penetration raids in Africa and Europe. Besides fuel and ammunition they were loaded with rations, water and the personal equipment for a two-man crew and stripped of all surplus weight

Ford, Willys and Bantam to submit fresh designs. The Ford and Bantam designs were within the weight limit but were deficient in performance, while the Willys was 120 kg (264 lb) over the weight but had almost 50% more engine power and consequently a better performance. Eventually after paring away every ounce which could be spared, Roos brought the Willys design to just within the weight limit and it was accepted for standardization early in 1941.

An initial order for 16 000 vehicles was given, and these were known as the MA model. Small changes were subsequently made, notably enlarging the fuel tank, and this became the Willys Model MB. The Ford company were then given a contract to manufacture to the Willys design, and these became the Truck, Command and Reconnaissance, ¼ ton, 4×4 Ford Model GPW.

The Jeep became the universal military runabout of the Allied nations during the war. Not only was it used as a utility vehicle behind the lines but it was also a combat vehicle in its own right, being armed and used by the Long Range Desert Group and other private armies. It was carried in gliders, dropped by parachute, and an amphibious version, a scaled-down DUKW in effect and shape, was developed by the Ford company and standardized in 1943. In postwar years it spawned innumerable imitations: one amphibious Jeep was driven across the Atlantic; and the original design was slightly modernized to become the Car Utility M38 for the US Army. In doing so it has lost some of the spartan simplicity of the original design.

A question never satisfactorily answered is that of the origin of the name Jeep. It has been suggested that it came from a corruption of GPW, the Ford model notation. It has also been suggested that the name was derived from a cartoon character. The only certain thing is that the various experimental models of light car were being called Jeep long before the Willys design appeared, and the probability is that it was derived from the letters GP for General Purpose, a phrase which appeared in the original specification.

(Willys Model MB) *Weight:* 1476 kg (3254 lb) *Length:* 3.36 m (11 ft) *Width:* 1.57 m (5 ft 2 in) *Height:* (without top) 1.32 m (4 ft 4 in); (with top up) 1.78 m (5 ft 10 in) *Powerplant:* 4-cylinder side-valve, 2200 cc, 54 bhp at 4000 rpm *Speed:* 105 km/h (65 mph) *Range:* 485 km (300 miles) *Towed load:* 454 kg (1000 lb) *Carried load:* 363 kg (800 lb)

(Ford Amphibious Model) *Weight:* 1950 kg (4300 lb) *Length:* 4.62 m (15 ft 1¾ in) *Width:* 1.63 m (5 ft 4 in) *Height:* (without top) 1.72 m (5 ft 8 in) *Powerplant:* As above *Speed:* (Land) 88 km/h (55 mph); (Water) 9 km/h (5½ mph) *Range:* (Land) 400 km (250 miles); (Water) 56 km (35 miles) *Payloads:* As above

IWM

A US-crewed Jeep, equipped for telephone-line laying in North Africa in the Second World War

Jeff

US assault hovercraft. Following the British success in developing the hovercraft principle the US Navy in 1965 initiated a programme of development designed to exploit the unique capabilities of the hovercraft. These are its considerable flexibility of movement, particularly the ease of transition between water and land, its ability to negotiate small obstacles, its high speed and its cost-effectiveness. Obviously a prime area for investigation was in amphibious assault roles where troops and heavy equipment have to be moved from large ocean-going ships with a deep draught and deposited on a hostile shore, possibly protected by mines and antishipping obstacles and probably under fire. The hovercraft's unique characteristics give it enormous advantages over the old-fashioned landing craft, and the US Navy began their 13-year study into the use of hovercraft in an assault role.

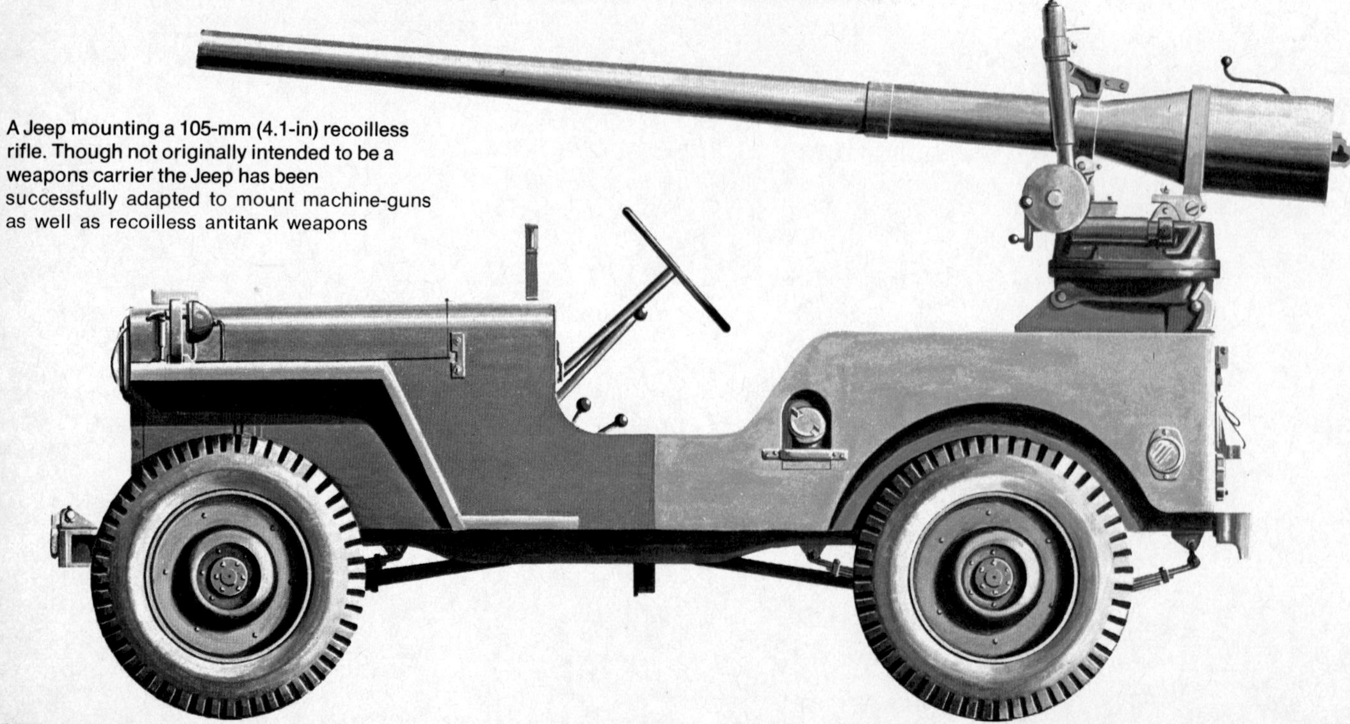

A Jeep mounting a 105-mm (4.1-in) recoilless rifle. Though not originally intended to be a weapons carrier the Jeep has been successfully adapted to mount machine-guns as well as recoilless antitank weapons

The programme led to the Jeff A and B assault craft designs. The contract for a Jeff A design for use by the US Marine Corps was awarded to Aerojet General Corporation in 1970. In March 1971 Bell Aerospace Textron was awarded the contract to design the Jeff B assault craft to an identical specification—a 160-ton craft capable of 50 knots with a 75-ton payload. The Jeff B was completed towards the end of 1977 and commenced trials early in 1978.

The Jeff B assault craft has a basic structure similar to that of a standard landing craft; a flat-bottomed craft with a large well deck for transporting vehicles, and high sides providing troop accommodation, etc. Six gas turbine engines provide power to four centrifugal impellers which lift the craft on a cushion of air; the gas turbines also power two large ducted fans aft on either quarter which provide horizontal thrust.

The assault craft are designed to be carried in the well decks of the American *Thomaston* and *Anchorage* LSDs (landing ship docks), *Raleigh* LPDs (amphibious transport docks) and *Tarawa* LHAs (amphibious assault ships). The LSDs can carry four Jeff assault craft and are fitted with bow and stern ramps for roll-on roll-off movement of tanks and vehicles. The assault craft can also operate alongside cargo ships for the transportation of palletized stores to troops ashore.

(Jeff A) *Weight:* 149 tons *Length:* 29.3 m (96 ft) *Beam:* 14.6 m (48 ft) *Height:* 7 m (23 ft) all dimensions on air cushion *Machinery:* 6 3750-hp gas turbines = 50 knots *Payload:* 75 tons *Crew:* 6

(Jeff B) *Weight:* 160 tons *Length:* 26.4 m (86 ft 9 in) *Beam:* 14.3 m (47 ft) *Height:* 7.2 m (23 ft 6 in) all dimensions on air cushion *Machinery:* 6 2680-hp gas turbines = 50 knots *Payload:* 75 tons *Crew:* 6

Bell Aerospace Textron

Jeff B, the US Navy's experimental assault hovercraft, comes ashore after the first overwater tests on December 16, 1977. It has a crew of six and payload of 75 tons

Jersey

British offshore patrol vessel class, built 1975-78. Faced with the need to replace the ageing 'Ton' Class minesweepers the British Ministry of Defence decided to build the cheapest possible type of ship to provide a vessel which could monitor ship movements, protect fishery rights, and release frigates from the mundane tasks of patrolling the oilfields.

The design chosen was a commercial trawler hull from the Aberdeen shipyard Hall Russell, which has long experience in this type of craft. The armament of one Mk 3 40-mm (1.57-in) Bofors of 1940 vintage caused great derision when it was announced, and the Royal Navy was harshly criticized for failing to produce a better-armed and better-equipped ship. In fact the ships have amply vindicated themselves, and the original five are to be followed by a further two. The Ministry of Defence made no attempt to improve on the commercial design, and merely drew up a series of parameters on the minimum length, beam, freeboard and other qualities needed to protect the crew against the worst effects of seasickness and tedium. A comprehensive navigation and communications outfit was provided, and the ships are highly manoeuvrable. They are fitted to replenish at sea, but even without refuelling can steam 11 300 km (7000 miles) at 15 knots.

Known as the 'Island' Class, the first five are *Jersey* (P.295), *Guernsey* (P.297), *Shetland* (P.298), *Orkney* (P.299) and *Lindisfarne* (P.300). The next two are to be called *Alderney* and *Anglesey.*

Displacement: 925 tons (standard), 1250 tons (full load) *Length:* 59.54 m (195 ft 4 in) oa *Beam:* 10.92 m (35 ft 10 in) *Draught:* 4.27 m (14 ft) *Machinery:* 1-shaft diesel, 4380 bhp = 16 knots *Armament:* 1 40-mm (1.57-in)/60-cal Bofors *Crew:* 24

Jet Provost, BAC

British trainer and light attack aircraft. Developed initially by the Hunting Aircraft Company, which later became part of the British Aircraft Corporation, the Jet Provost was based on the earlier piston-engined Provost which had in its time proved extremely successful as a trainer. The first of ten Jet Provost Mk 1 development aircraft flew on June 26, 1954, and the tenth aircraft of this evaluation batch became the T.Mk 2 prototype, which flew for the first time on

HMS *Orkney*, an 'Island' Class offshore patrol vessel, showing her bridge and stern with her controversial armament of one Bofors 40-mm (1.57-in)/60-cal AA gun

A J Watts Collection

A J Watts Collection

September 1, 1955. This was followed by the first production models for RAF Flying Training Command, the T.Mk 3 (201 built) with the 794-kg (1750-lb) st Viper 102 turbojet, and the T.Mk 4 (185 built), powered by a 1134-kg (2500-lb) st Viper 201. All had an unpressurized cockpit, with side-by-side ejection seats in the T.4. No armament was fitted.

The Jet Provost's potential as a close-support/light attack aircraft was soon realized, and armed versions of the T.Mk 3 (T.51s) went to Ceylon (12), Kuwait (six) and the Sudan (four). Armament comprised twin 0.30-in (7.62-mm) FN machine-guns mounted in the air-intake walls. Underwing attachments were provided for external loads of bombs, rockets, flares and rocket projectiles. T.Mk 4s, similarly armed, were exported as T.52s to Venezuela (15), Iraq (20), Sudan (eight) and South Yemen (four). All versions retained dual controls and could be used for armament training or operational combat.

The last two T.Mk 4s were converted as BAC 145 prototypes for the Jet Provost T.Mk 5. They had a new front fuselage, shorter rear fuselage, new pressurized cockpit, and additional fuel in the wings. Powerplant was the Viper 202 turbojet, and deliveries of 110 aircraft were made to the RAF between September 1969 and October 1972. During a three-year programme which ended in 1976, BAC installed VOR (VHF omnirange) and DME (distance measuring equipment) sets in 157 of the RAF's T.Mk 3s and T.Mk 5s; these then being redesignated T.Mk 3A and T.Mk 5A respectively. The BAC 167 Strikemaster light attack aircraft was developed from the BAC 145.

(T.Mk 3) *Span:* (over tip-tanks) 11.25 m (36 ft 11 in) *Length:* 9.88 m (32 ft 5 in) *Gross weight:* 3460 kg (7629 lb) *Maximum speed:* 550 km/h (342 mph)

'Jill' Allied codename for Nakajima B6N Japanese torpedo-bomber See **B6N**

JN-4 and JN-6, Curtiss

US training aircraft. Having produced a series of pusher biplane trainers for the US Army Signal Corps, in 1913 the Curtiss Aeroplane company built two model G two-seat tractor scouts for the army. These were not particularly successful, however, and in order to make up for his company's lack of experience with tractor aircraft, Glenn Curtiss engaged the English designer B Douglas Thomas, whose first design for Curtiss was the model J of 1914, an equal-span biplane powered by a 90-hp Curtiss OXX. It had a stick control for the elevators and a wheel to operate the rudder, but the ailerons were worked by a yoke on the pilot's shoulders. The J was succeeded by the Curtiss-designed model N, with interplane ailerons, and the best features of the two were combined to produce the JN. A modified J with double ailerons became the JN-2, ten of which were delivered to the army in 1915, and four modified JNs were built as N-8s before the JN-4 emerged in 1916.

The JN-4 was actually developed from the JN-3, a modified JN-2 with unequal-span wings, built by the Canadian subsidiary of Curtiss to provide trainers for the British Royal Flying Corps and Royal Naval Air Service. JN-3s were subject to various alterations requested by the RFC and carried out by the Canadian Aeroplanes company, and were given the new designation JN-4. Canadian-built machines were later designated JN-4Can by the US Army, becoming known as 'Canucks'. Before the United States joined the First World War on April 6, 1917, the army had ordered a total of 93 JN-4s, most powered by 90-hp OX-2s, though some had Hall-Scott A-7s of the same power. A further eight Twin JNs, with two 100-hp OXX-2 engines, were ordered, and these, along with a number of JN-4s, served along the Mexican border. The US Navy was also a customer, acquiring two JN-1W floatplanes.

Involvement in the war caused large orders to be placed with a variety of contractors for almost any type which was immediately available. The delivery of 603 JN-4s began in June 1917, and by November of that year JN-4A, B, C and D variants had been produced. Small numbers of each were supplied to the army and navy, but it was the D which was selected for large-scale production. The D was distinguished by a downward-thrusting engine, a 90-hp OX-5, and cut-out wing centre sections to improve rear cockpit visibility. A total of over 3000 Ds were built under wartime contracts, 1404 by Curtiss and the remainder by six other contractors.

The JN-4D-2 was an interim model with revised controls, and 101 were built before the introduction of the JN-4H with the 150-hp Hispano A engine. The more powerful engine was fitted to equip the type for advanced training, and as well as 402 JN-4H the army bought 100 JN-4HB bombardment trainers and 427 JN-4HG for instruction in aerial gunnery, some being supplied to the navy in 1918. Next came the JN-6, a slightly modified JN-4H with the same powerplant. Specialized versions were produced for training in bombardment (154, designated JN-6HB, were built), aerial gunnery, with one (560 HG-1) or two (90 HG-2) guns, observation (106 HO) and pursuit (125 HP), for a total of 1035. At the end of the war contracts for a total of 4450 of various JN-4 and JN-6 models were cancelled.

As well as the JN series, the model N was developed into the N-8, similar to the JN-3, four of which served with the army on the Mexican border, and the N-9 floatplane, with increased wingspan and 100-hp OX-6 engine, of which an eventual total of 610 were bought by the US Navy.

JN series aircraft were universally known as 'Jennys', and at the end of the war thousands of war-surplus machines were bought by civilian pilots and used for barnstorming, wing-walking and other stunting. The Hispano-powered types continued in military service until 1927, many rebuilt of steel tube being redesignated JNS, with A, E or I suffixes indicating different engine models.

(JN-4D) *Span:* 13.28 m (43 ft 7 in) *Length:* 8.33 m (27 ft 4 in) *Gross weight:* 871 kg (1920 lb) *Maximum speed:* 128 km/h (80 mph)

(JN-6HG-1) *Span:* 13.28 m (43 ft 7 in) *Length:* 8.2 m (26 ft 11 in) *Gross weight:* 1247 kg (2750 lb) *Maximum speed:* 128 km/h (80 mph)

João Coutinho

Portuguese frigate class. The first six vessels of the *João Coutinho* Class were ordered in April 1968 for delivery in 1970. The design was prepared by Blohm und Voss and the first three vessels F475, F476 and F477 were built in the firm's Hamburg yard. F471, F484 and F485 were built by the Spanish firm Empresa Nacional Bazan. The ships were designed as antisubmarine vessels and are officially rated as corvettes, but the armament of these first six vessels can no longer be considered adequate against modern nuclear submarines.

The principal A/S equipment consists of

Baptista de Andrade, a frigate of the *João Coutinho* Class, completed in the mid-1970s

obsolete depth charges and depth-charge throwers together with the Hedgehog A/S mortar dating from the Second World War. The armament is also outdated, consisting of a 76-mm (3-in) gun and an old-model 40-mm (1.57-in). The ships are also too slow (24.5 knots maximum) and lack modern A/S facilities such as a helicopter.

In March 1972 a further four vessels were ordered from Bazan with updated armament. A new antisubmarine torpedo-tube system replaced the obsolete depth-charge and Hedgehog equipment, and a new model French-built 100-mm (3.9-in) gun and single Bofors 40-mm (1.57-in) has replaced the outdated weapons on the earlier vessels.

The outdated armament aside, the class proved to be extremely reliable in service.

In 1977, *Baptista de Andrade, João Roby, Alfonso Cerqueira* and *Oliveira E Carmo* were sold to Colombia.

Displacement: 1203 tons (standard), 1380 tons (full load) *Length:* 84.6 m (277 ft 6 in) oa *Beam:* 10.3 m (33 ft 9 in) *Draught:* 3.6 m (11 ft 10 in) *Machinery:* 2-shaft diesels, 10 560 bhp = 24.5 knots *Armament:* (first six ships) 2 76-mm (3-in) (1×2); 2 40-mm (1.57-in) (1×2); 1 Hedgehog; 2 depth-charge throwers, (last four ships) 1 100-mm (3.9-in); 2 40-mm (1.57-in) (2×1); 2 depth-charge racks; 6 Mk 32 A/S torpedo tubes (2×3) *Crew:* 100

No and name	laid down	launched	completed
F471 *Antonio Enes*	4/68	8/69	6/71
F475 *João Coutinho*	9/68	5/69	3/70
F476 *Jacinto Candido*	4/68	6/69	6/70
F477 *General Pereira D'Eca*	10/68	7/69	10/70
F484 *Augusto de Castilho*	8/68	7/69	11/70
F485 *Honorio Barreto*	7/68	4/70	4/71
F486 *Baptista de Andrade*	1972	3/73	11/74
F487 *João Roby*	1972	6/73	3/75
F488 *Alfonso Cerqueira*	1973	10/73	6/75
F489 *Oliveira E Carmo*	1972	2/74	2/75

Joessel

French submarine class, built 1913-20. Under the 1914 Programme two submarines, *Q.109-110,* of a steam-driven Simonot design, were authorized and laid down. Work slowed down after August 1914, and eventually the turbines were used for the sloops *Ailette* and *Escaut.* The design was reconsidered before work started again late in the war, and the submarines were eventually given Schneider-Carel diesels. They were launched as *Joessel* and *Fulton* at Cherbourg in 1919.

Six more of the class had been planned by the Conseil Supérieur de la Marine (naval board) in April 1913, and orders were placed in January 1915, but they were suspended a month later and deferred until 1918 at the earliest. *Q.115-116* were to have been built at Cherbourg, *Q.117-118* at Toulon and *Q.119-120* at Rochefort, but they were all cancelled after the Armistice of 1918. *Joessel* and *Fulton* served successfully until 1935.

Displacement: 870/1247 tonnes (surfaced/submerged) *Length:* 74 m (242 ft 9 in) oa *Beam:* 7.4 m (24 ft 3 in) *Draught:* 3.62 m (11 ft 11 in) *Machinery:* (as designed) 2-shaft geared steam turbines/electric motors, 5000 shp/1640 ehp= 20/11 knots (surfaced/submerged), (as built) 2-shaft diesel/electric, 2900 bhp/1640 ehp= 16.5/11 knots (surfaced/submerged) *Armament:* 2 75-mm (2.95-in) (2× 1); 8 45-cm (17.7-in) torpedo tubes, 10 torpedoes *Crew:* 47

Joffre

French aircraft carrier class. Although the 1922 Washington Naval Treaty had allowed the French navy to build up to 54 000 tons of aircraft carriers, successive interwar French governments had lacked the will and the money to take advantage of the allowance. Only the *Béarn,* completed in 1927, but exempt from the treaty quota due to her 'experimental status', was commissioned.

The withdrawal of the French and Italian delegations from the 1930 London Naval Conference, as a result of mutual mistrust regarding Mediterranean ambitions, led to serious design work in both countries, culminating in the 15-in (381-mm) gun battleships of the *Richelieu* and *Littorio* Classes, but also embracing aircraft carriers. By 1936, when the need for rearmament became apparent to the democracies of Western Europe, the basis of a design of an 18 000-ton fast carrier had been worked out. Two years later, two ships, to be named *Joffre* and *Painlevé,* were ordered. The name-ship of the class was laid down at St Nazaire in November 1938, followed, at the same yard, a few months later by the second unit.

The design adopted was original. The island structure on the starboard side was the largest yet planned, with a cylindrical fire-control tower surmounting six decks of command and communications 'offices'. At each end of the island was a pair of twin 130-mm (5.1-in)/45-cal dual-purpose turrets, ideally situated for all-round defence but poorly placed if blast damage to aircraft on deck was to be avoided. Four 37-mm (1.46-in) AA guns were located on the island and seven quadruple 13.2-mm (0.52-in) heavy AA machine-guns were to have been installed around the deck edges.

The flight deck and hangar arrangement were unusual. The flight deck was offset to port, extending over the side while the starboard deck edge reached only to the inboard face of the island. The upper hangar was at forecastle and quarterdeck level and was bounded by the hull plating on the port side and the boiler uptakes and downtakes to starboard. The weight of the island was thus balanced by the flight-deck extension and the trunking to the boilers did not encroach on the hangar, which had a length of 195 m (640 ft) and a clear breadth of 20.8 m (68 ft) amidships. Below the main hangar deck was a 79×15.6 m (259×51 ft) area which was to be used primarily as a workshop and stowage for reserve aircraft. Two large 'T'-form lifts on the fore and aft axis of the hull, but offset to starboard in the flight deck and hangar, gave access to the upper hangar. The after lift also served the lower hangar.

A seaplane handling crane was to have been mounted on the quarterdeck, from which access to the upper hangar was gained via large doors. (The contemporary British *Illustrious* Class also had provision for handling seaplanes, but the Royal Navy preferred the amidships position for cranes as being less affected by pitching or 'corkscrewing' in the open sea.) The landplane complement was intended to consist of 25 divebombers and torpedo-reconnaissance bombers and 15 intercepters.

The hull of *Joffre* was almost half built when construction was halted in June 1940, following the Franco-German armistice; it was still there, though derelict, at the time of the Commando raid on St Nazaire in March 1942 and was not completely scrapped until after the end of the war. *Joffre*'s 120 000-shp machinery, which had been expected to give her a maximum speed of 33 knots, was built at Brest and when completed was incorporated into a thermal electricity generating station to provide power for the naval dockyard.

Displacement: 18 000 tons (standard) *Length:* 236 m (774 ft 3 in) oa *Beam:* 28 m (91 ft 10 in) hull (approx), 35 m (114 ft 10 in) max *Draught:* 8.2 m (26 ft 11 in) (approx) *Machinery:* 2-shaft geared steam turbines, 120 000 shp=33 knots *Aircraft:* 40 *Armament:* 8 130-mm (5.1-in) DP (4×2); 8 37-mm (1.46-in) AA (4×2); 28 13.2-mm (0.52-in) AA (7×4) *Crew:* not known

John C Butler

US destroyer escort class, built 1943-45. These ships resembled the *Rudderow* Class, a variant of the *Buckley* Class with lower bridgework and funnel, and two single 5-in (127-mm)/38-cal guns. Like the *Edsall* Class, they dispensed with electric drive as the shortages of turbine blades had been overcome by the time they were laid down.

The early ships of the group had a set of triple torpedo tubes, as in earlier destroyer escorts, but these were removed in 1945 to cope with the kamikaze threat. *Vandivier* and *Wagner* were launched in 1943 but not completed until 1955 as radar pickets (DER).

Built by Consolidated Steel Corporation, Orange, Texas: *John C Butler* (DE.339); *O'Flaherty* (DE.340); *Raymond* (DE.341); *Richard W Suesens* (DE.342); *Abercrombie* (DE.343); *Oberrender* (DE.344); *Robert Brazier* (DE.345); *Edwin A Howard* (DE.346); *Jesse Rutherford* (DE.347); *Key* (DE.348); *Gentry* (DE.349); *Traw* (DE.350); *Maurice J Manuel* (DE.351); *Naifeh* (DE.352); *Doyle C Barnes* (DE.353); *Kenneth M Willett* (DE.354); *Jaccard* (DE.355); *Lloyd E Acree* (DE.356); *George E Davis* (DE.357); *Mack* (DE.358); *Woodson* (DE.359); *Johnnie Hutchins* (DE.360); *Walton* (DE.361); *Rolf* (DE.362); *Pratt* (DE.363); *Rombach* (DE.364); *McGinty* (DE.365); *Alvin C Cockrell* (DE.366); *French* (DE.367); *Cecil J Doyle* (DE.368); *Thaddeus Parker* (DE.369); *John L Williamson* (DE.370); *Presley* (DE.371); *Williams* (DE.372)

Ordered from Consolidated Steel Corporation, but cancelled June 1944: *William C Lawe* (DE.373); *Lloyd Thomas* (DE.374); *Keppler* (DE.375); *Kleinsmith* (DE.376); *Henry W Tucker* (DE.377); *Weiss* (DE.378); *Francovich* (DE.379); DE.380 and 381

Built by Brown Shipbuilding, Houston, Texas: *Richard S Bull* (DE.402); *Richard M Rowell* (DE.403); *Eversole* (DE.404); *Dennis* (DE.405); *Edmonds* (DE.406); *Shelton* (DE.407); *Strauss* (DE.408); *La Prade* (DE.409); *Jack Miller* (DE.410); *Stafford* (DE.411); *Walter C Mann* (DE.412); *Samuel B Roberts* (DE.413); *Le Ray Williams* (DE.414); *Lawrence C Taylor* (DE.415); *Melvin R Nawman* (DE.416); *Oliver Mitchell* (DE.417); *Tabberer* (DE.418); *Robert F Keller* (DE.419); *Leland E Thomas* (DE.420); *Chester T O'Brien* (DE.421); *Douglas A Munro* (DE.422); *Dufilho* (DE.423); *Haas* (DE.424).

Built by Federal Shipbuilding, Kearny, NJ: *Corbesier* (DE.438); *Conklin* (DE.439); *McCoy Reynolds* (DE.440); *William Seiverling* (DE.441); *Ulvert M Moore* (DE.442); *Kendall C Campbell* (DE.443); *Goss* (DE.444); *Grady* (DE.445); *Charles E Brannon* (DE.446); *Albert T Harris* (DE.447); *Cross* (DE.448); *Hanna* (DE.449); *Joseph E Connolly* (DE.450); *Gilligan* (ex-*Donaldson*) (DE.508); *Formoe* (DE.509); *Heyliger* (DE.510).

Ordered from Federal Shipbuilding, but cancelled 1943-44: *Woodrow R Thompson* (DE.451); *Steinaker* (DE.452); DE.453-507, DE.511-515.

Built by Boston navy yard: *Edward H Allen* (DE.531); *Tweedy* (DE.532); *Howard F Clark* (DE.533); *Silverstein* (DE.534); *Lewis* (DE.535); *Bivin* (DE.536); *Rizzi* (DE.537); *Osberg* (DE.538); *Wagner* (DE.539); *Vandivier* (DE.540).

Ordered from Boston navy yard, but cancelled 1943-46: DE.425-437; *Sheehan* (DE.541); *Oswald A Powers* (DE.542); *Groves* (DE.543); *Alfred Wolf* (DE.544); *Harold J Ellison* (DE.545); *Myles C Fox* (DE.546); *Charles R Ware* (DE.547); *Carpellotti* (DE.548); *Eugene A Greene* (DE.549); *Gyatt* (DE.550); *Benner* (DE.551); *Kenneth D Bailey* (DE.552); *Dennis J Buckley* (DE.553); *Everett J Larson* (DE.554); DE.555-562; DE.801-832.

DE.833-840 were ordered from Mare Island navy yard, Vallejo, but were cancelled in 1943; DE.841-872 were ordered from Brown Shipbuilding, Houston, but were cancelled in 1943; DE.873-886 were ordered from the Dravo Corporation, Wilmington, but were cancelled in 1943; DE.887-898 were ordered from Western Pipe, San Pedro, but were cancelled in 1943; DE.889-904 were ordered from Federal Shipbuilding, Newark, but were cancelled in 1943.

As the last class of DEs authorized, they suffered the most drastic cutbacks in 1943-44, when the shortage of escorts in the Atlantic eased.

Oberrender was a constructive total loss after a kamikaze attack off Okinawa on May 9, 1945. *Shelton* was torpedoed by the Japanese submarine *RO.41* off Morotai, North Moluccas, on October 3, 1944, and on October 28, *I.45* sank *Eversole* off Leyte. *Samuel B Roberts* was sunk by gunfire from Japanese cruisers off Samar, East Philippines, on October 25, 1944. After the war the class saw considerable service.

In 1957 *McCoy Reynolds* and *Formoe* were transferred to Portugal as *Corte Real* and *Diego Cao*. Being too slow and too small to warrant modernization the class was disposed of between 1966 and 1972.

Displacement: 1350 tons (standard), 1660 tons (full load) *Length:* 93.3 m (306 ft) oa *Beam:* 11.2 m (36 ft 9 in) *Draught:* 4 m (13 ft 3 in) max *Machinery:* 2-shaft geared steam turbines, 12000 shp= 24 knots *Armament:* 2 5-in (127-mm)/38-cal (2×1); 4/10 40-mm (1.57-in) AA (2×2; or 1×4, 3×2); 10/16 20-mm (0.79-in) AA (10×1, 3×2); 3 21-in (53-cm) torpedo tubes (1×3) (early ships only); Hedgehog depth-charge mortar *Crew:* 200

John Ericsson

Swedish monitor class built 1864-66. Although it is hard to believe, the Swedish navy retained the three ships of this class dating from the time of the American Civil War until after the First World War. After John Ericsson had helped the US Federal navy to gain mastery over the Confederacy with *Monitor* and later developments, he and his colleague d'Ailly returned to their native Sweden to provide similar ships.

It was Sweden's willingness to adopt the latest technological innovations such as these ships which gave her a strong position militarily and politically. *John Ericsson* was launched at the Motala yard, Norrköping, on March 17, 1865. She was armed with two 15-in (381-mm) Dahlgren smooth-bore guns, mounted, like those of the American ships, in a single turret. Two similar ships, *Thordön* and *Tirfing,* were launched at the same yard on December 1, 1865, and August 1, 1866, respectively. The hulls of the later ships were 1.5 m (5 ft) longer, and they were given more efficient 24-cm (9.45-in) Krupp breech-loading guns.

In 1881, *John Ericsson* was rearmed in similar fashion, and in 1892-95 she was totally rebuilt at Karlskrona dockyard. The turret was replaced by an open barbette mounting with two 6-in (152-mm) quick-firers, and a new superstructure was provided in place of the flush deck devoid of fittings. In this guise she served as a coast-defence ship until 1918, when she was deleted and scrapped.

Thordön and *Tirfing* were also modernized,

The Swedish monitor *John Ericsson* as she appeared after completion at Norrköping in 1865

Swedish Naval History Museum

Below: *John Ericsson* after modernization in 1903. She served until 1918 when she was scrapped

in 1902-05, with two 4.71-in (120-mm) guns mounted inside the original turret. Both were stricken in 1922 and scrapped.

Displacement: 1500-1600 tons (normal) *Length:* 60.9 m (199 ft 10 in) (*Thordön* and *Tirfing* 62.4 m [204 ft 9 in]) wl *Beam:* 13.8 m (45 ft 3 in) *Draught:* 3.6 m (11 ft 10 in) *Machinery:* 1-shaft reciprocating, 380 ihp= 6.8 knots (max) *Protection:* 125 mm (5 in) belt, 43 mm (1.7 in) deck, 270 mm (10.6 in) turret (*Thordön* and *Tirfing* 118 mm [4.6 in] belt, 25 mm [1 in] deck, 261 mm [10.3 in] turret) *Armament:* 2 15-in/(380-mm) smooth-bore, muzzle-loading (1×2); 2 25-mm (1-in) machine-guns (from 1877); (*Thordön* and *Tirfing* 2 24-cm [9.4-in] breech-loading [1×2]; 2 25-mm [1-in] machine-guns [from 1877]; 8 57-mm [2.24-in] [from 1902-05]) *Crew:* 80

Johnson

US self-loading rifles and light machine-guns. Melvin M Johnson, born in 1909, was a reserve officer in the US Marine Corps and an inventor of automatic weapons. In late 1938 he had developed a satisfactory rifle with recoil operation and was on the way to perfecting a light machine-gun on the same principle. Both were unusual but effective weapons of radically different appearance from their contemporaries.

The recoil principle employed by the Johnson weapons required the barrel and bolt to recoil while locked together. After 4.8 mm (0.19 in) of travel, the barrel unlocked from the bolt and returned to battery by its own spring. The bolt was forced backwards by the residual gas pressure in the chamber, and then acted in the usual way. The system used blowback to some extent, and in this respect had similarities with the Hispano cannon.

The barrel of the Johnsons was carried in a tubular-steel jacket which provided a mount for the front bearing and a housing for the spring. The receiver was also tubular and smooth in outline. However, it was difficult to make and required careful machining and fitting. The bolt locked by eight radial lugs, much the same as in the present-day Armalite system. The lugs turned and engaged inside a barrel extension which had recesses machined in it. Both the barrel and extension were held into the body by a simple lock which could be quickly released with the nose of a bullet. The barrel could then be dismounted and a replacement inserted equally fast. In one demonstration a barrel-change took as little as six seconds.

The magazine was, perhaps, the most interesting part of the rifle. Johnson believed that damaged magazine lips were a common cause of weapon stoppage. He therefore designed a rotary magazine, without lips, located inside the weapon. The magazine was detachable, but the lips were machined into the receiver. This unusual feature complicated the rifle and allowed only ten rounds to be carried.

The light machine-gun (LMG) was very similar in operation to the rifle, but used a conventional box magazine which fed in from the left-hand side. However, the fixed and machined lips were retained and, like the rifle, the magazine could be topped up when it was fitted to the gun. The receiver was shorter than the rifle's, and a tubular housing for the return spring ran out over the butt.

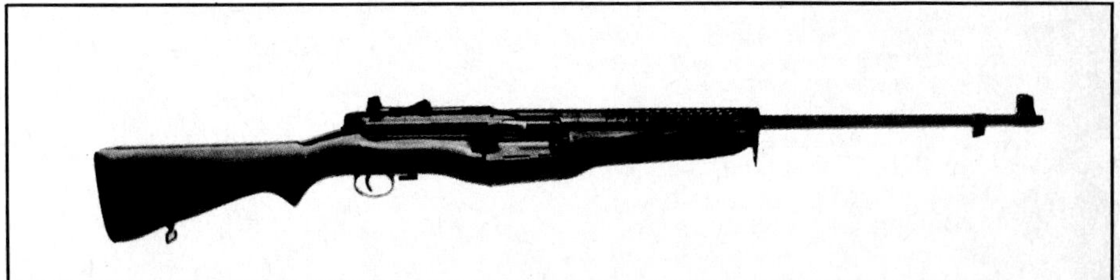

I V Hogg

Above: **The Johnson M 1941 self-loading rifle with its unusual ten-round rotary magazine.** ***Below:*** **The light machine-gun M 1941. The return spring housing extends over the butt**

I V Hogg

Both rifle and LMG had a straight-line design to improve control of fire, particularly when on automatic. The LMG was quite light in weight, and could be handled like a rifle if necessary. Both weapons had a high-set sightline, and were fitted with a folding back-sight and a tall foresight.

The US Army and the Marine Corps tested the Johnsons in 1940 and 1941, but did not adopt them. The army claimed it did not like the gun because of the magazine feed. This was an odd comment since the Browning automatic rifle was fed in this way. But the likelihood is that both weapons were discovered to be insufficiently robust for service use. Their barrels were long and unsupported, and have always appeared vulnerable to damage. The Dutch also carried out trials with the Johnson guns and decided to buy them. Johnson, therefore, set up a factory and supplied some weapons to the Dutch troops in the East Indies before the Japanese invasion. As soon as the United States entered the war in 1941 there was a great need for automatic weapons of all kinds; the US Marine Corps took the remaining batch of Johnsons, and later the Special Operations Executive (SOE) used them in Europe, as did the US Army 1st Special Force which operated in Italy.

Two basic LMG models were manufactured, the M1941 and the M1944. The former was given a bipod and a wooden butt, and the M1944 had a light tubular monopod and a butt consisting of two parallel pieces of tubing closed by a butt plate.

There were complaints about the lack of strength of both weapons, but praise for their reliability. Throughout the Second World War Johnson continued to make improvements, but his guns were never officially accepted. Under test the M1944 version of the LMG performed no better than the earlier model. A total of 70000 rifles and 10000 LMGs were manufactured by the Cranston Arms Company, Providence, Rhode Island. Production ceased in the winter of 1943-44. Some of the rifles were sold on the open market in the 1950s and 1960s, and were eagerly snapped up by collectors.

The Johnson guns represented a brave attempt to produce new and different weapons, but they failed mainly because of insufficient development. In the early 1950s, Israel manufactured a few Johnson LMGs under licence as the Dror, though the project was soon dropped.

(Rifle, Model 1941) *Calibre:* 0.30 in M1906 (7.62 mm) *Weight:* 4.31 kg (9 lb 8 oz) *Length:* 115.6 cm (3 ft 9½ in) *Barrel length:* 55.9 cm (1 ft 10 in) *Operation:* recoil, partial blowback *Magazine:* 10-round detachable rotary box *Muzzle velocity:* 808 m/sec (2650 ft/sec)

(LMG, Model 1941) *Calibre:* 0.30 in M1906 (7.62 mm) *Weight:* 6.49 kg (14 lb 5 oz) *Length:* 106.7 cm (3 ft 6 in) *Barrel length:* 55.9 cm (1 ft 10 in) *Operation:* recoil, partial blowback *Magazine:* 20-round detachable box *Rate of fire:* 300-900 rds/min *Muzzle velocity:* 853 m/sec (2800 ft/sec)

Jolly Green Giant USAF nickname for HH-3E rescue version of Sikorsky S-61 Sea King helicopter See **Sea King**

Josef Stalin

Soviet heavy tank, introduced in 1944. When Germany invaded the USSR the two standard tanks were the T-34 medium and the KV heavy, and both proved to be extremely effective. Within a year, however, it was apparent that the Germans were recovering from their initial shock and were developing new and more powerful tanks and antitank guns, so the Soviets had to make improvements to retain their advantage.

The first move was to put an improved, thicker, turret with an 85-mm (3.35-in) gun on to both tanks, replacing the 76-mm (3-in) guns previously used. But it was obviously wasting the potential of a heavy tank to arm it with the same weapon as that mounted in the medium tank. After tests with a 100-mm (3.9-in) gun, a fresh design of turret was produced which allowed the mounting of a 122-mm (4.8-in) gun. After testing in October 1943 this was approved for service and put into production as the Josef Stalin 1.

The JS-1 used the same hull as the KV tank, differing only in the larger turret and gun, and after studying combat reports of the new tank, some modifications were seen to be necessary. The principal defect was the old type of hull with vertical surfaces and several 'shot traps'. The hull was therefore redesigned to incorporate more sloped surfaces so as to deflect projectiles instead of catching them. This became the JS-2 model, which went into production early in 1944. Over 2200 were built.

During 1944 the performance of the JS-2 was carefully studied, and a design team was employed to remedy the remaining defects and produce the definitive version. The entire tank, apart from the suspension and tracks, was redesigned. The hull was given even more sloped surfaces and the glacis plate shaped into a pointed prow. The turret was changed for a low, turtle-like outline with hardly a straight line in it. The gun was improved and a better muzzle brake fitted.

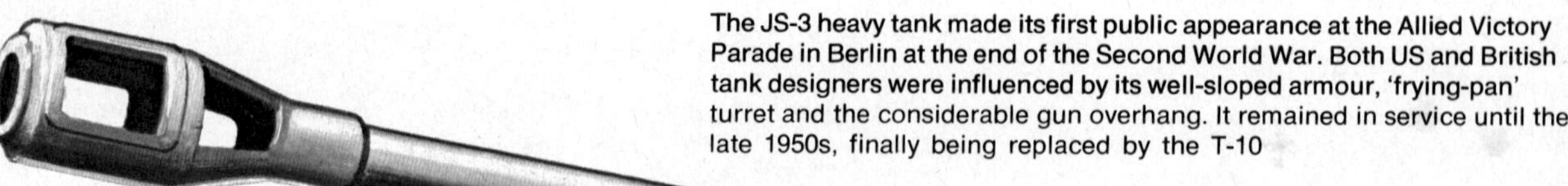

The JS-3 heavy tank made its first public appearance at the Allied Victory Parade in Berlin at the end of the Second World War. Both US and British tank designers were influenced by its well-sloped armour, 'frying-pan' turret and the considerable gun overhang. It remained in service until the late 1950s, finally being replaced by the T-10

Production of this new model, the JS-3, began early in 1945 and only a handful were ready in time to be used in combat. The first inkling the Western Allies had of it was when it was displayed on the Victory Parade in Berlin, and its shape, armament and presence were to have considerable influence on Western tank design for several years.

In postwar years the Josef Stalin continued in service and was supplied in some numbers to Warsaw pact and satellite countries. A JS-4 with thicker armour and a more powerful engine was developed but few were built and it was not placed into service. The JS series was finally replaced by the T-10 in 1957.

At the time of their inception, the JS tanks were the most powerful tanks in the world, combining good armour protection with ample firepower and adequate performance, all in a package which was not unduly heavy. It achieved this by making some sacrifices —the crew accommodation was cramped and the ammunition carried was only 28 rounds. But it was still successful and ranks as a milestone in tank development.

(JS-3) *Length:* 6.8 m (22 ft 4 in) *Width:* 3.44 m (11 ft 3½ in) *Height:* 2.44 m (8 ft) *Armour thickness:* 19-132 mm (0.75-5.2 in) *Armament:* 1 122-mm (4.8-in) M1943 gun; 1 12.7-mm (0.5-in) DShK machine-gun (AA); 1 7.62-mm (0.30-in) DT or DTM machine-gun *Powerplant:* Diesel, V-12, 520 bhp at 2000 rpm *Speed:* 40 km/h (24 mph) *Range:* 150 km (93 miles) *Crew:* 4

Ju 52/3m, Junkers

German multipurpose transport and bomber aircraft. This low-wing monoplane with a distinctive angular fuselage and wing configuration, was developed from the single-engined Ju 52 which was designed by Ernst Zindel in 1928. The latter was first flown in prototype form in October 1930, powered by a 750-hp Junkers Jumo six-cylinder engine, but was not built in large numbers.

Six months later, in April 1931, the three-engined Ju 52/3m made its first flight. This was ordered into production in 1932 utilizing three 575-hp BMW-built Pratt & Whitney Hornet radials. Prior to the Second World War Ju 52/3ms were used extensively as commercial transports by Deutsche Lufthansa and various foreign airlines, especially in South America. Some of these aircraft were fitted with two-step metal floats, in which configuration they were designated Ju 52/3mW. One thousand six hundred machines had been built by 1939, including several hundred for the emerging Luftwaffe as four-seat bombers.

The bombers were intended for interim service, to bridge the gap between the failure of the Do 11 and the arrival of He 111s and Do 17s. Designated Ju 52/3m g3e, they were used initially to transport troops and military supplies to the Nationalist forces in the Spanish Civil War. Later, 20 of the aircraft undertook their first bombing missions. The g3e was armed with a 7.9-mm (0.311-in) MG 15 machine-gun in a semiretractable ventral 'dustbin', and another of similar calibre was installed in an open dorsal position for rearward defence.

By the end of 1937 more modern types such as the Ju 86, He 111 and Do 17 had begun to arrive for Luftwaffe service and the Ju 52/3m reverted to its original role as a troop and supply transport. Given the affectionate nickname Tante Ju (Auntie Ju), it was to become world-renowned during the Second World War. The dorsal gun was retained for defence, but the lower position was removed.

Subsequent military versions were distinguished by suffixes ranging from g4e to g14e, which indicated the specific role of the aircraft, the variant of the BMW 132 (licence-built version of the Hornet) engine installed, or a particular structural modification. A typical production model was the Ju 52/3m g7e of 1941, equipped with an automatic pilot, larger cabin doors and powered by three 830-hp BMW 132T radial engines.

On the outbreak of the Second World War all available aircraft of the type were pressed into Luftwaffe service, either as troop transports or ambulance aircraft, in which latter role they could carry 12 stretchers. They also received yet another nickname: Iron Annie. Armament was improved during production of the g8e: calibre of the dorsal gun was increased to 13-mm (0.51-in). On the g14e an additional MG 15 was installed in the flight-deck roof, two others in beam positions, and armour protection was provided for the crew.

Ju 52/3ms were used extensively in the invasions of Norway and Denmark in April 1940, when approximately 600 saw operational service, and a smaller number figured in the battles for France and the Netherlands. Although about a quarter of those involved were lost, the remainder continued in service throughout the war on the Eastern Front, the Balkans, North Africa and the airborne invasion of Crete. As well as more normal transport duties, these aircraft were used to drop paratroops and/or supplies; and some acted as glider tugs. Others were fitted with electrically energized hoops braced beneath the wings and fuselage, and employed on magnetic mine clearance. The suffix ms (*Minensuche,* mine search) was added to the designation of the aircraft so used. Ju 52/3ms acted in the support role wherever necessary although loss rates continued to be quite high. They were easily adapted to ski or float landing gear and many such conversions

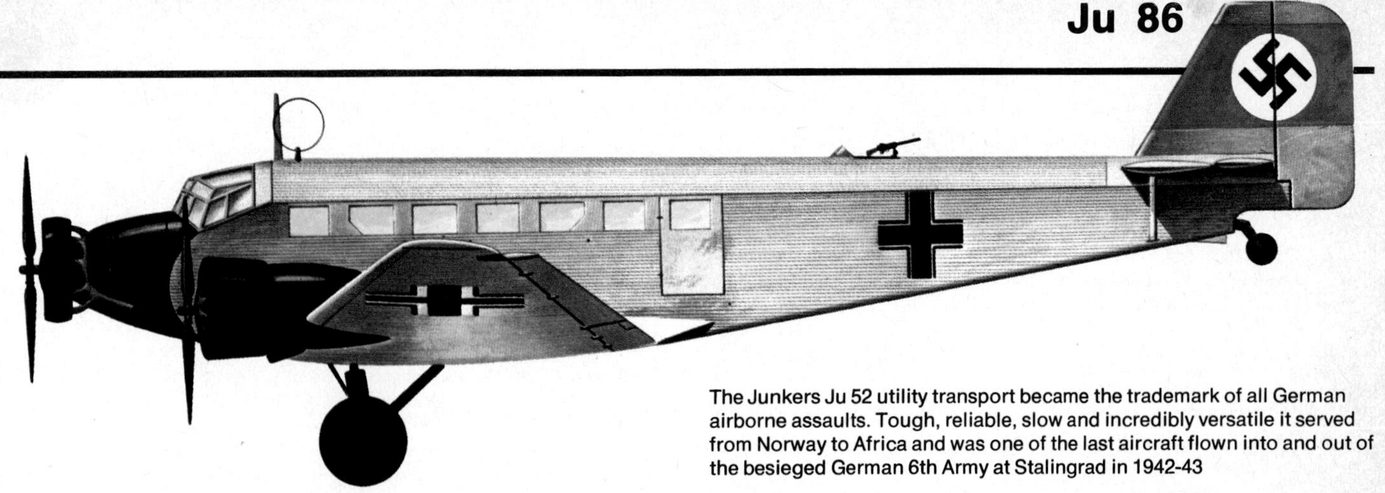

The Junkers Ju 52 utility transport became the trademark of all German airborne assaults. Tough, reliable, slow and incredibly versatile it served from Norway to Africa and was one of the last aircraft flown into and out of the besieged German 6th Army at Stalingrad in 1942-43

were done under German supervision at the Dutch Fokker factory.

Production in Germany continued until July 1944, when the total number built had reached about 4850 of both civil and military types. Some of the later batches were built in France (361), Hungary (26), Spain (70) and Holland. It had been intended to replace these ageing machines with the newer Ju 252s and Ju 352s, but the latter were not produced in sufficient numbers to be of any real use. The Ju 52/3m therefore continued to serve throughout the war and for many years afterwards, mainly in the service of foreign airlines and air forces. In Spain, CASA began building the Ju 52/3m in 1945 as the CASA 352L primary transport for the Spanish air force, with three 750-hp ENMASA Beta E-9C radials, under the designation T.2B. Of the 170 built, some were still in Spanish service in 1973 but were phased out during the next two years. A few also remained in service as transports in Switzerland until 1969.

Apart from its robust corrugated-skin structure, the most outstanding feature was STOL performance. Except in the most adverse conditions, 400 m (1300 ft) was a sufficient airstrip. A typical load was 3 tonnes (6600 lb) or 17 passengers.

(Ju 52/m g7e) *Span:* 29.25 m (96 ft) *Length:* 18.90 m (62 ft) *Gross weight:* 11 030 kg (24 317 lb) *Maximum speed:* 286 km/h (178 mph)

Ju 86, Junkers

German transport and bomber aircraft. The Ju 86 was designed by Ernst Zindel of the Junkers company in 1934 to a joint civil and military requirement for a fast, twin-engined commercial transport or bomber. (The He 111 was designed for the same purpose at the same time.) Five original prototypes were built, the first of which, the Ju 86 V1, was flown for the first time on November 4, 1934, powered by two Siemens radial engines. The 600-hp Jumo 205C six-cylinder diesel power-plants, around which the Ju 86 had been designed, were not available in time; they were, however, installed in the Ju 86 V2 second prototype which first flew in April 1935. A preproduction batch of 13 bombers designated Ju 86A-0 were built for service trials.

The four-seat first production model, the Ju 86A-1 (of which about 20 were built) began

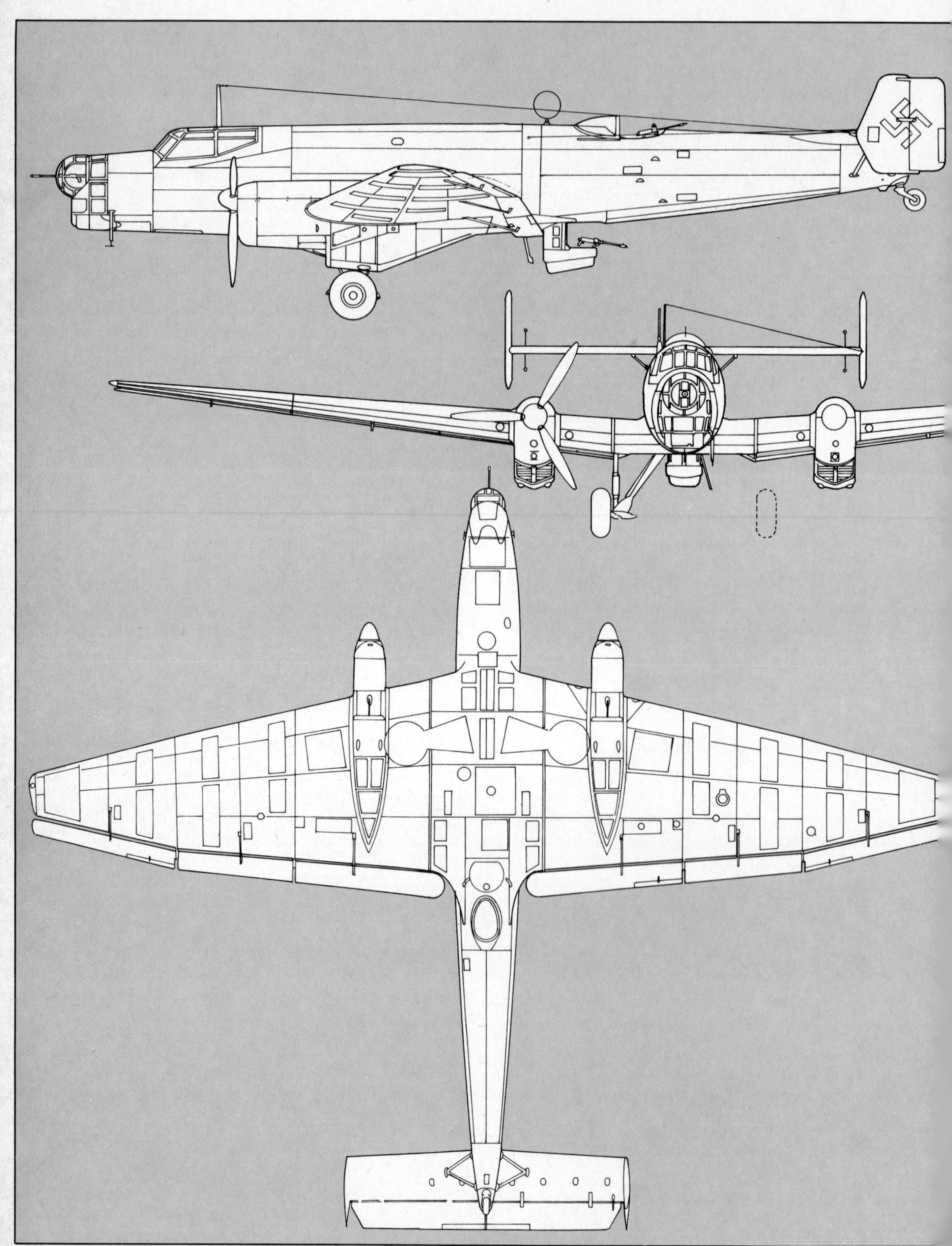

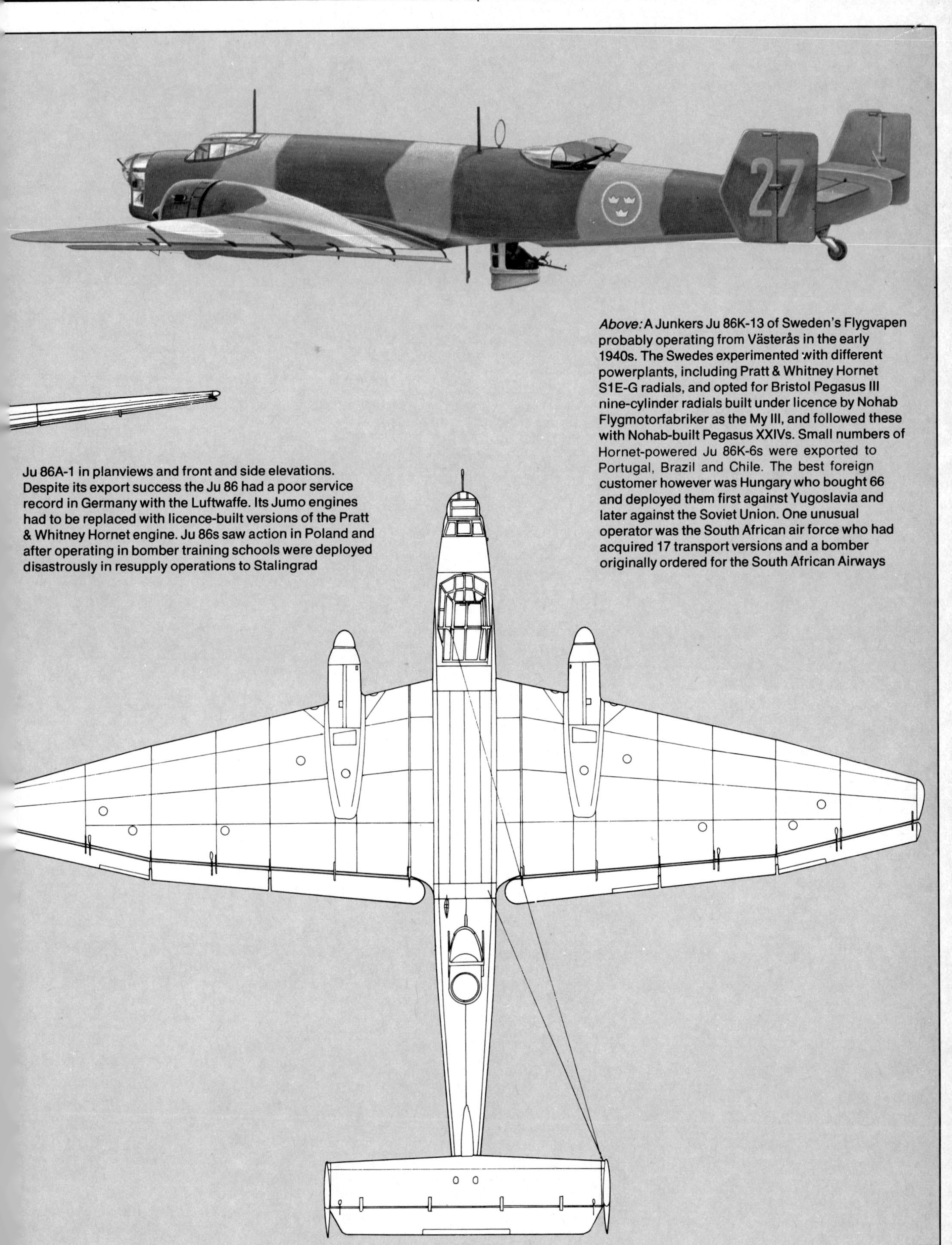

Above: A Junkers Ju 86K-13 of Sweden's Flygvapen probably operating from Västerås in the early 1940s. The Swedes experimented with different powerplants, including Pratt & Whitney Hornet S1E-G radials, and opted for Bristol Pegasus III nine-cylinder radials built under licence by Nohab Flygmotorfabriker as the My III, and followed these with Nohab-built Pegasus XXIVs. Small numbers of Hornet-powered Ju 86K-6s were exported to Portugal, Brazil and Chile. The best foreign customer however was Hungary who bought 66 and deployed them first against Yugoslavia and later against the Soviet Union. One unusual operator was the South African air force who had acquired 17 transport versions and a bomber originally ordered for the South African Airways

Ju 86A-1 in planviews and front and side elevations. Despite its export success the Ju 86 had a poor service record in Germany with the Luftwaffe. Its Jumo engines had to be replaced with licence-built versions of the Pratt & Whitney Hornet engine. Ju 86s saw action in Poland and after operating in bomber training schools were deployed disastrously in resupply operations to Stalingrad

to enter squadron service in May-June 1936, powered by 600-hp Jumo 205C-4 engines and capable of carrying an internal bombload of 800 kg (1764 lb). The Ju 86B and 86C, of which only a few were built, were used as commercial transports.

Next military variant was a development of the A, the Ju 86D-1, with an extended fuselage and tail cone to improve stability, and increased fuel capacity. Armament comprised three 7.9-mm (0.311-in) MG 15 machine-guns (nose, dorsal and ventral) and a maximum bombload of 1000 kg (2205 lb).

After some service by the D-1 in the Spanish Civil War it was realized that the Ju 86's performance as a bomber was not adequate under combat conditions, and the Jumo diesels were proving unsuited to the frequent changes of speed which combat service demanded. Experiments with the Pratt & Whitney Hornet radial and the German BMW 132 licence-built counterpart led to the production of the Ju 86E, utilizing the 810-hp BMW 132F engine. These began to enter service in the later summer of 1937 and approximately 50 were built, including about 20 E-2s with 865-hp BMW 132N powerplants. Forty more of a similar model were completed as Ju 86Gs, with a redesigned front fuselage and the cockpit further forward to improve pilot view. The 235 D, E and G models began to be withdrawn from frontline Luftwaffe service in the autumn of 1938 in favour of the more effective He 111 and Do 17.

Prior to this, several models had been exported. After three evaluation bombers (Ju 86K-1) had been sent to Sweden in 1936-37, they were followed by 20 with Swedish-built Bristol Pegasus III engines (Ju 86K-4) and 17 with Pegasus XII powerplants (Ju 86K-5). Swedish air force designations for these were B 3A and B 3B respectively. The Saab company then built 16 under licence as Ju 86K-13s, with various versions of the Pegasus engine, for the Swedish air force. Other export orders included small batches for Brazil, Chile and Portugal; and 66 Ju 86K-2s for Hungary, fitted after their arrival in that country with Gnome-Rhône 14K-series engines. Eighteen Ju 86s, which had been supplied to South Africa as airliners, were converted to bomber configuration in 1939 for the South African Air Force.

After the beginning of the Second World War the Ju 86P was evolved, powered by two 950-hp Jumo 207A diesel engines, with an increased wing span and redesigned nose. Bombload remained the same as the D model but the armament was reduced to one rearward-firing defensive 7.9-mm (0.311-in) MG 17 machine-gun. The Ju 86R was developed as a further conversion of the P series for high-level photo-reconnaissance duties. Two 1000-hp Jumo 207B engines were fitted and the wing span was increased to 32 m (105 ft). Both P and R types served during the early years of the war, most being produced by the conversion of airframes of the earlier models. Two projected developments, the Ju 186 and 286, with four and six engines respectively, did not get beyond the design stage.

(Ju 86D-1) *Span:* 22.5 m (73 ft 10 in) *Length:* 17.87 m (58 ft 8 in) *Gross weight:* 8060 kg (17 770 lb) *Maximum speed:* 325 km/h (202 mph)

(Ju 86R-1) *Span:* 32 m (105 ft) *Length:* 16.46 m (54 ft) *Gross weight:* 11 530 kg (25 420 lb) *Maximum speed:* 420 km/h (261 mph)

Ju 87, Junkers

German dive-bomber and multirole tactical aircraft. Partly because of its sharply cranked wing and spatted fixed landing gear, which likened it to a swooping bird of prey, and partly because of the fear engendered by its popular name of Stuka—actually short for *Sturzkampfflugzeug*, the German word for any dive-bomber—the Ju 87 was one of the classic military aircraft of aviation history.

It is often thought that the design of the Ju 87 was based on the Junkers K-47 two-seat fighter built by Swedish Junkers, AB Flygindustri, at Limhamm-Malmö in 1927, and also that the Luftwaffe's interest in dive-bombing stemmed from US Navy displays watched by Ernst Udet. In fact, from 1918 the covert German defence and air ministries had never ceased to have the most intense interest in dive-bombing, and the Ju 87 was a completely fresh design by Dipl-Ing Hermann Pohlmann. While the little Hs 123 biplane won the stop-gap *Sofort* (immediate) competition, Pohlmann's submission had a

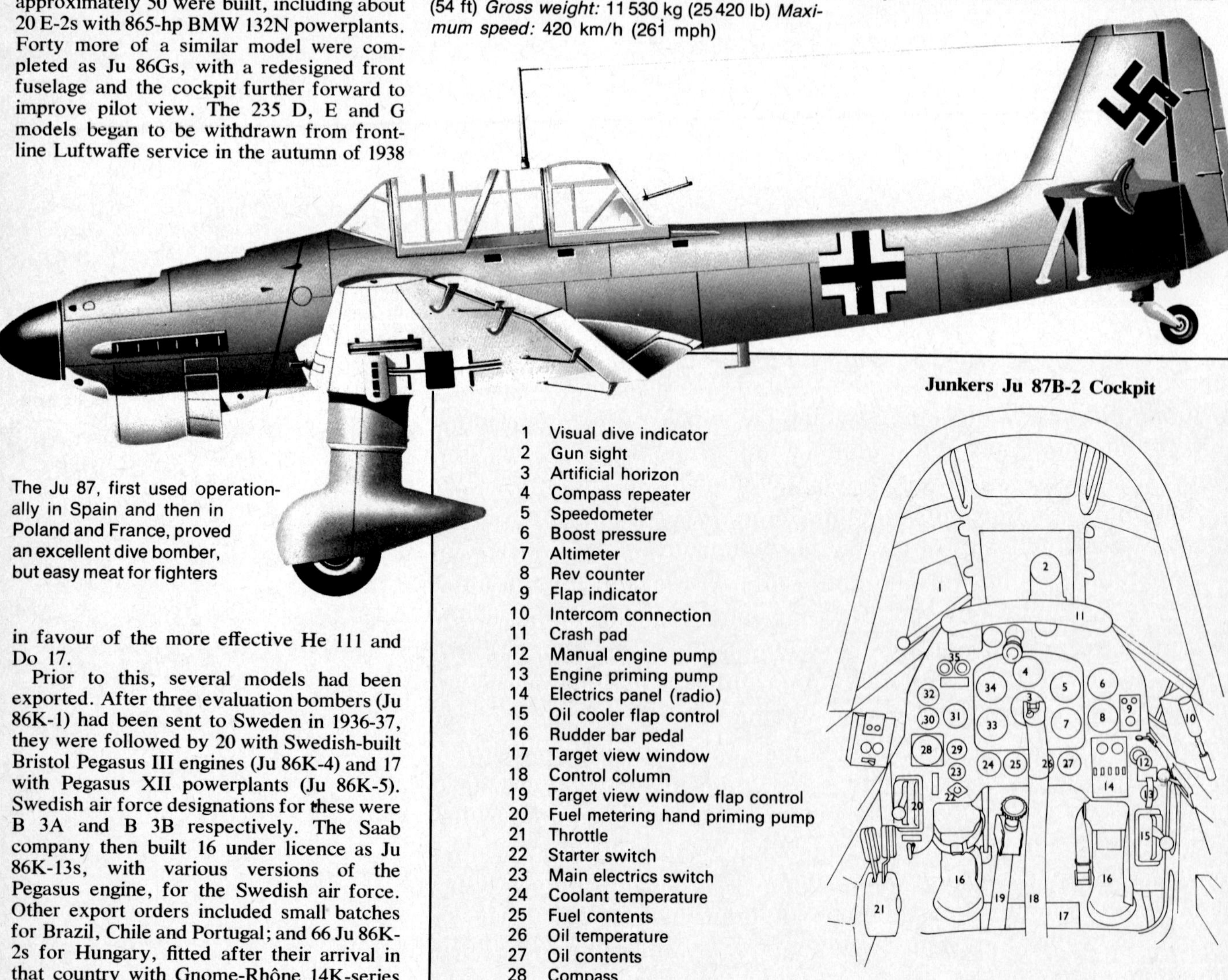

The Ju 87, first used operationally in Spain and then in Poland and France, proved an excellent dive bomber, but easy meat for fighters

A Junkers Ju 87B 'Stuka' waits to be loaded with a 500-kg (1100-lb) bomb during attacks in Greece in 1941

The Ju 87B-2 with its bomb swung forward ready for releasing. The Stuka could deliver very accurate attacks against such targets as road and rail links and military concentrations. Effective as they were, Stukas also had considerable psychological value as the pitch of diving engine reached a scream at the bottom of the dive. Some Stukas had sirens fitted to the wings to add to this effect

rather unfair advantage in the definitive Sturzbomber contest. Junkers designed the Ju 87 in 1934 and began to build the prototype, while the RLM (air ministry) wrote the specification around it.

The rivals, the Ar 81, Ha 137 and He 118, would have had to be exceptionally good to beat the Ju 87, and in fact the first two did not have a chance. On paper the He 118 was superior, but it did badly in trials at Rechlin—Udet even managed to leave it by parachute, through his own error of technique—and the Ju 87 became possibly the most important attack aircraft of the Luftwaffe.

The V1 prototype, flown on an unknown date in the spring of 1935, was an ungainly machine, with trousered landing gears and square twin fins. Like the first Bf 109, building at the same time, it had a Kestrel powerplant imported from Rolls-Royce. The second Ju 87 had a Jumo 210 of 610 hp and, on the V1's crashing through tail failure, was hurriedly given single fin. Another three prototypes were tested, and by late 1936 the Luftwaffe was receiving the preproduction Ju 87 A-0 series, with a 7.92-mm (0.312-in) MG 17 in the right wing, an MG 15 aimed from the rear cockpit and a hinged belly crutch for a 250-kg (550-lb) bomb (or 500-kg [1100-lb] if flown as a single-seater).

Structurally a tough, modern stressed-skin machine, the Ju 87 had superb flying qualities—quite the opposite of the impression fostered by Allied propaganda during the Second World War—and was so light on the controls that pilots at first tended to overcontrol. Red lines on the side windows helped the pilot to set up the correct dive angle. The technique was to fly until the target appeared to be passing along the left wing-root, invisible to the pilot, who then had to shut the cooling gills, set the propeller to

full coarse, open slat-type airbrakes hinged below the outer wings and wing over to the left and point at the target, usually at an angle of about 85°. The bomb was swung out on its crutch to avoid hitting the propeller, and release was a matter of pilot judgement. Experience showed that an autopilot was needed to assist in recovery to level flight in the high-g pull-out. Later subtypes had further automatic aids which relieved the pilot of the need to fiddle with gills and propeller, but dive-brake actuation remained manual (red rods projected above the wing when they were open).

Even with brakes closed the A-0 could reach only 320 km/h (200 mph) unladen, and a mere 295 km/h (183 mph) when carrying the bombload. The A-1 production version, with simplified airframe, and the A-2, with 680-hp Jumo 210Da, accounted for about 200 aircraft by May 1938. These equipped the four chief Stukagruppen, and many of the aircrew were rotated for a spell of actual operations with three A-1 aircraft detached to the Legion Kondor. Their results were out of all proportion to their small number, and they were especially effective in demolishing port facilities and sinking ships at such major Republican bases as Barcelona, Valencia and Tarragona. They met little effective opposition. Other nations appeared not to take in the lesson that a single Stuka, with a single heavy bomb, had a fair chance of causing severe damage or even of sinking all classes of ship.

In early 1938 the underpowered A-series was being replaced by the Ju 87B-1 with 1200-hp Jumo 211Da. This had a completely new fuselage, sliding canopies, spatted wheels and many other changes, and could easily carry a 500-kg (1100-lb) bomb and four 50-kg (110-lb) bombs on wing racks, with both crew members. Responsibility for the whole Ju 87 programme was passed to the Weser works, which subsequently managed not only the increasingly dispersed production but also the development of new versions. The total number of aircraft produced at the new works was 557. The first new version, in late 1939, was the B-2, with various refinements which allowed it, flown as a single-seater, to carry an SC 1000 bomb of 1000 kg (2200 lb).

By the start of the Second World War there were nine Stukagruppen, all equipped with the excellent B-1, a combat force of 336 machines. This total was briefly reduced by 13 when, immediately before the assault on Poland, 13 aircraft hit the ground as a result of sudden ground mist in a dive-bombing display watched by several high-ranking officers including Oberst Wolfram von Richthofen, chief of the development section of the technical dept, and an opponent of the technique. But in the Polish campaign the Stuka fully vindicated its supporters.

The first mission of the war was flown by a *kette* (flight) of three aircraft from 3/StG.1 led by Hauptman Bruno Dilley, which temporarily succeeded in the nearly impossible task of hitting the demolition crew and detonation cables waiting to blow the Dirschau bridges over the Vistula. Other actions included virtual annihilation of an infantry division caught changing trains at Piotrkow, and the near-annihilation of the Polish navy with most of the major vessels sunk. The Ju 87B-1 proved to have unprecedented ability to absorb battle damage, and Generalfeldmarschall Albert Kesselring, Chief of Air Staff, publicly commented on the 'miracle' of the return to base of aircraft almost demolished in mid-air, and thanked Dr Koppenberg, Junkers director-general.

The Ju 87C, developed for the carrier *Graf Zeppelin*, never entered production, but the long-range Ju 87R with outer-wing tanks and provision for two drop tanks was delivered in April 1940, in time to make an important contribution to the Norwegian campaign, and to the chagrin of Allied naval staff who thought them out of Stuka range. Several Allied ships went to the bottom including the destroyers *Afridi*, *Bison* and *Grom*, and the AA ship *Bittern*. *Bittern*'s sister, *Black Swan*, was hit squarely by a Stuka's bomb, but the bomb was released from such a low altitude that it went straight through the ship and exploded in the water below. In the advance in the West it was the same story, Fliegerkorps VIII providing the vital cornerstone of the Blitzkrieg. The Korps commander, von Richthofen, had by then become a passionate advocate of the Stuka.

Part of its effect was to destroy morale, even among seasoned troops. The dive-bomber appeared to be aiming straight at each man, and the fitting of loud sirens on the landing gear (called Trombones of Jericho by the Luftwaffe) heightened the effect. Operating in the closest partnership with the Panzer formations, the Stukas, by now mostly B-2s of various subtypes, worked around the clock and yet suffered only 14 casualties in the first four days.

In the assault on English Channel shipping and then on RAF Fighter Command airfields and the Chain Home radar stations, however, the Ju 87 suddenly ran into formidable fighter opposition. Its sweeping success had so permeated the Luftwaffe thinking that previous

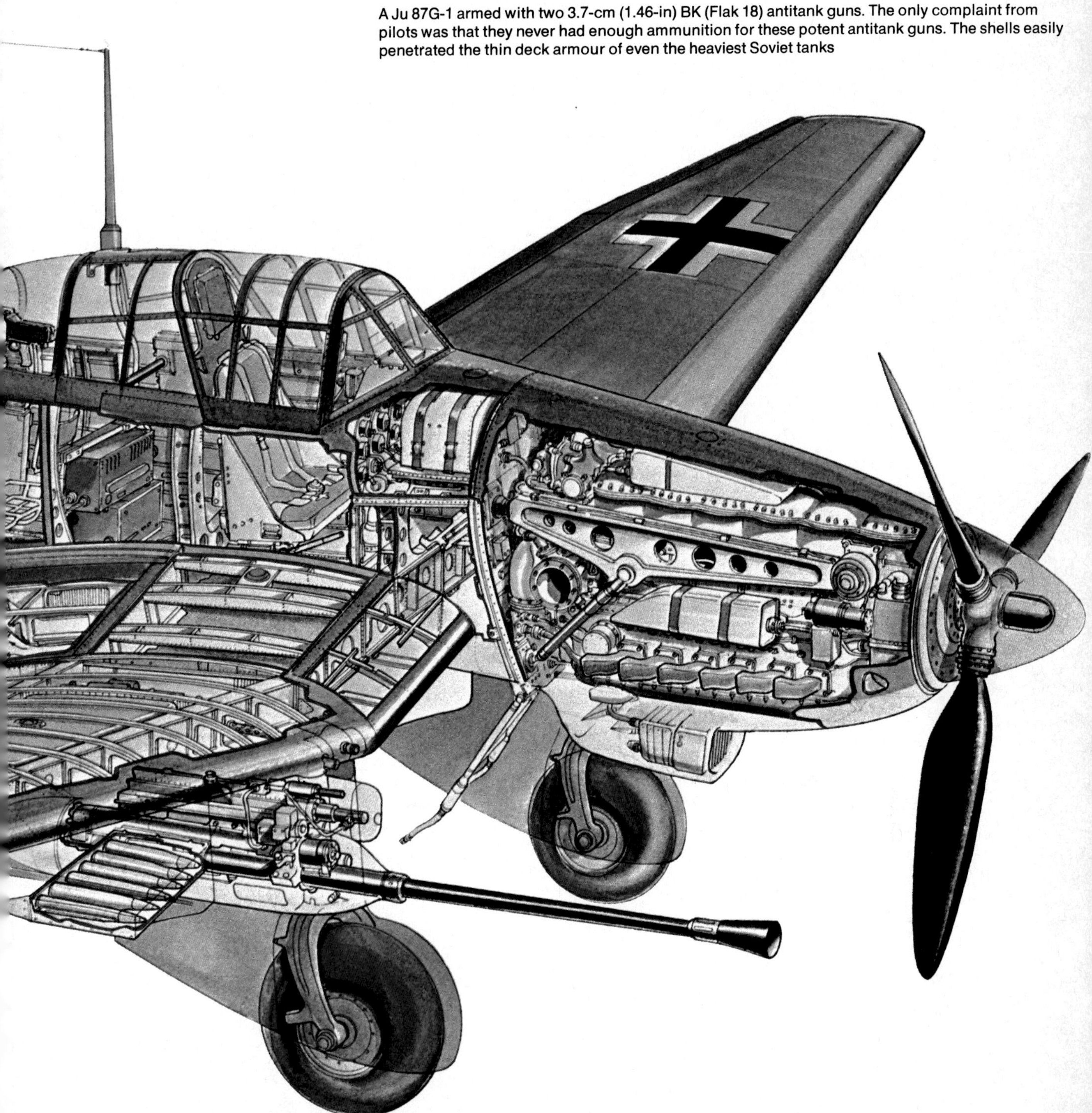

A Ju 87G-1 armed with two 3.7-cm (1.46-in) BK (Flak 18) antitank guns. The only complaint from pilots was that they never had enough ammunition for these potent antitank guns. The shells easily penetrated the thin deck armour of even the heaviest Soviet tanks

belief in its obsolescence had been overturned and replaced by an increase in production and it was weeks before the unpalatable truth was accepted: the loss-rate was unacceptable. Despite strong fighter escort, more than 20% of the total Stuka strength was shot down in the first ten days, and on August 18, 1940, the Ju 87 was pulled out of the battle, a remarkable decision.

Subsequently the Stuka wings again proved instrumental in defeating organized opposition in the Balkans, Greece and Crete, and several versions were extremely important in North Africa until, by 1942, the sky had become too dangerous except by night.

In North Africa the Ju 87D quickly became the chief version, this model coming into production around May 1941. Aerodynamically much improved it had the 1400-hp Jumo 211J-1 engine with very broad propeller blades, and completely new cockpit canopy and cooling system. For short ranges it could carry the remarkable bombload of 1800 kg (3968 lb). Normal armament comprised twin MG 17s firing ahead and twin MG 81 guns in the rear cockpit, and crew and tank protection were considerably improved. This was to become the chief production version with numerous subtypes, and versions were supplied to most Axis air forces. The Allies were led to believe it was made by Breda in Italy, and therefore invented the designation Breda 201 Picchiatelli for it.

In the Soviet Union the Ju 87 became one of the foremost Axis warplanes. By this time it was truly obsolescent, but its toughness, versatility and general popularity caused output to be increased dramatically. From a total of 557 in 1939, the total for 1943 was 1844. There were very many subtypes including the important D-7 night assault machine with two 20-mm (0.79-in) MG 151 cannon in the wings. The D-7 was one of the later subtypes with increased span to improve behaviour at extremely high weights. It had no dive-bombing equipment, reflecting the fact that from 1942 onward most Ju 87 missions had not involved the original form of attack at all. Indeed the most numerous model, the D-3, was the first configured as a Schlachtflugzeug (attack aircraft), and in the final three years of the war all the once proud Stukagruppen became Schlacht, Nachtschlacht (night attack) or other kinds of unit, and most re-equipped with the Fw 190.

On wheels or skis the 87 in many versions served as a close-support machine, glider tug, assault transport (in one odd modification with 'personnel containers' above the wings which were released by parachute) and, in the Ju 87G-1, two 37-mm (1.46-in) BK 3,7 (Flak 18) antitank guns, each with a clip of six rounds, hung on reinforced wing panels. One pilot, Hans-Ulrich Rudel, flew the proving trials with the G-1 in late 1942 and later was credited with the amazing score of 519 Soviet armoured vehicles, winning the Knight's Cross. Rudel's III/SG.2 was the only surviving Ju 87 unit on day operations at the end of 1944. Elsewhere the Ju 87 was being used mainly in night attack missions creeping at about 200 km/h (124 mph) over the trees and hedges to harass Allied armies with antipersonnel bombs.

Span: (prior to D-5) 13.1 m (43 ft); (D-5 and later) 15 m (49 ft 3 in) *Length:* (B) 11.1 m (36 ft 5 in); (D) 11.5 m (37 ft 9 in) *Gross weight:* (B-1) 4336 kg (9560 lb); (D-1) 6600 kg (14 550 lb) *Maximum speed:* (B-1) 383 km/h (238 mph); (D-1) 410 km/h (255 mph)

Stukas in 1940. Over a target they would stack up in an oblique line and peel off in succession to dive down and release their bombs

Ju 88, Junkers

German multirole combat aircraft. Though planned as a *schnellbomber* (high-speed bomber) the Ju 88 first flew as a civil record-breaker and subsequently served as a dive-bomber, torpedo carrier, night fighter, strategic reconnaissance aircraft, long-range intruder, tank-buster and close-support attack aircraft, and in many other roles including the missile portion of most Mistel composite aircraft. It was unquestionably the most versatile Axis aircraft of the Second World War, and the best Luftwaffe offensive aircraft. Unlike such machines as the Ju 87 and He 111, which were kept in production until near the end of the war through failure to find a replacement, the Ju 88 was still a first-class front-line machine at the end of the European war. It was built in numbers far exceeding those of all other German aircraft excepting the Bf 109 and Fw 190.

To help achieve a modern stressed-skin structure Junkers hired two American stress-men, and to the end of its days the Ju 88 airframe was outstanding, though in its initial development in 1938-39 the weight rose so much that reinforcement was necessary. The first prototype, with two 990-hp DB 600Aa engines, flew at Dessau on December 21, 1936, but was written off in high-speed tests only a few weeks later. The V2 was similar, but the V3, flown on September 13, 1937, had 1000-hp Jumo 211A engines and the specified armament of 800 kg (1770 lb) of bombs and a 7.92-mm (0.312-in) MG 15 in the upper rear of the rather cramped cabin. At Rechlin it proved the most popular aircraft ever to be officially tested, and it never had to be evaluated against the rivals, the Hs 127 being too late and the Bf 162 being dropped to allow Messerschmitt to concentrate on fighters. Instead Junkers were told to plan dispersed production, and this began with five Junkers and five other plants in 1938 and by 1944 embraced more than 135 factories throughout Nazi-occupied Europe.

In 1938 the V5 set important world records,

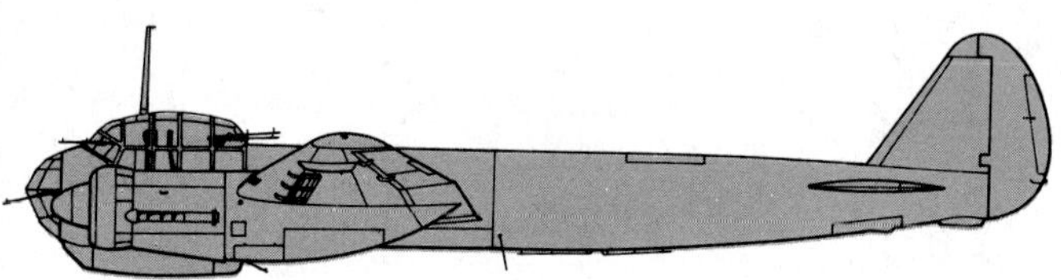

The Junkers Ju 88A-5 went into action in September 1939. It was similar to the A-1, but its larger bombload reduced its maximum speed to 439 km/h (273 mph)

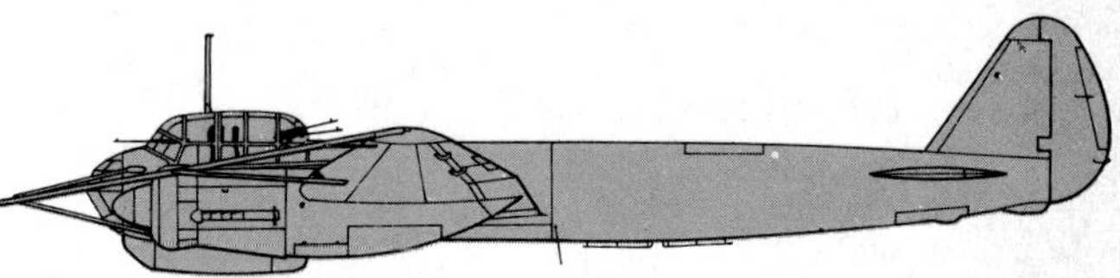

The Ju 88A-6 was an A-5 equipped with a barrage-balloon fender designed to cut balloon cables. However, it was so unwieldy that it was withdrawn

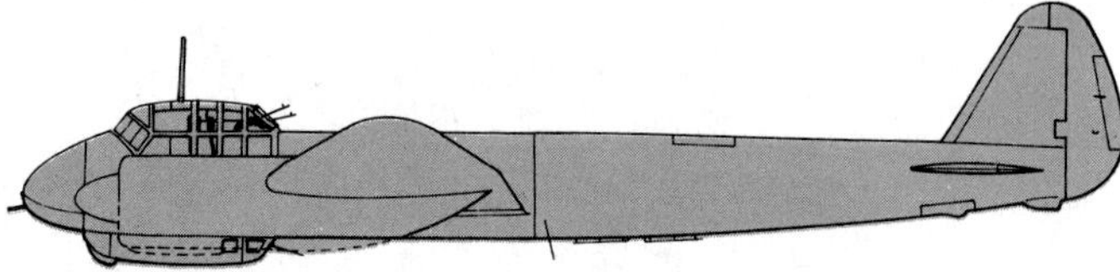

The Ju 88C-4 was a fighter version. It could carry additional armament of two Waffenbehälter weapons pods containing a total of 12 MG 81 machine-guns

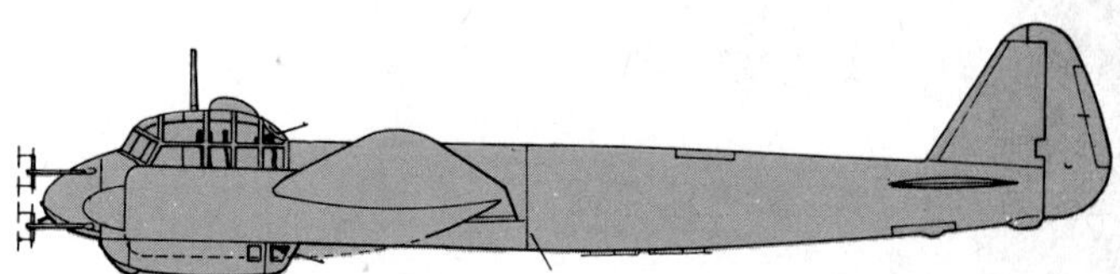

The Ju 88C-6b was the first radar-equipped night-fighter version of the Ju 88. It carried either FuG 202 Lichtenstein BC AI or FuG 212 C-1 radar

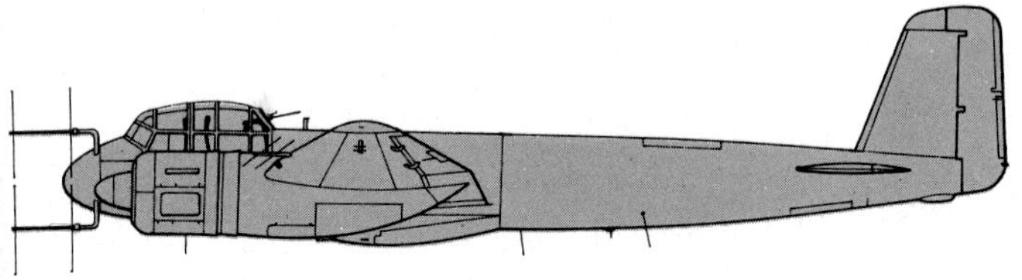

The Ju 88G-4 included features like rearward-facing Lichtenstein SN-2 radar for tail warning and schräge Musik MG 151 cannon with 200 rounds per gun

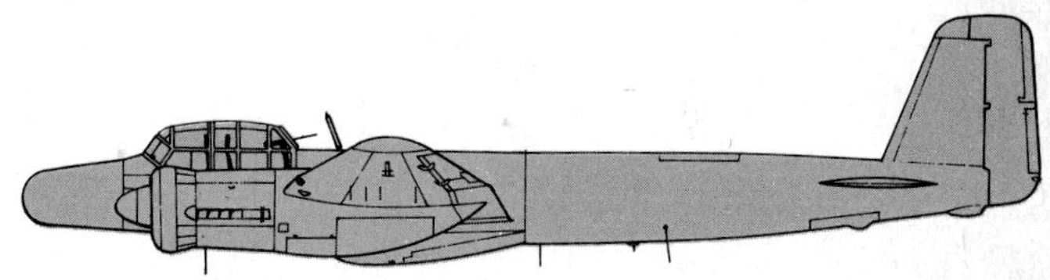

The Ju 88G-7c used FuG 240 Berlin N-1a radar protected by a wooden nose fairing. The radar was based on a captured British H_2S set and was unaffected by Window

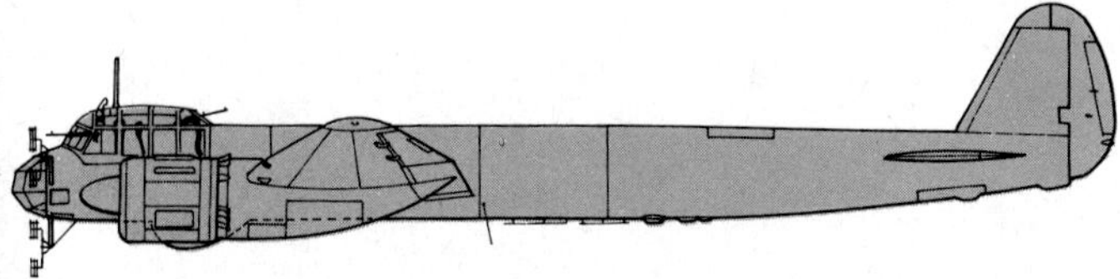

The Ju 88H-1 was a reconnaissance aircraft fitted with FuG Hohentwiel radar and remotely controlled cameras. Its enlarged fuel tanks gave it a very long range

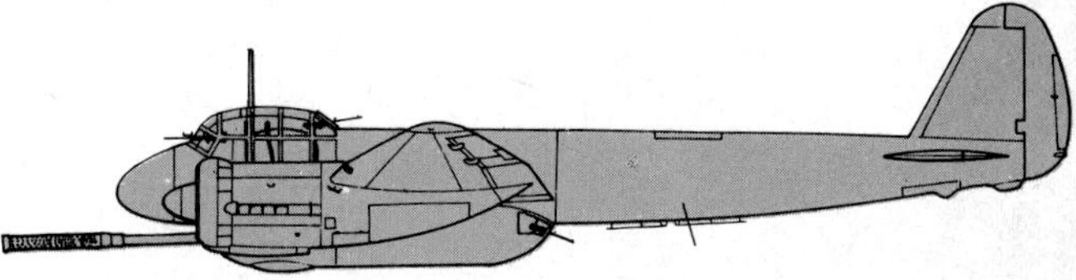

The Ju 88P-1 had a 75-mm (2.95-in) PaK 40 cannon for antitank work. If it was intercepted or hit by ground fire the gun could be jettisoned

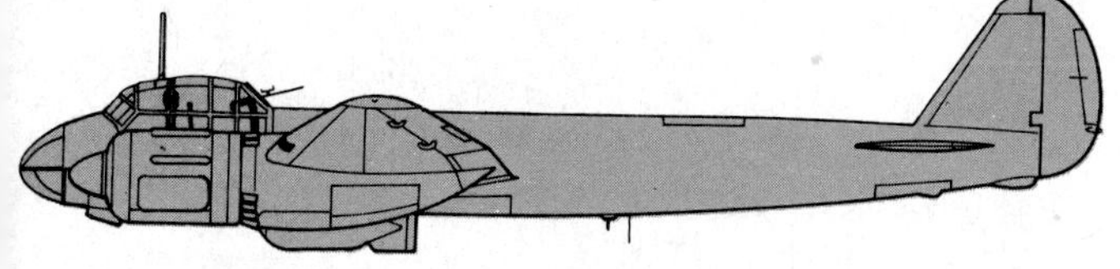

The Ju 88S-1 had powerful BMW 801G-2 engines with GM 1 nitrous-oxide injection power-boost with two rates, 'normal' and 'emergency'. The latter lasted for 27 minutes

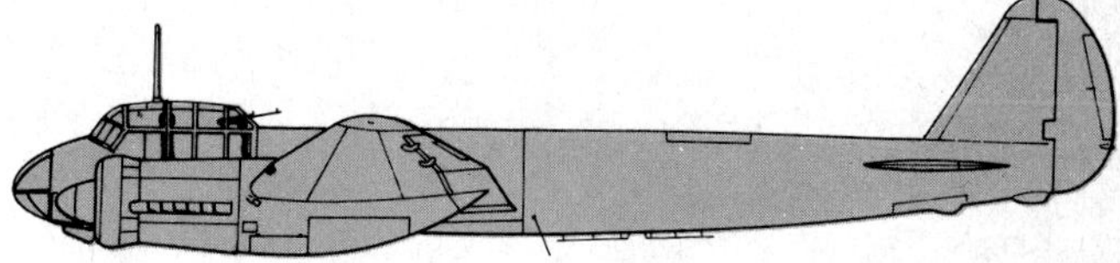

The Ju 88S-3 was similar to the S-1 with nitrous-oxide injection to give a high-altitude performance which would make interception very difficult

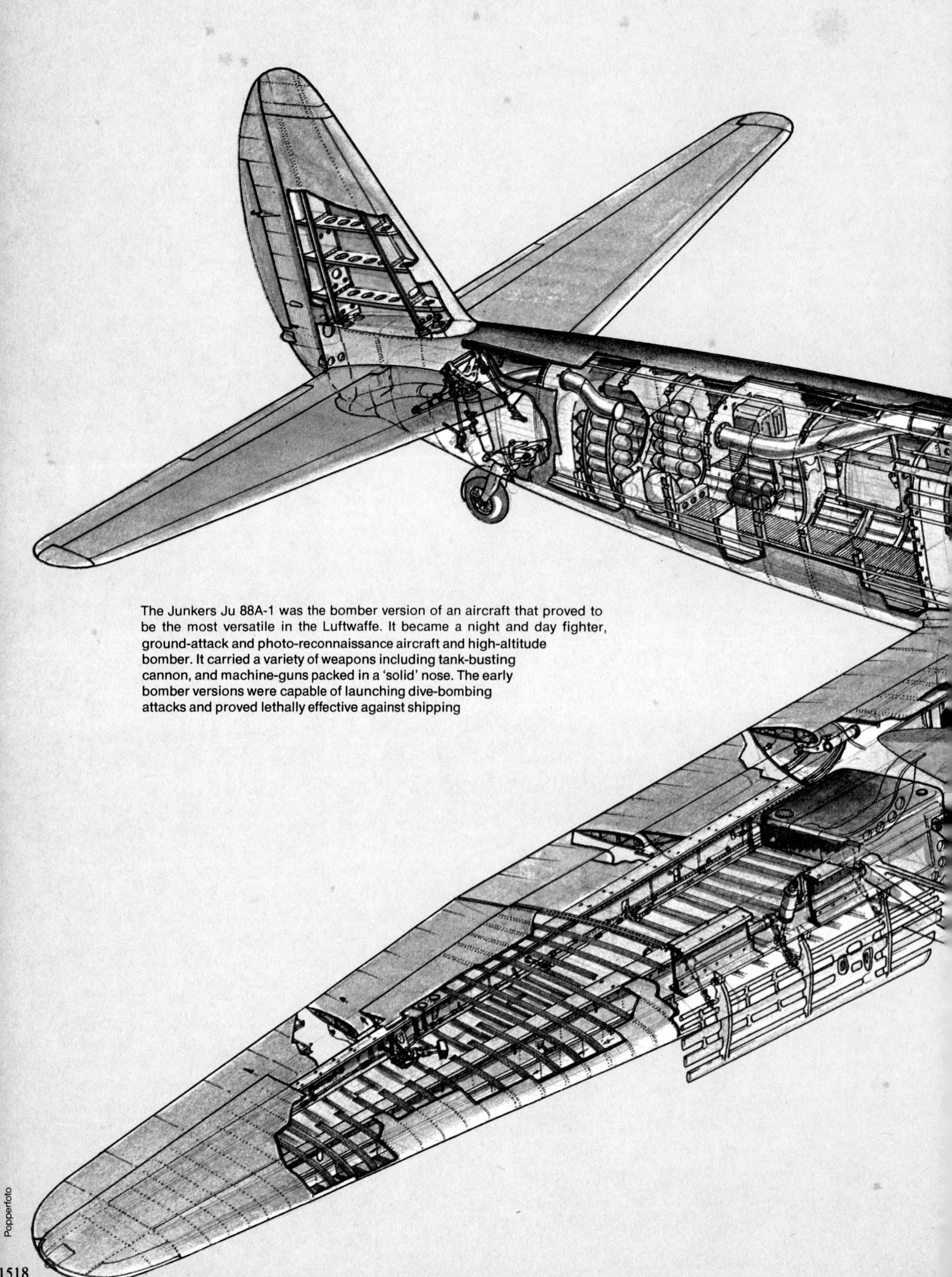

The Junkers Ju 88A-1 was the bomber version of an aircraft that proved to be the most versatile in the Luftwaffe. It became a night and day fighter, ground-attack and photo-reconnaissance aircraft and high-altitude bomber. It carried a variety of weapons including tank-busting cannon, and machine-guns packed in a 'solid' nose. The early bomber versions were capable of launching dive-bombing attacks and proved lethally effective against shipping

Popperfoto

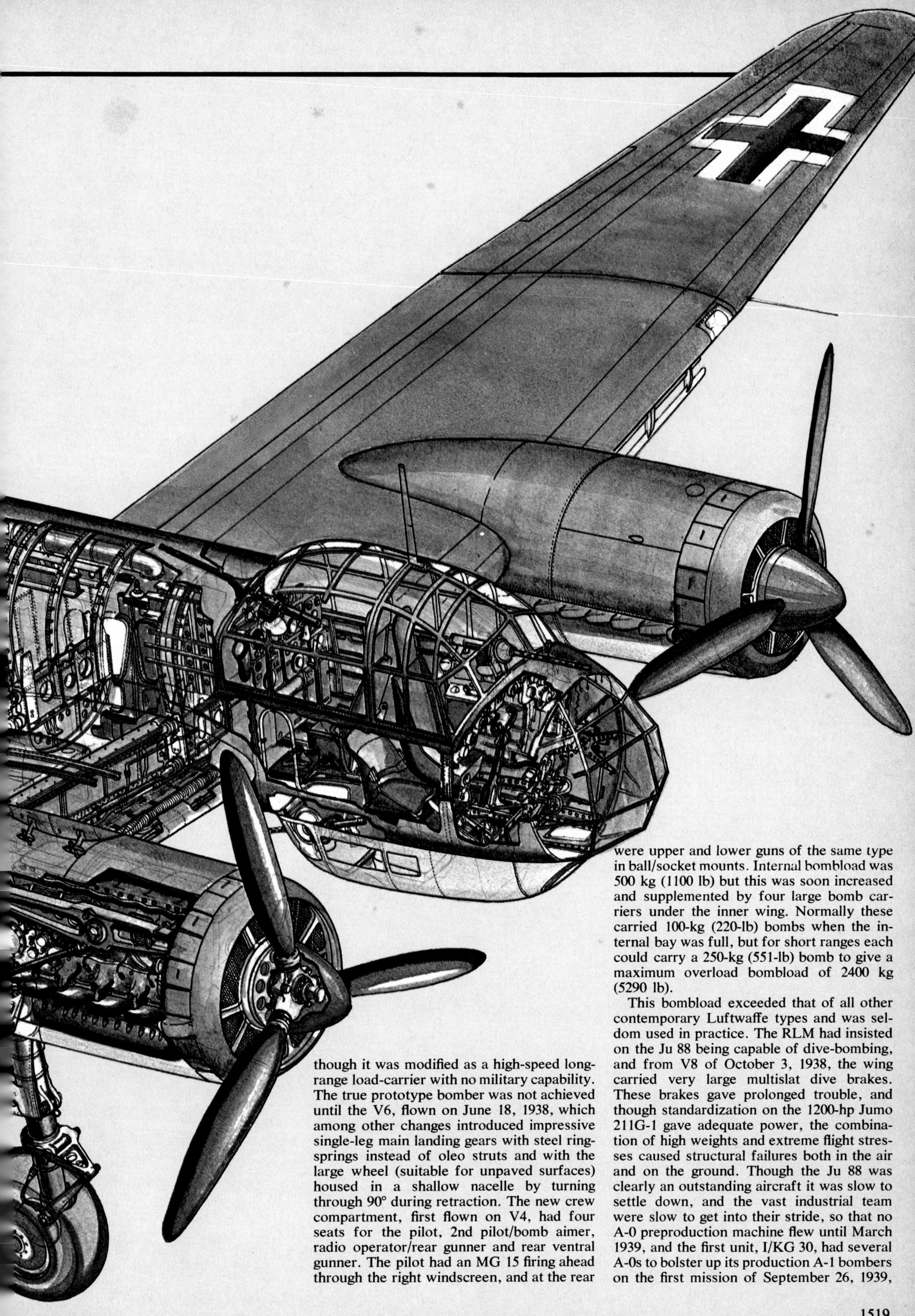

though it was modified as a high-speed long-range load-carrier with no military capability. The true prototype bomber was not achieved until the V6, flown on June 18, 1938, which among other changes introduced impressive single-leg main landing gears with steel ring-springs instead of oleo struts and with the large wheel (suitable for unpaved surfaces) housed in a shallow nacelle by turning through 90° during retraction. The new crew compartment, first flown on V4, had four seats for the pilot, 2nd pilot/bomb aimer, radio operator/rear gunner and rear ventral gunner. The pilot had an MG 15 firing ahead through the right windscreen, and at the rear were upper and lower guns of the same type in ball/socket mounts. Internal bombload was 500 kg (1100 lb) but this was soon increased and supplemented by four large bomb carriers under the inner wing. Normally these carried 100-kg (220-lb) bombs when the internal bay was full, but for short ranges each could carry a 250-kg (551-lb) bomb to give a maximum overload bombload of 2400 kg (5290 lb).

This bombload exceeded that of all other contemporary Luftwaffe types and was seldom used in practice. The RLM had insisted on the Ju 88 being capable of dive-bombing, and from V8 of October 3, 1938, the wing carried very large multislat dive brakes. These brakes gave prolonged trouble, and though standardization on the 1200-hp Jumo 211G-1 gave adequate power, the combination of high weights and extreme flight stresses caused structural failures both in the air and on the ground. Though the Ju 88 was clearly an outstanding aircraft it was slow to settle down, and the vast industrial team were slow to get into their stride, so that no A-0 preproduction machine flew until March 1939, and the first unit, I/KG 30, had several A-0s to bolster up its production A-1 bombers on the first mission of September 26, 1939,

The Ju 88G-6c was powered by two Jumo 213A engines driving VS 111 wooden propellers. It was equipped with Lichtenstein SN-2, Flensburg rad and Naxos Z which received British H_2S navigation radar emissions

A Ju 88A-5 loaded with two SC 250 bombs starts up its engines before leaving on a bombing mission early in the Second World War

J G Moore Collection

when it dropped SC500 armour-piercing bombs on British warships (one bounced off *Hood* without exploding).

By January 1940 the A-1 was scheduled to be replaced in production by the A-4, with long-span wing and 1340/1410-hp Jumo 211J-1 engines, but delay with the engine led to the A-5 being substituted with the new wing only. By the Battle of Britain there were as many A-5s as A-1s, and the Ju 88 proved itself the most successful of all German bombers though this was due to performance and manoeuvrability rather than defensive armament. By September 1940 most aircraft used against Britain had been modified in the field to have four upper guns, two at the rear and one in each side window, all requiring to be aimed, fired and reloaded individually. The A-6, with tip-to-tip balloon cable fender, was unpopular and soon withdrawn or converted to A-4 standard.

Small numbers were delivered of the A-3, and some A-5s, with dual pilot controls for use as conversion trainers, but by the spring of 1941 the A-4 was established as the standard Ju 88, and it served as the basis for nearly all subsequent versions. The development of the Ju 88 was more complex than that of any other aircraft, and more than 240 subtypes appeared in seemingly haphazard order, some losing the designation Ju 88; for example the Ju 88B-0 with much improved crew compartment was the jumping-off point for the Ju 188. In the matter of armament there were often numerous schemes for each subtype, which in turn could be modified by Rüstsätz modification kits. Thus, the basic A- commonly carried an MG 81 in the right windscreen, a single 13-mm (0.51-in) MG 131 r twin MG 81 aimed by the bomb aimer through the nose, the same choice of weapons for the ventral gunner and twin MG 1 firing aft dorsally.

Right to the close of production the basic -series remained important, many being modified or even remanufactured for different roles. Among the subtypes were the -8 with Kutonase balloon-cable cutters, the opicalized A-11, stripped A-12 conversion ainer, heavily armoured A-16 close-support rcraft with up to 16 forward-firing guns and umerous antipersonnel bombs, the A-14 tishipping aircraft (though most torpedo rriers were subtypes of A-4), A-15 with 00 kg (6614 lb) of bombs in a cavernous ooden bomb bay which was later resurcted for the S-2, and purpose-designed A-' torpedo bomber carrying two LT F5b eapons externally. Other Ju 88 A-series, ostly rebuilt A-4s, tested nearly all the erman air-to-surface missiles, including L Friedensengl and L 11 Schneewittchen d many other weapons other than the Hs 293 and Fritz X. The A-series were also the chief German testbeds for new guns, including large recoilless weapons, and turbojets.

The B-series, with more capacious and streamlined forward fuselage, introduced the BMW 801 radial engine and, though ten preproduction B-0 built in 1940 saw action as reconnaissance aircraft, this family served to lead to the turret-armed E-series which were the basis of the Ju 188 and later 388. In contrast, the C-series did see production as Ju 88s, but only after long delay. The first of several families of Ju 88 fighter, the C derived from the rebuilt V7 prototype in September 1939, but complete priority on bomber versions halted work despite Junkers' proposals for various fighter (Zerstörer) versions of Ju 88B. In 1940 the existence of the BMW-powered B-series resulted in a limited go-ahead on the C-1 but this was then negated by the radial engine being reserved for the Fw 190, and by the summer of 1940 there were only a handful of C-2 Zerstörers with Jumo engines and fixed nose armament of two 20-mm (0.79-in) MG FF and two MG 17. Some saw limited action with a special staffel of KG 30 which became I/NJG 2 in September 1940 in the newly created night-fighter force. Though concerned primarily with the development of night-fighting techniques and the testing and evaluation of new night-fighting aids, the C-2s did make many scattered night-intruder missions over RAF Bomber Command bases until prohibited by order of the Führer in October 1941.

By this time the purpose-designed C-4 was in use, based on the A-4 and with a potential forward-firing armament of four MG FF cannon, 12 MG 81 and two MG 17. BMW 801D-2 radials of 1700 hp were fitted to the C-3 but reservation of this engine to the Fw 190 thwarted Junkers' efforts until early 1942, when at last the radial-engined C-5 entered production, closely followed by the C-6 family. The BMW 801 raised speed with full load from 475 km/h (295 mph) to 570 km/h (354 mph), while the Jumo-powered C-6 reflected the lack of radials. C-6b night fighters were among the first fully equipped NJG aircraft with FuG 202 Lichtenstein BC AI radar. Later, in 1943, the much better FuG 220 Lichtenstein SN-2 was fitted, often in addition to the BC system. The cumbersome arrays of dipole aerials were at first not popular, but the proven results of NJG pilots, both in Germany and (in the case of the Ju 88) the Mediterranean, gradually overcame prejudice. Speed was cut by some 40 km/h (25 mph) but the radar was in many ways very effective, and by sheer chance the later SN-2 proved not to be significantly bothered by Allied Window ECM foil clouds.

The first BMW-powered night-fighter version produced in quantity was the R-series. Frantic work by Allied agents and 'boffins' eventually showed that Lichtenstein BC operated on a frequency of 490 MHz, but the device itself—called Emil-Emil by Luftwaffe crews talking on the R/T—remained tantalizingly unknown. Then on May 9, 1943, an almost-new Ju 88R-2 landed at RAF Dyce, Aberdeen. It was an extraordinary case of a multiseat Luftwaffe aircraft defecting, with the whole crew; the aircraft greatly impressed the RAF and is still in perfect condition at RAF St Athan. There were many later subtypes of C-series, and this Zerstörer became one of the most important versions, second only to the A-series with about 3200 delivered, nearly all in the winter 1943-44 when production of the Ju 88 was at its peak of some 380 per month.

To complete the Zerstörer story, the high weights at which the later C-series had to fly, with over 2000 kg (4400 lb) of combat equipment and 3000 kg (6600 lb) of armament, combined, with makeshift airstrips and deteriorating pilot experience, to result in very high attrition. There was a need for a Ju 88 fighter that was easier to fly, and V58 (the 58th development aircraft), a converted R-2, flew in spring 1943 with the larger tail of the Ju 188. With considerable further development this led to the G-series, delivered with both BMW 801D and 801D radials (G-1 and G-6b) and the new 1750-hp Jumo 213A (G-6c and G-7). In all respects the G-series were superb aircraft, with a great variety of equipment and weapon options. Typical armament comprised six 20-mm (0.79-in) MG 151, two of them in an oblique Schräge Musik installation, and an MG 131 for rear defence. By another amazing stroke of luck a new Ju 88G-1 landed at RAF Woodbridge on July 13, 1944, this time because the pilot flew a reciprocal course; this allowed a full examination of Lichtenstein SN-2, the Naxos Z in the cabin roof which homed on RAF bombers' H_2S radars and the Flensburg in the wings which homed on the RAF Monica tail-warning radars which were specially added to the bombers to protect them against night fighters. Sadly for the Luftwaffe the G-series arrived at a time when everything except day fighters was being abruptly cancelled and only about 750 were built in late 1944.

The D-series were various subtypes of strategic reconnaissance aircraft, the P were a family of not very successful heavily gunned antiarmour aircraft which were also used against USAAF bombers, the S was a family of high-speed bombers, the T were related reconnaissance machines and the H were grossly stretched long-range models for use over the Atlantic, the H-1 having FuG 200 Hohentwiel radar and cameras while the H-2 had six forward-firing cannon. Of these only the S was made in numbers, there being several slim smooth-nosed versions, mainly with the BMW engine, which suffered either by having to carry the bombs externally or else by having the large wooden bomb bay of the old A-15. All S-series bombers had either GM-1 (nitrous oxide) engine boost or else turbosupercharged engines; the S-2, with the wooden bomb cell, had BMW 801TJ engines giving 1500 hp at 12 000 m (40 000 ft), and a 3000-kg (6614-lb) bombload could be carried close to this altitude—which was certainly at least 5000 m (16 000 ft) higher than any RAF heavy bomber could fly with a full load. Surprisingly, none of the S-series were quite as fast as the best G-series night fighters, which with radar and flame dampers removed, but with full armament, could reach 647 km/h (402 mph), an outstanding figure for so large an aircraft whose design made no sacrifices to ease of handling, weapon load or range. Most later Ju 88s had endurance in the order of seven hours.

The Ju 88 was also the standard lower component in the Mistel (mistletoe) series of composite aircraft. As will later be described these strange man-guided missiles, which carried a piloted fighter on their backs until in the target area, were an attempt to place extremely large demolition charges on targets where by late 1944 Luftwaffe bombers seldom dared venture. Most lower components were rebuilt A-series bombers, some having Ju 188-type tails, and in the development and crew-training phases in late 1943 and early 1944 the excessive stresses imposed on the Ju 88 landing gears on takeoff caused several crashes. The definitive Mistel replaced the normal crew compartment by a giant hollow-charged warhead containing 3800 kg (8380 lb) of explosive triggered by a set of fuzes on a long conical stand-off probe. Tests showed that a properly aimed Mistel could punch clean through any warship, or through some 18 m (60 ft) of reinforced concrete. The ultimate model was the so-called Führungsmaschine (leading machine) in which an Fw 190A-8 rode on a doubly stretched Ju 88H-4 with 2½ times the fuel capacity of standard Ju 88 bombers and centimetric radar in the nose.

It would be pointless to describe the Ju 88 as a war-winning aircraft because Germany lost the war. But no aircraft did more, in all kinds of missions and on all fronts, to stave off defeat. After its rather long and prickly development it matured as an aircraft in which every desirable quality resided. Like the Lancaster it was not only a great load-carrier but it could be flung about like a single-seater. Total production was about 14 980, some 5000 being fighters. Only small numbers served with other Axis air forces.

Span: (up to A-3, with derived models) 18.35 m (60 ft 3 in), (A-4 and subsequent) 20 m (65 ft 7 in) *Length:* (A-4) 14.4 m (47 ft 3 in) *Gross weight:* (A-1) 10 360 kg (22 840 lb), (most later versions) 14 000 kg (30 865 lb) *Maximum speed:* (A-1, A-4) 450 km/h (280 mph), (C-6c) 495 km/h (308 mph), (G-7b) 648 km/h (402 mph), (S-1) 610 km/h (379 mph)

The Ju 188E-2 was a torpedo-carrying version equivalent of the Ju 188A-3. Some models of this aircraft were delivered without an EDL 131 dorsal turret. It could carry a pair of 800-kg (1764-lb) LT 1B or 765-kg (1686-lb) LT F5b torpedoes under the wings

Ju 188, Junkers

German medium bomber and reconnaissance aircraft. The first prototype of the Ju 188 was flown in the spring of 1942, being basically a refined version of the classic Ju 88, developed via the Ju 88 V27, the Ju 88E-0, and the Ju 88B-0. The Ju 188 featured a considerably revised, enlarged and extensively glazed nose section; larger-span wings, characterized by pointed tips; and bigger, more angular tail surfaces.

The first major production version was the Ju 188E-1, powered by two 1700-hp BMW 801D-2 radial engines. Armament comprised one 20-mm (0.79-in) MG 151 cannon in the nose; one 13-mm (0.51-in) MG 131 machine-gun in a dorsal turret; another MG 131 in the rear of the cockpit ; and one rearward-firing twin 7.9-mm (0.311-in) MG 81Z in a ventral position. Maximum bombload was 3000 kg (6615 lb), and a crew of four was carried. The Ju 188E-2 was a torpedo-bomber variant, and the Ju 188F-1 and F-2 were reconnaissance versions equipped with FuG 200 Hohentwiel maritime search radar. These models first appeared in service in the summer of 1943.

They were followed in 1944 by the Ju 188A-2 production version (the A-1 not being built) with two V-12 1776-hp Jumo 213A engines. It was armed with one MG 151 cannon in the nose and another in the power-operated dorsal turret, one MG 131 in the rear of the cockpit, and a twin MG 81Z mounting in the ventral position. The Ju 188A-3 was the torpedo-bomber counterpart, with the same powerplant but carrying two 765-kg (1685-lb) or 800-kg (1765-lb) torpedoes under the wings (as did the E-2) and a FuG 200 installation in the nose.

An experimental development was the Ju 188C-0, a modified A model with two remote-controlled 13-mm (0.51-in) MG 131 guns in a barbette in the tail cone. A Ju 188G-0 prototype, deriving from the C-0, was completed with a manually operated tail turret and deeper rear fuselage. Neither the C-series nor the G-series entered production. The Ju 188H-2 reconnaissance equivalent of the G remained a project only; other project-only models were the Ju 188M-1 and M-2 (long-range reconnaissance) designs.

Still further developments from the A model were the Ju 188D-1 and D-2 reconnaissance variants (both with a three-man crew and the nose gun deleted); the former was equipped with cameras, while the latter had FuG 200 Hohentwiel radar installed. The Ju 188J, K and L variants were intended as pressurized high-altitude bad-weather intercepter, bomber and reconnaissance models respectively. These three were eventually developed separately under the new designation Ju 388. The Ju 188R-0 experimental radar-carrying night fighter, evaluated in mid-1944, offered little improvement over the existing Ju 88G in that role, and did not progress beyond the prototype stage.

Final operational variants were the normally unarmed Ju 188S and T for high-altitude intruder and reconnaissance roles, with a redesigned forward fuselage section, pressurized cabin, and two 2168-hp (with power boost) Jumo 213E-1 engines. The Ju 188S-1 had a bomb capacity of 800 kg (1763 lb); some were armed with a 50-mm (1.97-in) BK 5 cannon in a ventral fairing and used in the close-support role. The latter aircraft, designated Ju 188S-1/U, were unpressurized and had no engine power boost. A long-range, high-altitude reconnaissance counterpart, the Ju 188T-1, was equipped with two Rb cameras.

Total German production of all Ju 188 models was approximately 1100 aircraft. They operated as pathfinders over the UK during the winter of 1943-44 and were widely used on the Western and Eastern Fronts, in Italy and in Arctic regions, until 1945. Rather more than half of the total built were of the Ju 188D and F reconnaissance series, comparatively few being operated in the bombing role with the Kampfgeschwadern (bomber groups). After VE-Day, the SNCA du Sud Est at Toulouse, using captured German components, completed 12 Ju 188Es for use by the French Aéronavale, and this service also acquired a number of additional ex-German Es and Fs which were used mainly for test purposes.

(Ju 188E-1) *Span:* 22 m (72 ft 2 in) *Length:* 14.95 m (49 ft 1 in) *Gross weight:* 14 510 kg (31 990 lb) *Maximum speed:* 500 km/h (310 mph)

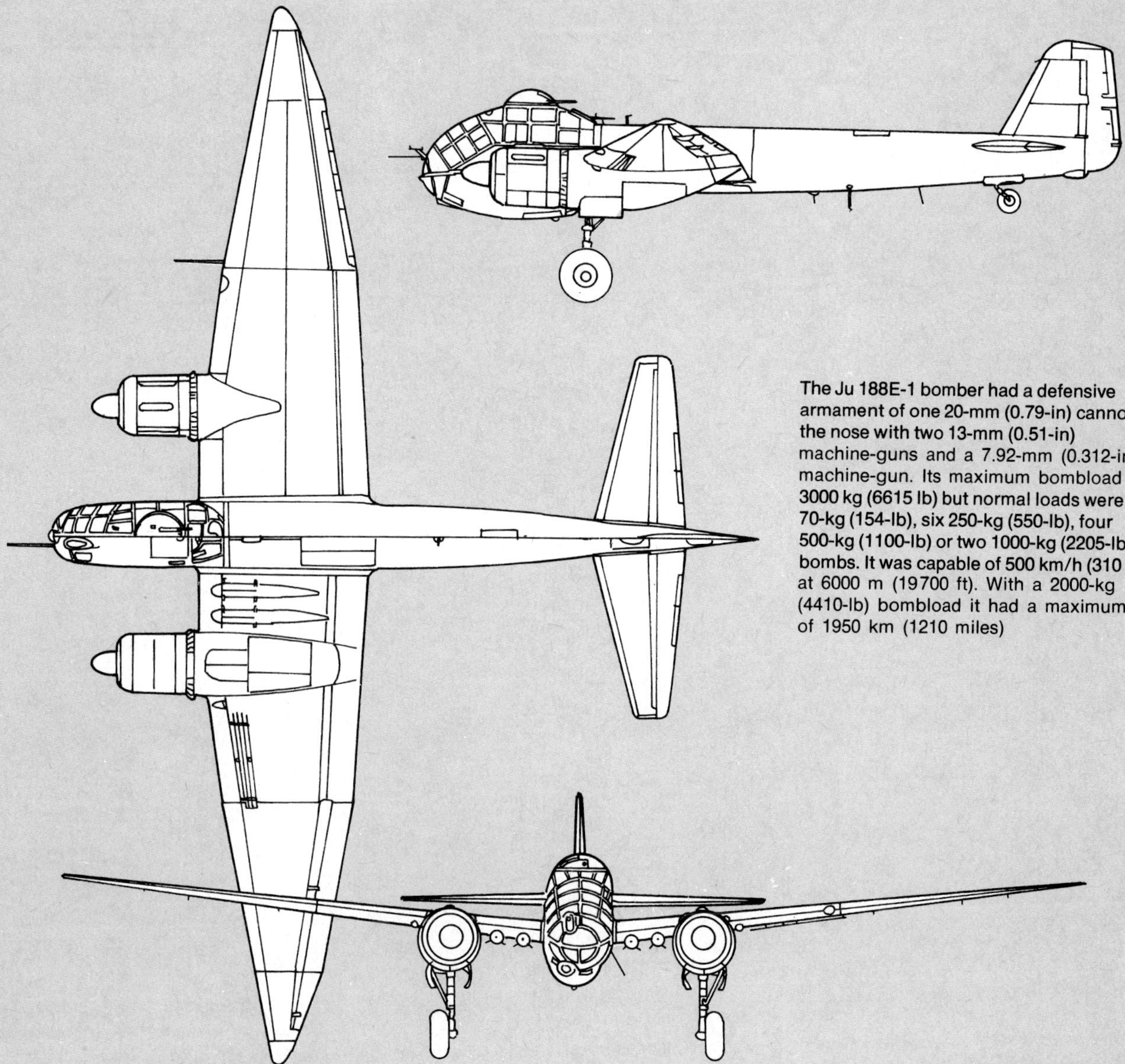

The Ju 188E-1 bomber had a defensive armament of one 20-mm (0.79-in) cannon in the nose with two 13-mm (0.51-in) machine-guns and a 7.92-mm (0.312-in) machine-gun. Its maximum bombload was 3000 kg (6615 lb) but normal loads were 20 70-kg (154-lb), six 250-kg (550-lb), four 500-kg (1100-lb) or two 1000-kg (2205-lb) bombs. It was capable of 500 km/h (310 mph) at 6000 m (19700 ft). With a 2000-kg (4410-lb) bombload it had a maximum range of 1950 km (1210 miles)

Ju 252, Junkers

German transport aircraft. Design work on a replacement for the Ju 52/3m was begun in 1939 for Deutsche Lufthansa, who required an aircraft with better performance to keep in line with foreign commercial aircraft of that time. In the Ju 252, Junkers retained the general arrangement of the earlier transport, but utilized a smooth metal skin, retractable undercarriage, and a pressurized cabin for the three-man crew and passengers. Three unarmed prototypes (Ju 252 V1-V3) were produced, each powered by three 1340-hp Junkers Jumo 211F 12-cylinder liquid-cooled engines, and the first flight was made at Dessau at the end of October 1941.

At this juncture the original Lufthansa order for 25 was overridden by demands to adapt the Ju 252 for use by the Luftwaffe. A fourth prototype (V4) was built with turret armament, a modified rudder, and a ventral loading ramp which could be lowered and raised hydraulically (with the tail wheel retracted) for loading. This formed the basis for the production model, designated Ju 252A-1, which was armed with one 13-mm (0.519-in) MG 131 machine-gun in a power-operated turret aft of the flight deck and two 7.9-mm (0.311-in) MG 15 machine-guns in beam positions. Eleven A-1s were built, and during the Second World War they were used as cargo transports, troop carriers, and for dropping agents.

Although the Ju 252 was a successful design, plans for further development, including increased armament and a float-plane variant, were dropped in favour of the Ju 352 Herkules, due mainly to the shortage of the metal alloys required for the construction of the Ju 252.

(Ju 252A-1) *Span:* 34.1 m (111 ft 10 in) *Length:* 25.1 m (82 ft 4 in) *Gross weight:* 24 000 kg (52 910 lb) *Maximum speed:* 439 km/h (273 mph)

Ju 287, Junkers

German jet bomber. Much study and research had gone into the possibilities of using the jet engine in German fighters and bombers around the middle of the Second World War. In 1943 a contract was placed with the Junkers Flugzeug und Motorenwerke to develop a high-speed jet-propelled heavy bomber. Under the direction of Hans Wocke, two prototypes were begun using the revolutionary swept-forward wing configuration. After extensive wind-tunnel tests the first prototype, utilizing the fuselage of a Heinkel He 177A and the tail unit of a Junkers Ju 388, was completed in 1944. After being transferred from the Dessau factory to the airfield at Brandis, near Leipzig, it began its flight-test programme on August 16. The basic structure was orthodox enough, with an all-metal fuselage and a cabin in the extreme nose for the two-man crew to sit side by side. The tricycle undercarriage was fixed and 'spatted' since research work was to be carried out at low speeds. (On production machines the undercarriage was to have been fully retractable into the fuselage.) The twin-nosewheel unit, salvaged from B-24 Liberators, was fitted with oleo-pneumatic shock absorbers and the main wheels, of Ju 352 type, were braced externally to the underside of the wing. A small tail wheel was also fitted, to absorb shocks in the event of a tail-down landing.

Test flights of the Ju 287 V1 were carried out using four 900-kg (1984-lb) thrust Junkers Jumo 004B-1 turbojets, one under each wing and one on each side of the fuselage nose, each fitted with a 1200-kg (2645-lb) thrust jettisonable, rechargeable Walter 109-502 liquid-fuel rocket to assist takeoff. The

The Ju 287 heavy jet bomber with fixed, spatted tricycle undercarriag intended for low-speed trials. Prototypes were completed but Allied raids and the demands for fighters prevented full production before war ended. The surviving aircraft were captured by the USSR

development programme was cancelled in mid-1944, when the high-speed V2 was partly built, as the German authorities required all available facilities to concentrate on fighter production.

It was revived in 1945 and a V3 production prototype was initiated. Wing structure remained the same, but there were to be other modifications: the front fuselage was redesigned to closely resemble the Ju 388, and the three-seat nose cockpit was pressurized. Behind this were the bomb bay and fuel tanks. A remote-controlled barbette mounting two 13-mm (0.51-in) MG 131 machine-guns in the extreme tail was operated by the gunner from the cockpit using periscopic sights. The two 3500-kg (7720-lb) st BMW 018 turbojets ultimately intended for the aircraft were still in the development stage and various alternatives, including four Heinkel-Hirth HeS 011 or six BMW 003A turbojets, were considered. Although preparations for a production line had been made at a Junkers factory, no aircraft were actually produced.

The partially completed V2 prototype was captured at Rechlin by the Soviet forces, the V1 having earlier been badly damaged there in an Allied air raid. Subsequently, the V2 was completed and tested in the USSR in 1947.

(Ju 287 V1) *Span:* 20.12 m (66 ft) *Length:* 18.28 m (60 ft) *Gross weight:* 20 000 kg (44 090 lb) *Maximum speed:* 559 km/h (347 mph); estimated speed for Ju 287 V3 was 334 km/h (537 mph)

Ju 288, Junkers

German medium bomber aircraft. Still searching for a Ju 88 replacement, in 1939 the RLM (German aviation ministry) favoured the Junkers contender for the 'Bomber B' competition of the same year. Over a four-year development period many setbacks were encountered, not the least of which was the non-availability of the expected Junkers Jumo 222 engines.

No fewer than 21 prototypes were built in an attempt to produce an acceptable production model. First of these were the Ju 288A-series prototypes, the Ju 288 V1-V5, four of them powered by two 1600-hp BMW 801MA engines; the V5 was fitted with 2500-hp Jumo 222A/B powerplants. First flight of the Ju 288 V1 was made in January 1941. Each aircraft was equipped to carry a three-man crew, and various wing, dive-brake and armament layouts were tried. Though no contract was issued, intended production models were the Ju 288A-1 and A-2, to be armed with two 13-mm (0.51-in) MG 131 machine-guns in each of the remote-controlled dorsal and ventral barbettes and having a capacity for an internal bombload of 3000 kg (6614 lb).

The next three aircraft (the V6, 7 and 8, prototypes for the Ju 288B series) were adapted for a four-man crew, with a redesigned wing configuration and enlarged tail surfaces. They also were powered by Jumo 222A/B engines except for the V7, which had BMW 801Cs installed. Five more Ju 288B prototypes (V9, 11, 12, 13 and 14) were completed, but production plans were again cancelled due to development problems with the Jumo 222.

It was decided instead to proceed with the proposed Ju 288C, for which a further eight prototypes were built, designated Ju 288 V101-108. These had redesigned, lengthened nose sections and an additional ventral barbette with twin 13-mm (0.51-in) MG 131 machine-guns. Instead of the troublesome Jumo 222, they were powered by 2700-hp DB 606A/Bs or 2950-hp DB 610A/Bs. The Ju 288 V101 first flew in the late summer of 1942. A proposed night-bomber variant was the Ju 288C-3, preceded by the variously armed Ju 288C-1 and C-2 day-bomber models.

Eventually the entire 'Bomber B' programme was cancelled in the summer of 1943. Work on the Ju 288 was continued privately by Junkers, which carried out a further year or so of flight testing. With the tide of the Second World War turning in late 1944, all available aircraft were allocated to the Luftwaffe, and some of the surviving Ju 288 prototypes (17 of which had crashed) were sent to operational units in the closing stages of the war, equipped with a 50-mm (1.97-in) BK 5 cannon in an under-fuselage pod.

(Ju 288B, estimated) *Span:* 22.66 m (74 ft 4 in) *Length:* 17.80 m (58 ft 5 in) *Gross weight:* 20 950 kg (46 190 lb) *Maximum speed:* 623 km/h (387 mph)

Ju 290, Junkers

German maritime patrol bomber and transport aircraft. The Ju 290 had its origins in the pre-Second World War Ju 90 commercial transport. It was originally known as the Ju 90S, and several Ju 90 prototypes were used in its developments. The Ju 290 was designed

Above: The Ju 288C-1 medium day bomber. The 288 was Junkers' attempt to find a replacement for the 88, but despite extensive trials and 21 prototypes it was not a success

in 1940 under the direction of Dipl-Ings Zindel and Kraft of the Junkers Flugzeug und Motorenwerke, and had a wider wing span and larger fuselage than its predecessor. Two Ju 290A-0 preproduction models were built in 1942, powered by four 1600-hp BMW 801L engines. The initial production model, designated Ju 290A-1 carried a crew of nine; five were built and entered service in early 1943. Armament comprised one 20-mm (0.79-in) MG 151 cannon under the nose, three 13-mm (0.51-in) MG 131 machine-guns, two further MG 151s in dorsal and tail turrets, and two side-firing 7.9-mm (0.311-in) MG 15 machine-guns.

Three Ju 290A-2 maritime reconnaissance aircraft were built, with increased fuel capacity, FuG 200 Hohentwiel radar equipment and an additional 20-mm (0.79-in) MG 151 cannon in an aft dorsal turret. The next five aircraft were A-3s; two of them were powered by 1700-hp BMW 801D engines, and all had a modified gun blister in the tail. Five Ju 290A-4s, with low-drag forward and aft dorsal turrets, were followed in late 1943 by a much improved model, the A-5, with armour protection for the fuel tanks and the nine-man crew. The beam machine-guns were replaced by two 20-mm (0.79-in) MG 151 cannon. Eleven of these were built by Junkers and about 18 other Ju 290As, of various models, came off a production line which had been set up at the Letov plant, near Prague in Czechoslovakia.

A solitary A-6 model, capable of carrying 50 passengers, was built by Junkers for Hitler's personal transport flight. After a journey to Barcelona in April 1945 it served with the Spanish air force until the mid-1950s.

The Ju 290A-7, of which 12 were built, was a reconnaissance bomber model, developed from the A-5. Provision was made for increased range and weight, which arose from the additional 20-mm (0.79-in) cannon in the redesigned, glazed nose section plus three racks (one under the fuselage and one under each wing) which could carry an external bombload of 3000 kg (6610 lb) or three missiles of the Hs 293 or Fritz X type.

A 13-man crew was carried by the A-8 model, which had four dorsal turrets, slightly revised armament and BMW 801G powerplants. Only two or three of this model were completed, and it was followed by a long-range reconnaissance version with decreased armament but increased fuel capacity, designated Ju 290A-9; of these only three were built and used for flights to assist the Japanese in Manchuria.

In late 1943 work began on a Ju 290B bomber series, eliminating the cargo-loading *Transpoklappe* (rear-loading ramp) fitted to the A series. The first prototype to appear was for the Ju 290B-1, a long-range high-altitude heavy bomber; first flown in mid-1944, it was basically the same as the A-7, but with pressurized nose, dorsal and tail turrets, plus a further increase in armament. An unpressurized variant, again with revised armament detail, was the B-2, but none were completed. Other project-only models were the Ju 290B MS (mine countermeasures), the Ju 290C (reconnaissance and transport), and the 290D and E (long-range bombers). Total production of the entire series did not exceed 70 aircraft.

(Ju 290A-5) *Span:* 42 m (137 ft 9 in) *Length:* 28.6 m (94 ft) *Gross weight:* 44 970 kg (99 140 lb) *Maximum speed:* 440 km/h (273 mph)

Ju 352 Herkules, Junkers

German general-purpose transport aircraft. The Ju 352 (named Herkules by Junkers) was a progressive development of the all-metal Ju 252. Built during the latter stages of the Second World War, it was designed to use as much non-strategic material as possible. It was generally similar to the earlier aircraft, but the fuselage was partly metal-and partly fabric-covered with all-wooden wings.

The first of two unarmed prototypes (Ju 352 V1 and V2) flew for the first time on October 1, 1943, powered by three 1000-hp BMW-Bramo 323R-2 radial engines. These were followed by a preproduction batch of ten Ju 352A-0s (V3 to V12). A production batch of 33 aircraft followed, designated Ju 352A-1. All were armed with a single 20-mm (0.79-in) MG 151 cannon in a power-operated forward dorsal turret, with provision for two lateral-firing 13-mm (0.51-in) MG 131 machine-guns. The central nose-mounted engine extended well out in front of the aircraft to accommodate the somewhat unusual exhaust pipes which emerged from the rear of the cowling, giving it a very distinctive appearance.

Deliveries of the A-1 began in the spring of 1944 and, like the Ju 252, it was used on special-duty missions as well as in the regular transport role—mostly on the Eastern Front during the later months of the war. The Herkules carried a four- or five-man crew and had a useful load capacity of 4300 kg (9480 lb) or up to 32 troops. The Ju 352B-1 and B-2 projects had not reached development stage by the end of the war.

(Ju 352A-1) *Span:* 34.2 m (112 ft 2 in) *Length:* 24.6 m (80 ft 9 in) *Gross weight:* 19 595 kg (43 200 lb) *Maximum speed:* 370 km/h (230 mph)

Ju 388, Junkers

German multipurpose combat aircraft. Making its first appearance in autumn 1943, the Ju 388 was intended as a high-performance successor to the Ju 188. It was developed from the Ju 188S and T models as a stand-in until pure-jet types could be produced. It was to have been built in three main versions all having a three-man crew: high-altitude pressurized night and all-weather fighter (J); high-altitude bomber (K); and high-altitude photographic reconnaissance aircraft (L). Numerous prototypes were built, but the versions mentioned above were the only ones to be produced in any numbers, and the Ju 388L was the only one to enter squadron service.

The first prototype was converted from a Ju 188T-1 and flew for the first time in late 1943. Ten preproduction Ju 388L-0s, converted from Ju 88S-1s, were produced by the Allgemeine Transportanlagen GmbH (ATG), and 45 production Ju 388L-1s by the ATG and Weser companies. Soon after trials had been made from August 1944, the L-1 began to enter service with two Luftwaffe experimental units, the Versuchsverbänd Oberbefehlshaber der Luftwaffe (3rd Staffel) and Erpröbungskommando 388. Many standard wing and tail units of Ju 188s were used on these aircraft, which were powered by two 14-cylinder 1800-hp BMW 801TJ radial engines. Standard armament was two remote-controlled 13-mm (0.51-in) MG 131 machine-guns in a tail barbette, though slow development and delays in delivery of this equipment resulted in the L-0s being fitted instead with a ventral fairing containing two rearward-firing 7.9-mm (0.311-in) MG 81s. The L-1 had the tail barbette, FuG 217 Neptun warning radar (also in the tail), a ventral wooden pannier for two cameras, and an auxiliary fuel tank. A few Ju 388L-1s were converted to carry an additional MG 131 in the rear of the cockpit, and two were re-engined with 1750-hp Junkers Jumo 213Es and designated L-3.

The main prototypes (V2, V4 and V5) built for the Ju 388J Stortebeker night and bad-weather fighter variant, were to have been equipped with Lichtenstein SN-2 radar in a 'solid' nose, the twin MG 131 tail barbette of the Ju 388L, a ventral pack of two 30-mm (1.18-in) MK 108 cannon, two 20-mm (0.79-in) MG 151 forward-firing cannon, and two upward-firing MG 151 cannon in the dorsal position. Only the prototypes were built.

The Ju 388 V3 high-altitude bomber variant, with BMW 801TJ engines and a bombload of 3000 kg (6614 lb), was flown in early 1944. This was followed by ten preproduction models designated Ju 388K-0 and five K-1 production models, none of which were ever used operationally. The proposed K-2 (Jumo 213Es) and K-3 (Jumo 222E/Fs) were never flown. Yet another projected version was the four-seat Ju 388M-1 torpedo carrier. Total production of the Ju 388 series amounted only to approximately 77 aircraft by early 1945, when the programme was halted.

(Ju 388L-1) *Span:* 22 m (72 ft 2 in) *Length:* 15.20 m (49 ft 10 in) *Gross weight:* 14 675 kg (32 350 lb) *Maximum speed:* 616 km/h (383 mph)

Ju 390, Junkers

German transport/heavy bomber/reconnaissance aircraft. Derived through the Ju 90 and 290 series, only two aircraft of this type were built. The first was a transport prototype based on the Ju 290A, but with a longer fuselage and increased wing span. It was powered by six 1700-hp BMW 801D engines and incorporated a *Transpoklappe* (rear-loading ramp) and retractable main undercarriage with twin wheels under each of the four inner nacelles. Designated Ju 390 V1, it was flown for the first time in August 1943.

The V2, prototype for a long-range maritime reconnaissance version, had an extended front fuselage section and was armed with four 20-mm (0.79-in) MG 151 cannon, one in each of the forward and rear dorsal turrets, one in the nose of a ventral gondola, and one in the tail; two 13-mm (0.51-in) MG 131 machine-guns were mounted in beam positions with a third in the tail. The V2 was also equipped with FuG 200 Hohentwiel radar. It first flew in October 1943.

The third prototype, the Ju 390 V3, was to have formed the basis for the production Ju 390A-1, heavy-bomber and reconnaissance variant, with a BMW 801E powerplant and revised armament (four MG 131 machine-guns in each of the two dorsal turrets as well as two in the ventral barbette; and two lateral-firing MG 151s in the beam positions). The Ju 390A-1 was to have been capable of carrying a 7200-kg (15 870-lb) bombload or four Hs 293 or other missiles on the underwing racks. No bomber variants were produced, but evidence of the aircraft's long-range potential was provided in early 1944 when the V2, then operating with Fernaufklärungsgruppe 5 (long-range reconnaissance wing) made a return flight from Mont de Marsan in France to within 20 km (12 miles) of the American coast, just north of New York. It is also claimed, though confirmation is lacking, that one or both of the prototypes flew between Odessa and Manchuria, allegedly in service with Hitler's personal transport squadron.

(Ju 390A-1, estimated) *Span:* 50.3 m (165 ft) *Length:* 34.2 m (112 ft 2 in) *Gross weight:* 75 500 kg (166 450 lb) *Maximum speed:* 505 km/h (314 mph)

Judy Allied codename for Yokosuka D4Y Suisei Japanese dive-bomber See **D4Y**

Julian Ordonez

Spanish torpedo boat class. The 1st Class torpedo boats *Julian Ordonez* and her sister *Acevedo* were built by the British firm of Thornycroft, and were part of a series of torpedo boats ordered by Spain from British, French and German firms in the 1880s. They were not large enough to operate effectively at sea for any length of time, and were really meant purely for local and harbour defence.

Acevedo (builder's no 209) and *Julian Ordonez* (builder's no 210) were typical of the torpedo boats that Thornycroft were building for a large number of countries in the middle of the 1880s. Both were built in 1885, and had a steel hull with a short turtledeck forecastle over the fixed bow torpedo tubes. At the aft end of the turtledeck was a very prominent conning tower, with a searchlight mounted above it. There was a single raked mast and funnel, and a long deckhouse over the machinery. The gun armament was two 25-mm (1-in) Nordenfelt machine-guns, one of which was mounted to starboard between the funnel and conning tower, and the other sited well aft.

The vessels were fitted with locomotive boilers, with a working pressure of 8.86 kg/sq cm (126 psi). On trials, *Ordonez* developed 666 ihp and *Acevedo* 587 ihp to make 20 knots. The former had a range of 480 nautical miles and the latter of 400 at full speed, on 20 tons of coal. They had both bow and stern rudders, and were almost as manoeuvrable going astern as ahead.

Like most of the Spanish torpedo boats, they had an uneventful career, spending most of their time at anchor or alongside at the major Spanish naval dockyards. In the early years of this century *Ordonez* was renumbered *No 43* and *Acevedo* became *No 44.* Both were discarded about 1913.

Displacement: 66 tons *Length:* 35.86 m (117 ft 8 in) *Beam:* 3.81 m (12 ft 6 in) *Draught:* 1.65 m (5 ft 5 in) *Machinery:* 1-shaft compound reciprocating, 600 ihp=20 knots *Armament:* 2 25-mm (1-in) machine-guns; 2 36-cm (14-in) torpedo tubes *Crew:* not known

Juliet

Soviet submarine class, built 1961-67. The *Juliet* submarines were diesel-electric boats designed to launch SS-N-3 surface-to-surface missiles in the same manner as their contemporary nuclear counterparts the *Echo* Class. The *Juliet* boats had a smaller hull, however, and could accommodate only four missile launchers in the casing. It is reported that 72 boats were planned, but the number was reduced to 16 in 1962, when production problems were encountered with the launchers. In any case the *Juliet* submarines have now been overtaken by later developments, and would stand little chance of firing their SS-N-3s on the surface.

The *Juliets* have a very unusual appearance, with high freeboard and a very long fin. As in the *Echo* boats the missile tubes are elevated to 20-30° for firing, and when stowed are concealed under hatches. Behind each tube the casing is indented to form a blast deflector.

See also *Echo.*

Displacement: 2200/3550 tons (surfaced/submerged) *Length:* 87 m (285 ft 5 in) oa *Beam:* 9.4 m (30 ft 10 in) *Draught:* 6 m (19 ft 8 in) *Machinery:* 1-shaft diesel/electric, 6000 bhp =19/10 knots (surfaced/submerged) *Armament:* 4 SS-N-3A SSM launchers (4×1); 6 53-cm (21-in) torpedo tubes (bow); 4 40-cm (15.7-in) A/S torpedo tubes (stern); 36 mines (in place of torpedoes) *Crew:* 79

Jumbo, Messerschmitt-Bölkow-Blohm

German air-to-surface missile. In 1972 Messerschmitt-Bölkow-Blohm began project definition of a heavy, long-range rocket-powered missile to arm the Tornado multirole combat aircraft from 1981. Two Jumbos would have been carried by Tornado, one each side of a command/video-link guidance pod beneath the fuselage. The weapon was intended to be launched at high or low level and to carry a variety of interchangeable warheads weighing up to 800 kg (1765 lb). This was to allow the weapon to be used

The *Juliet* Class are counterparts of the Soviet *Echo* Class submarines. They have a smaller hull but retain the same large fin. Their inability to launch missiles submerged has rendered them obsolescent

A Soviet *Juliet* Class missile submarine pictured in 1973. The black shadows in the casing indicate the blast deflectors for the SS-N-3 missiles

US Navy

Messerschmitt-Bölkow-Blohm

The Messerschmitt-Bölkow-Blohm Jumbo air-to-surface heavy long-range missile, which is under development as a stand-off weapon for the Tornado MRCA for deployment in 1981

against hard structures such as bridges as well as against dispersed targets including tank formations.

The US and Italy both expressed some interest in joining the project, but in late 1975 Jumbo was cancelled as a result of the German government's policy of developing major weapons on a multilateral basis only. The design has since been re-examined by MBB and McDonnell Douglas, which have carried out joint studies on long-range air-to-surface missiles, but was rejected in favour of a design using flip-out wings and probably a turbojet powerplant.

Length: 5.24 m (17 ft 2 in) *Span:* 1.25 m (4 ft 1 in) *Diameter:* 50 cm (20 in) *Weight:* 1150 kg (2535 lb) *Range:* 30-40 km (19-25 miles)

RAF men examine a captured Bücker Bü 131B Jungmann two-seat primary trainer. The Bü 131 was used not only for training but also for night ground attack on the Eastern Front

IWM

Jungmann Bü 131, Bücker

German trainer and light attack aircraft. Carl Clemens Bücker was a seaplane pilot in the Imperial German Navy during the First World War. He spent the 1920s in Sweden, but in 1932 set up Bücker Flugzeugbau at Berlin-Johannisthal and got the Swedish designer Anders J Andersson to design a succession of light aircraft. Virtually every one was a great success. The very first, the Bü 131 Jungmann (young man), became a standard primary trainer in the Luftwaffe.

The prototype flew on April 27, 1934. Powered by an 80-hp Hirth HM 60R inverted four-in-line engine, it had typical steel-tube fuselage and identical upper and lower wooden wings, all with ailerons and with marked stagger and sweepback. Pupil and instructor were in tandem open cockpits.

Deliveries of the Bü 131A began in December 1934 to the *Deutscher Luftsportverband* (German Air Sport League), followed in July 1935 by the more powerful Bü 131B with 105-hp HM 504A-2. This was adopted as a standard Luftwaffe trainer, and several thousand were built, nearly all of standard Bü 131B type. In winter many operated on skis. Jungmanns equipped units at more than ten pilot schools *(Flugzeugführerschulen)* from late 1935 until the final Nazi collapse.

In 1942 light aircraft were urgently sought to equip the newly formed Nachtschlachtgruppen (night close-support/ground attack groups) to serve on the Eastern front in night harassment sorties with light guns, antipersonnel bombs and various other capacities both over the front line and against partisans. The Bü 131B was one of the types selected, several hundred seeing action with NSGr 2, 8, 11, 12 and possibly other units.

The Imperial Japanese Navy adopted the Jungmann as a standard trainer and 339 were built by Watanabe (later Kyushu) and Hitachi as the K9W1, with 110-hp Hitachi GK4A engine. The army followed suit, 1037 being built by Nippon Kokusai as the Ki-86a in 1944-45. The Allied codename was Cypress. Captured Jungmanns, both German and Japanese, were popular with the Allies, and many were still airworthy in the late 1970s.

Span: 7.4 m (24 ft 3 in) *Length:* 6.62 m (21 ft 9 in) *Gross weight:* (typical) 680 kg (1500 lb) *Maximum speed:* 183 km/h (114 mph)

Jungmeister Bü 133, Bücker

German aerobatic trainer aircraft. Based on the Jungmann, this machine was a single-seater with a more powerful engine. Built at the new factory at Berlin-Rangsdorf, the *Jungmeister* (young champion) was another instant success and it went into production in 1936 as the Bü 133C powered by the 160-hp Siemens Sh 14A-4 radial. Though built in smaller numbers than the two-seater the 133C served at numerous Luftwaffe pilot and fighter-pilot schools, though so far as is known no examples carried armament. The Jungmeister was a standard type for formation flying, aerobatics and the teaching of combat tactics. Skis were used in winter.

Dornier-Werke in Switzerland built 47 Bü 133C for the Swiss air force and CASA in Spain built 50, including a few with the

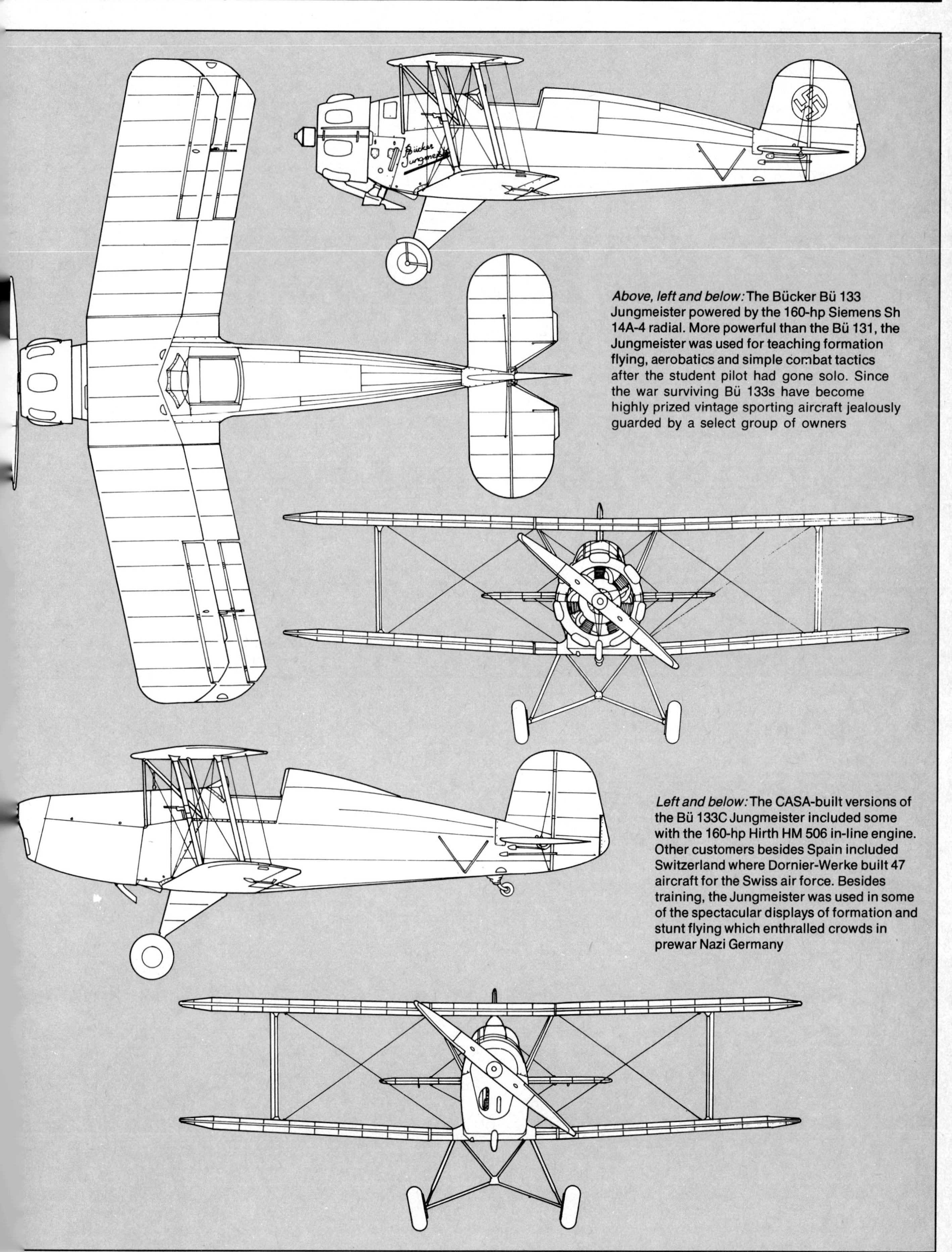

Above, left and below: The Bücker Bü 133 Jungmeister powered by the 160-hp Siemens Sh 14A-4 radial. More powerful than the Bü 131, the Jungmeister was used for teaching formation flying, aerobatics and simple combat tactics after the student pilot had gone solo. Since the war surviving Bü 133s have become highly prized vintage sporting aircraft jealously guarded by a select group of owners

Left and below: The CASA-built versions of the Bü 133C Jungmeister included some with the 160-hp Hirth HM 506 in-line engine. Other customers besides Spain included Switzerland where Dornier-Werke built 47 aircraft for the Swiss air force. Besides training, the Jungmeister was used in some of the spectacular displays of formation and stunt flying which enthralled crowds in prewar Nazi Germany

IWM

A Jungmeister trainer with ski undercarriage takes off from a frozen lake in prewar Germany

160-hp Hirth HM 506 in-line engine, for the Spanish air force. The Jungmeister is now one of the most prized vintage sporting aircraft.

Span: 6.6 m (21 ft 8 in) *Length:* 6.02 m (19 ft 9 in) *Gross weight:* 585 kg (1290 lb) *Maximum speed:* 220 km/h (137 mph)

Junkers German aircraft See **J.1, Ju 52, Ju 86, Ju 87, Ju 88, Ju 188, Ju 252, Ju 287, Ju 288, Ju 290, Ju 352, Ju 388, Ju 390, Junkers CL, Junkers D, Junkers R, Junkers W, R.42**

Junkers CL

German fighter aircraft. The J.8, which appeared in early 1918 (itself virtually a two-seat version of the Junkers D.I), served as a prototype for the J.10 which went into production in 1918, designated CL.I. An all-metal low-wing monoplane, with cantilever wings, the CL.I was intended to re-equip the Schlachtstaffeln (battle flights) for close tactical support of the German army.

Of typical Junkers construction, the CL.I incorporated thin corrugated metal skin on wings and fuselage, resulting in a distinctive angular outline. It was powered by a 180-hp Mercedes IIIa engine, and carried armament of two synchronized 7.92-mm (0.312-in) Spandau machine-guns and a ring-mounted 7.92-mm Parabellum machine-gun. The CL.I was too late to see extensive service during the war, a total of only 47 machines having been constructed by the Armistice in 1918, but several examples were modified for civil passenger and communications use in the years immediately after the war in Germany.

Three CLS.I variants, serialled 7501-03, were converted to floatplanes, and were later used for civil purposes. They differed from the CL.I in having an additional fin fitted to the tail unit and employing a 200-hp Benz engine.

(CL.1) *Span:* 12 m (39 ft 6 in) *Length:* 7.9 m (25 ft 11 in) *Gross weight:* 710 kg (1560 lb) *Maximum speed:* 161 km/h (100 mph)

Junkers D.I

German fighter aircraft. Continuing his policy of building all-metal aeroplanes, Dr Hugo Junkers produced his J.7 (factory designation) in 1917. A low-wing single-seat fighter, with metal sheet skinning on fuselage and wings, the J.7 was powered by a 160-hp Mercedes D.III engine. It took part in the June 1918 D-types competition for new fighter designs, but was not ordered for production.

The J.7 served as the prototype for the J.9, officially titled D.I, which appeared in late 1918. A clean, neat design, the D.I production version had a slightly longer fuselage than the J.7, and had a 185-hp BMW engine installed in a rather neater fuselage layout. Like the CL.I, it was armed with two fixed and one ring-mounted 7.92-mm (0.312-in) machine-guns. Though ordered into limited production, only a few reached front-line units for operational evaluation before the end of hostilities in November 1918.

Span: 9 m (29 ft 6 in) *Length:* 7.25 m (23 ft 9 in) *Gross weight:* 832 kg (1835 lb) *Maximum speed:* 191 km/h (119 mph)

Junkers H

German/Soviet reconnaissance aircraft, first flown 1922. The H 21 reconnaissance aircraft was the first of a series of Junkers military

The Junkers CLS.1 floatplane variant, serialled 7501-03, was later used for civil purposes. They were powered by a 200-hp Benz engine

IWM

The Junkers D.1 all-metal monoplane fighter aircraft saw limited service on the Western Front at the close of the First World War

aircraft produced at a factory at Fili, near Moscow, under the secret clauses of the Treaty of Rapallo. With its typical all-metal construction and corrugated duralumin skin, the H 21 backed up the reputation of the F 13 transport—the first Junkers seen in the Soviet Union—in being more able to withstand severe conditions than any other aircraft.

The Fili plant delivered at least 100 H 21s as reconnaissance aircraft, with 195-hp Junkers L2 water-cooled engines. They were parasol monoplanes with tandem cockpits, and overload fuel tanks forming large blisters on the fuselage sides. Armed with one fixed and one free 7.62-mm (0.30-in) gun, the H 21 had interchangeable wheel and ski landing gear. It was rumoured to be short on range.

The H 22 was a single-seat version built in 1922-23, with the wing brought down to touch the fuselage ahead of the windscreen. Armed with two synchronized machine-guns, it was apparently not outstanding since only a small number were built. Production of Junkers aircraft at Fili was terminated by the Soviet government in March 1927.

Span: 10.77 m (35 ft 4 in) *Length:* 6.7 m (22 ft) *Gross weight:* (H 21) 990 kg (2185 lb); (H 22) 850 kg (1875 lb) *Maximum speed:* (H 21) 220 km/h (137 mph); (H 22) 250 km/h (155 mph)

Jupiter, Chrysler

US intermediate-range ballistic missile. The SM-78 Jupiter was the US Army's first and only strategic ballistic missile. The US Army Ballistic Missile Agency (ABMA) was established with the primary aim of developing a mobile IRBM as a logical extension of conventional artillery. The US Air Force, however, saw such a weapon as a threat to its bomber forces and was developing its own IRBM, Thor. Subsequently the USAF succeeded in preventing the army from developing long- and intermediate-range weapons, and responsibility for them was transferred to the USAF.

In November 1955, as a result of concern about development of thermonuclear weapons in the Soviet Union, the US Navy was ordered to join the army on the Jupiter project. The navy examined both the standard liquid-propellant Jupiter (four of which would have been carried on a submarine, and launched from the surface) and the Jupiter-S, which was to be powered by a cluster of solid-propellant rocket motors. Both were too large to be practicable, and in mid-1956 the navy set up its Special Projects Group to examine alternative designs making use of recent advances in warhead miniaturization. The navy's involvement with Jupiter officially ended in December 1956, and development of the solid-propellant Polaris submarine-launched ballistic missile was begun the following month.

In June 1956 Chrysler had been awarded a full-scale development contract for Jupiter by the US Army, and in September the first of nine Jupiter-C re-entry test vehicles was flown successfully. Jupiter-C was built up from a modified Redstone missile with increased propellant capacity as the first stage, and clusters of solid-fuel rockets forming the other three stages. The Jupiter IRBM was the first ballistic missile to have a re-entry vehicle which used ablative cooling rather than a heat sink, and much of the design was proved with Jupiter-Cs.

The first two test launches of the standard Jupiter were failures, but on May 31, 1957, one flew the full 2400-km (1500-miles) design range. The army placed the first production order in August, and in May 1958 a full-scale ablative nose cone was flown over the design range and recovered. Two months later the missile began fully guided flights to extreme range, and the US Army fired its first production missile from Cape Canaveral in January 1959. The research and development programme ended in February 1960, having involved 29 Jupiters and four Juno space boosters.

The standard Jupiter was a single-stage (more accurately 'one-and-a-half-stage') missile with an aluminium-alloy airframe. The main stage contained a single Rocketdyne S-3D rocket motor burning RP-1 (kerosene) fuel with liquid oxygen and producing 68 000 kg (150 000 lb) of thrust. The engine could be swivelled to steer the missile in pitch and yaw, roll control being provided by the turbopump exhaust. Following burn-out of the main engine, which was commanded by an on-board computer fed by data from an accelerometer, the exact final velocity was achieved by firing a small solid-propellant motor in the nose. The missile was maintained on its correct azimuth by an inertial guidance system known as Delta Minimum, developed by ABMA and built by Ford Instrument. The desired heading was determined before launch by theodolites and fed into the guidance system. Once the final trajectory had been established by the solid rocket motor the warhead was separated by explosive bolts.

The Goodyear nose cone was protected by an ablative surface built up from glass/phenolic laminates and was stabilized by four attitude-control jets and a spin rocket to ensure even ablation. Heat generated by friction during re-entry was carried away as the ablative material melted and was scoured off the nose cone. This method of cooling, adopted for the first time in Jupiter, resulted in a much lighter re-entry vehicle than was possible with missiles such as Thor and the early models of Atlas, which used a copper block as a heat sink. A bigger payload could therefore be carried, and delivered more accurately. Jupiter was fitted with a thermonuclear warhead of 1.5 megatons yield.

Although developed under the sponsorship of the US Army, Jupiter was inherited by the USAF. The missile was operated by 864, 865 and 866 Squadrons of Strategic Air Command, initially in the US and later in Italy (two squadrons) and Turkey (one squadron). Control of the missiles in these countries was handed over to the respective air forces and the weapons were assigned to NATO, with the warheads under US control.

Each squadron had 15 missiles, of which six were normally kept at 'instant' readiness and could be launched within 15 minutes. Each missile was delivered in two parts: the thrust unit, including rocket motor and propellant tanks; and the warhead unit, including the arming and fuzing mechanisms. Once assembled, the IRBM was mounted vertically and enclosed in a segmented 'rose-petal' shelter to protect it from the weather. In the autumn of 1962 the Cuba crisis focused attention on IRBMs capable of being fired against the superpowers from neighbouring countries, and the following year the Jupiters in Italy and Turkey were withdrawn and replaced by Polaris submarines.

Length: 18 m (59 ft) *Diameter:* 2.7 m (8 ft 9 in) *Launch weight:* 47 600 kg (105 000 lb) *Range:* 2400 km (1500 miles) *Velocity:* 16 000 km/h (10 000 mph)

HM Submarine *K.11* as she was completed, with a low bow and conning tower. Her twin 18-in (46-cm) torpedo tubes located amidships have been trained to port. These tubes were intended for surface attacks at night and enabled the submarines to engage targets from a beam position. Other armament included two 4-in (102-mm) guns and a 3-in (76-mm) AA gun as well as bow-mounted tubes. The Admiralty had proposed 21-in (53-cm) torpedoes, but 18-in were adopted at Vickers' suggestion since no design work had been done on 21-in tubes.

Jurien de la Gravière

French protected cruiser, built 1897-1901. The *Jurien de la Gravière* was intended to be a fast commerce-destroyer, capable of outrunning and outfighting any British cruiser afloat. She was launched at Lorient on June 26, 1899, but the leisurely pace of work in French shipyards meant that by the time she was completed she had been outclassed by the latest British cruisers. In any case she was a dismal failure on her speed trials. Although repeatedly flogged up and down the measured mile she never made more than 21.7 knots, compared with the 23 for which she was designed; and she could not maintain 21 knots for more than an hour. In layout and appearance she was a reduced edition of the *Kleber* Class, though she was protected only by deck armour and had her guns in splinter-proof shields, not turrets.

In August 1914 she joined the Armée Navale at Lorient, and she was immediately sent to the Mediterranean, escorting the submarines of the 2nd Flotilla to Bizerta. On August 16 she was in action against the Austro-Hungarian fleet in the Adriatic, and fired at the destroyer *Uhlan*. In September 1916 she and the destroyer *Lansquenet* were sent to Crete to put down the insurrection there. She also took part in the Salonika campaign. In August-September 1918 she was refitted at Palermo and was stationed off the Syrian coast in 1919. She was condemned at Toulon in 1922 and sold for scrap.

Displacement: 5700 tons (normal) *Length:* 137 m (449 ft 6 in) pp *Beam:* 15 m (49 ft 3 in) *Draught:* 6.4 m (21 ft) *Machinery:* 3-shaft reciprocating steam, 17 000 ihp=23 knots (designed) *Protection:* 65 mm (2.56 in) deck, 54 mm (2.13 in) gun shields, 45 mm (1.77 in) casemates *Armament:* 8 164.7-mm (6.48-in)/45-cal (8×1); 10 47-mm (1.85-in) QF (10×1); 2 45-cm (17.7-in) torpedo tubes (above water, beam) *Crew:* 511

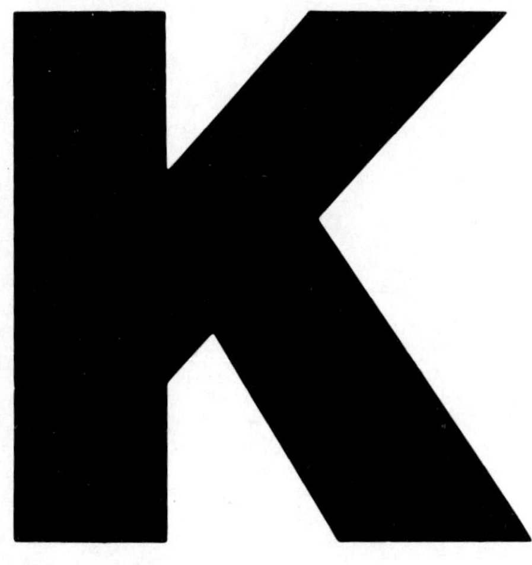

'K' Class British destroyers (1911)
See ***Acasta***

'K' Class British destroyers (1957)
See ***Javelin***

K.1

British submarine class, built 1915-17. On April 15, 1915, Vickers forwarded to Commodore Hall, the officer in charge of British submarine flotillas, a design for a large submarine driven by steam turbines. Vickers were building the 'J' Class, diesel-driven boats designed for high speed, and were experiencing great difficulty in producing engines of the required power.

Whether Vickers were influenced by the long French experience with surface steam propulsion is not known, but what is clear is that they grasped the fact that existing diesels had reached the limit of development, and only steam power could provide a surface speed of 21 knots. Vickers produced a design which had a length of 85.3 m (280 ft), 8.5 m (28 ft) beam, 7 m (23 ft) draught and a displacement of 2000/2760 tons. Triple screws were to be driven by 14 000-shp steam turbines on the outer shaft and a diesel engine on the centre one; 1500-hp electric motors would be driven by a 284-cell battery. The armament would include eight 18-in (46-cm) torpedo tubes on bow and beam positions, as well as a 4-in (102-mm) and a 12-pdr (3-in) gun.

In reply, the Director of Naval Construction put forward a design which his department had drawn up as early as 1913. It was smaller than the Vickers design but had a maximum speed of 24 knots as against 23. The official design was adopted, but many features of the Vickers design were incorporated, including the diesel engine on the centre shaft and 18-in torpedo tubes as replacements for the 21-in (53-cm). The diesel engine provided power during the tricky changeover from steam to electric drive and vice versa. The 18-in tubes which had already been designed for the 'J' Class were chosen to speed construction, no design work having been done on a 21-in tube. As completed, the design also included a twin 18-in tube in a trainable deck-mounting for use at night. The gun armament was increased to two 4-in guns and a 3-in (76-mm) antiaircraft gun, and the last three of the class were to receive 5.5-in (140-mm) guns instead of 4-in. For security reasons the ships were officially referred to as the 'K' Class flotilla leaders, even on official drawings. Their main intended purpose was, however, to accompany the battle fleet in order to take part in a fleet action.

It was decided to build *K.1* and *K.2* at Portsmouth dockyard, and *K.3* and *K.4* at Vickers, and the outline details were passed to Vickers at the beginning of May 1915, less than a month after the idea had been put forward. Subsequently an extra boat, *K.5*, was ordered from Portsmouth, *K.6* and *K.7* from Devonport, *K.8, K.9, K.10* and *K.17* from Vickers, *K.11* and *K.12* from Armstrong, *K.13* and *K.14* from Fairfield, *K.15* from Scotts, and *K.16* from Beardmore.

During later detailed design work it was decided to abandon the diesel engine on the centre shaft, and replace it by an 800-bhp diesel from the 'E' Class design driving a 700-hp dynamo supplying current to the electric motors on the outer shafts. This is believed to be the first example of diesel-electric drive in submarines, as opposed to separate diesel or electric drive. Two Yarrow boilers were provided in a single boiler room, with the stokehold between them. To allow the boilers to work under pressure it was necessary for the first time to have a fore-and-aft gangway, so that crew passing through did not have to go through the air-lock. Two funnels were provided. They folded down before diving, and the apertures were sealed by heavy metal lids, operated by shaft-gearing from the turbine room. Specified time for sealing the apertures was 30 seconds.

The first boat to be completed was *K.3*, in September 1916, and she reached 23.8 knots on trials, a world record for a submarine. They were much bigger than previous boats, and the fast diving speed caused problems. In theory they dived on electric motors like conventional submarines, but in practice the funnels were down and all openings sealed while the turbines continued to run on steam in the boilers, with the result that a 'K' boat could dive at twice her designed speed. It was found that a small obstruction such as a loop of wire rope under the ventilators could jam the vents open while the indicator showed that they were shut tight. The steam drive required a profusion of apertures both for smoke and for air to provide draught, far more than in a normal submarine, and this multiplied the risk of a diving accident. As a safety measure the boats were modified with a huge quick-blowing tank forward to help get the bows up quickly if the boat dived out of control. This gave the characteristic 'swan bow' which lent the class considerable distinction. The conning tower had then to be raised to give adequate view over the bow, and the 4-in (102-mm) gun was moved on to the superstructure. At the same time the twin torpedo tubes, which were concealed behind hinged doors in the superstructure, were removed to reduce weight.

Although they were a considerable technical achievement, the class very quickly earned a bad reputation for accidents. *K.1* was rammed and sunk by *K.4* on November 18, 1917, and *K.13* sank on trials in the Gareloch in January 1917. She was raised and renumbered *K.22,* but during an exercise in the Firth of Forth on the night of January 31, 1918, she triggered off a terrible series of accidents known as the 'Battle of May Island', in which *K.4* and *K.17* were rammed and sunk and two more ships were damaged. The 'K' Class design could not be blamed for this tragedy, but it did prove that the tactical concept behind these boats was faulty. Submarines lack the navigating capability of surface ships, and the 'K' boats were asked to manoeuvre at high speed with surface ships, inviting collisions at night or in fog. Submarines were simply not suited for this kind of operation.

There was one more casualty, *K.5,* which was lost in a diving accident, on January 20, 1921. *K.3* and *K.7* were sold for scrap in 1921, *K.15* and *K.16* in 1924 and the others in 1926 as part of the postwar rundown. Orders for four more boats, *K.18-21,* were cancelled in 1916 before being laid down. An improved

K.12 showing the characteristic 'swan bow' and 4-in (102-mm) gun which were features of the later 'K' Class. The class earned a dire reputation after a series of accidents. There were a number of vents and openings which had to be sealed before diving, and indicators within the submarine had a tendency to show these closed when in fact they were jammed open by obstructions like wire rope. *K.1* was rammed and sunk by *K.4* and *K.13* sank on trials, on January 31, 1918; *K.4* and *K.17* were lost in a series of accidents which earned the grim name the 'Battle of May Island'. Before the type was finally withdrawn the *K.5* was lost in a diving accident on January 20, 1921. Yet despite this grim record the 'K' Class were of revolutionary design capable of 24 knots on the surface

class, the *K.23* type, was laid down in 1917, but only *K.26* was completed.

See also *J.1, K.26.*

Displacement: 1883/2560 tons (surfaced/submerged) *Length:* 103 m (338 ft) oa *Beam:* 29.4 m (96 ft 6 in) *Draught:* 4.9 m (16 ft) *Machinery:* 2-shaft steam turbines diesel-electric, 10 000 shp/1400 bhp=24/9 knots (surfaced/submerged) *Armament:* 10 18-in (46-cm) torpedo tubes (4 bow, 4 beam, 2 deck); 1 4-in (102-mm) QF; 1 3-in (76-mm) AA *Crew:* 50

K.1

Dutch submarine, built 1911-14. Following the success of *O.2* and her sisters, the East Indies marine decided to order an enlarged version with endurance increased from a nominal 800 km (500 miles) to 2500 km (1500 miles) on the surface. To distinguish her from the boats paid for by the home government she was given a K prefix (for *Kolonien*) instead of an O prefix, and a roman numeral. (For simplicity arabic numerals have been used here.) The design was provided by the Electric Boat company but the boat was built by K M de Schelde at Flushing, with diesels instead of gasoline motors. She was scrapped in the early 1920s.

See also *O.2.*

Displacement: 320/380 tons (surfaced/submerged) *Length:* 45.2 m (148 ft 3 in) oa *Beam:* 4.3 m (14 ft 2 in) *Draught:* 2.9 m (9 ft 6 in) *Machinery:* 2-shaft diesel/electric, 1800 bhp/650 shp=16/9 knots (surfaced/submerged) *Armament:* 3 45-cm (17.7-in) torpedo tubes (2 bow, 1 stern) *Crew:* 17

K.1

Soviet submarine class, built 1936-44, also known as the *Katyusha* Class. A class of large ocean-going submarines, known as project KE-9 or Series XIV *bis,* was designed in the mid-1930s. The K designation is an abbreviation of *kreiser* (cruiser), and it is believed that the original intention was to embark a small SPL floatplane in a hangar, as in contemporary Japanese submarines. Two prototypes of the aircraft were flown in 1933-35, but the submarines were never fitted to operate them.

The class proved only a qualified success, and as they were large and complex, production was cut back during the Second World War. Only 13 boats were apparently completed: *K.1-3* and *K.51-56* by the Marti yard, Leningrad and *K.21-23* by the Ordzhonikidze yard. The others were apparently not built, and postwar reports of submarines numbered *K.57-60* and *K.77-78* probably refer to some of the original boats being renumbered after assignments to different fleets, or merely an attempt to confuse Western intelligence.

The first to complete were *K.2* and *K.3* in 1939, while *K.54* and *K.55* joined the fleet in 1945. On June 22, 1941, when the Germans launched Operation Barbarossa (the attack on the Soviet Union), *K.1* and *K.2* were with the Northern fleet and *K.3* and *K.21-23* were

in the Baltic. In August 1941 the four Baltic fleet boats were transferred to the Arctic via the White Sea or the Stalin Canal. *K.1* was lost about September 30, 1943, in the Kara Sea, probably to a German mine; *K.2* failed to return from a patrol off the Norwegian coast in August-September 1943; and *K.3* was sunk by German ships off Batsfjord on March 21, 1943.

K.21 was given credit by both the Soviets and their Western allies for scoring a torpedo-hit on the battleship *Tirpitz*, but as German records show no record of any damage from a torpedo, this claim is almost certainly false. However, Soviet histories still maintain the claim. The submarine was decommissioned in 1959 for use as a permanent training unit and was preserved as a memorial at Polyarnoe, near Murmansk.

K.22 was lost early in February 1943, probably to a mine. *K.23* was sunk on May 12, 1942, by German warships off Oksafjord. In August 1948 *K.52-56* were transferred from the Baltic to the Arctic via the Great Belts. All the survivors were out of service by the early 1960s.

Displacement: 1480/2095 tons (surfaced/submerged) *Length:* 97.65 m (320 ft 4 in) oa *Beam:* 7.4 m (24 ft 3 in) *Draught:* 4.51 m (14 ft 9 in) *Machinery:* 2-shaft diesel/electric, 4200 bhp/1200 shp=22.5/10 knots (surfaced/submerged) *Armament:* 2 100-mm (3.9-in) (2×1); 2 45-mm (1.77-in) AA (2×1); 10 53-cm (21-in) torpedo tubes (4 bow, 4 stern, 2 above water in casing); 20 mines *Crew:* 60

K.1

US submarine class, built 1912-14. Eight boats were ordered to the Electric Boat company design EB 30-B in 1911 as the *Haddock* Class, but in November 1911 the numbers *K.1-8* were allocated. The names *Haddock, Cachalot, Orca* and *Walrus* were chosen for *K.1-4*, but the remainder were given numbers only.

K.1, K.2 and *K.5-6* were built by Bethlehem, Fore River, *K.3* and *K.7-8* by Union Iron Works, San Francisco, and *K.4* by Seattle Construction and Dry Dock company. All were commissioned in 1914. In 1920 they were designated *SS.32-39.* All boats of the class were scrapped in 1931.

Displacement: 392/521 tons (surfaced/submerged) *Length:* 46.8 m (153 ft 7 in) oa *Beam:* 5.1 m (16 ft 9 in) *Draught:* 4 m (13 ft 1 in) *Machinery:* 2-shaft diesel/electric, 950 bhp/680 shp=14/10.5 knots (surfaced/submerged) *Armament:* 4 18-in (46-cm) torpedo tubes (bow), 8 torpedoes *Crew:* 28

K.1

US submarine class, built 1949–52. Three small hunter-killer submarines were built under the Fiscal Year 1948 Programme for high-speed antisubmarine work. The displacement was kept as small as possible to break away from what was felt to be the excessive size of the *Tang* Class attack submarines and the fleet types modified under the GUPPY (greater underwater propulsive power) programme. They were given numbers *K.1-3* to underline this, and it was hoped to mass produce them to counter the big Soviet fleet. They were unique in having a massive square bow housing the big BQR-4 passive sonar, although this was later removed.

In December 1955 they were named *Barracuda* (SSK.1), *Bass* (SSK.2) and *Bonita* (SSK.3). By 1959 they were considered to be outclassed as they lacked the speed, range and weaponry for modern A/S warfare. In that year *Bass* and *Bonita* were reclassified as SS.551 and SS.552 but *Barracuda* became a training submarine (SST.1). The first two were stricken from the navy list in April 1965 but *Barracuda* was not finally retired until October 1973.

Displacement: 765/1160 tons (surfaced/submerged) *Length:* 59.7 m (196 ft) oa *Beam:* 7.5 m (24 ft 9 in) *Draught:* 4.9 m (16 ft) *Machinery:* 2-shaft diesel/electric, 1050 bhp=10/8 knots (surfaced/submerged) *Armament:* 4 21-in (53-cm) torpedo tubes (2 forward, 2 aft) *Crew:* 50

K.2

Dutch submarine class, built 1914-22. Four submarines were built to the British Hay-Denny design, a modification of the saddle-tank type. The design work was done jointly by Marley F Hay and William Denny and Brothers, Dumbarton. The firm had done some tank-testing and theoretical design work before the First World War, and in 1915 the design staff were all transferred to the Netherlands to supervise the work at the Fijenoord shipyard.

Work proceeded slowly as the supply of components and material was held up by the war. The original MAN diesels ordered for *K.5-7* were never delivered from Germany and the incomplete engines for *K.2* had to be finished by the Dutch firm KM de Schelde. All four, *K.2* and *K.5-7,* were built by Fijenoord at Rotterdam and, apart from the machinery, were virtually identical. The disposition of torpedo tubes was unusual, with two forward, two aft and two in a revolving mounting in the deck casing forward of the conning tower. Profiting by the war experience of the belligerents, each boat was completed with a 75-mm (2.95-in) deck gun.

K.2, K.5 and *K.6* were scrapped in the late 1930s, but *K.7* was still in service in the East Indies when the Second World War broke out. She was sunk by Japanese bombs at Soerabaya on February 18, 1942.

Displacement: 507/639 tons (surfaced/submerged) *Length:* 57.3 m (188 ft) oa *Beam:* 5.1 m (16 ft 9 in) *Draught:* 3.8 m (12 ft 6 in) *Machinery:* 2-shaft diesel/electric, 1200 (*K.2,* 1800) bhp/500 shp=13.5/8 knots (surfaced/submerged) *Armament:* 1 75-mm (2.95-in); 1 12.7-mm (0.5-in) machine-gun; 6 45-cm (17.7-in) torpedo tubes (2 bow, 2 stern, 2 in superstructure [1×2]) *Crew:* 31

Above: The Soviet prewar 'K' Class or *kreiser* (cruiser) large ocean-going submarines were also known as *Katyushas* by their crews

K2Y, Yokosuka

Japanese training aircraft. Produced for the Imperial Japanese Navy in the late 1920s as the Type 3 Primary Trainer Model 1, the K2Y1 was basically a development of the British Avro 504K then in use by the Japanese naval air force.

Designed by the Yokosuka naval air arsenal, the K2Y was a land-based aircraft, with the main wheels carried on side Vs and a cross-axle, with a tail skid under the rear fuselage. It was an equal-span, two-bay biplane, with two open cockpits set in tandem, and first flew in prototype form in 1928. Five different factories built a total of 360 K2Ys during 1929-30. The K2Y1 version was powered by a 130-hp Armstrong Siddeley Mongoose radial engine. The predominant version, however, was the K2Y2, fitted with an uncowled 160-hp Hitachi Kamikaze 2 seven-cylinder radial, and a few of these still remained in service in the early part of the Second World War.

(K2Y2) *Span:* 10.9 m (35 ft 9 in) *Length:* 8.6 m (28 ft 3 in) *Gross weight:* 890 kg (1960 lb) *Maximum speed:* 160 km/h (99 mph)

K.3

Dutch submarine class, built 1914-20. Following experience with *K.1* two of an enlarged type were ordered from the same builders, K M de Schelde of Flushing. As with the Hay-Denny boats of the *K.2* Class, completion was greatly delayed by the shortage of materials; *K.3*'s MAN diesels had to be completed by the builders as the parts were not delivered from Germany, and *K.4* was equipped with Suizer diesels instead.

The two boats were given 75-mm (2.95-in) deck guns on disappearing mountings and had the same arrangement of torpedo tubes as the *K.2* Class: two bow, two stern and two in a revolving deck-mounting inside the casing. Both were scrapped in the late 1930s.

See also *K.1, K.2*.

Displacement: 560/715 tons (surfaced/submerged) *Length:* 64.3 m (211 ft) oa *Beam:* 5.6 m (18 ft 4 in) *Draught:* 3.5 m (11 ft 6 in) *Machinery:* 2-shaft diesel/electric, 1800 bhp/630 shp=16/9.5 knots (*K.4* 1200 bhp/630 shp) *Armament:* 1 75-mm (2.95-in); 6 45-cm (17.7-in) torpedo tubes (2 bow, 2 stern, 1×2 in superstructure) *Crew:* 29

K3M, Mitsubishi

Japanese naval training aircraft. Known as 'Pine' under the Allied wartime codename system, the K3M aircrew trainer was a braced, high-wing monoplane of mixed construction with a fixed tailwheel-type landing gear. The first of four K3M1 prototypes was flown in the late spring of 1930, design having been started in 1929 by the engineer Hattori. Cooling and vibration problems were encountered with the 340-hp Mitsubishi-built Hispano-Suiza V-8 engines in these aircraft. However, at the request of the Japanese naval air force the first production model, the K3M2, changed to a Hitachi Amakaze 11 nine-cylinder radial, enclosed in a Townend ring. During 1932-35, Mitsubishi built 70 of this version, known alternatively as the Navy Type 90 Crew Trainer Model 1, and a further 247 were completed by Aichi. Two examples were built in 1933 of a counterpart for the Japanese army, the Ki-7, but no production order was placed. The second Ki-7, re-engined in 1934 with a 420-hp Japanese-built Bristol Jupiter VI radial, was offered as a four- or five-seat civil transport, designated MS-1 but, again, no orders resulted. The K3M2 was, however, followed in 1939 by the K3M3 trainer, with larger tail surfaces and a 580-hp Nakajima Kotobuki 2 Kai 2 Jupiter engine, and during the next two years a total of 301 of this model were built by Watanabe. Seating a pilot and gunner in separate open cockpits, the K3M2 and K3M3 accommodated an instructor and two pupils in an enclosed cabin. There was a ring-mounted 7.7-mm (0.303-in) Type 92 machine-gun in the rear cockpit, and four 30-kg (66-lb) bombs could also be carried. A few K3M3s were modified as light cargo transports during the Second World War and designated K3M3-L.

(K3M3) *Span:* 15.78 m (51 ft 9 in) *Length:* 9.54 m (31 ft 4 in) *Gross weight:* 2200 kg (4850 lb) *Maximum speed:* 235 km/h (146 mph)

K5Y, Yokosuka

Japanese naval training aircraft, prototype first flown 1933. Although comparatively little known, the Yokosuka K5Y was in production for 12 years and was the most extensively-built trainer ever used by the Japanese armed forces. It was an improved version of the Navy Type 91 Intermediate Trainer, two prototypes of which were completed in 1931 by the First Naval Air Technical arsenal (Dai-Ichi Kaigun Koku Gijitsusho) at Yokosuka. Development was entrusted to Kawanishi in 1932, with design collaboration from Yokosuka, the prototype making its first flight in December 1933. An unequal-span, single-bay biplane of wood, metal and fabric construction, it had swept-back upper wings and non-swept lower wings. Both sets were equipped with ailerons. The aircraft had a wheel undercarriage. Instructor and pupil sat in tandem open cockpits amidships, and the powerplant was a single 340-hp Hitachi Amakaze 11 nine-cylinder radial engine, fitted with a Townend ring and driving a two-blade wooden propeller.

Only a short flight test programme was necessary before the aircraft was accepted by the Japanese naval air force, and in January 1934 Kawanishi began building an initial batch of land-based Navy Type 93 Intermediate Trainers, alternatively designated K5Y1. Kawanishi built only 60 K5Y trainers (1934-36), a proportion of which were of the second major production model, the K5Y2, identical to the K5Y1 except for the substitution of a twin-float landing gear. Subsequent manufacture was undertaken by Nakajima, which built 24 K5Y1s in 1935-36; Mitsubishi (60 K5Y1s); Watanabe (393 K5Y1s and 163 K5Y2s between 1936-39); Nihon (2025 K5Y1s and 706 K5Y2s between 1940-45); Hitachi (1393 K5Y1/2s during 1940-44); Fuji (869 K5Y1/2s during 1942-45); and the Yokosuka arsenal itself, which in 1944 completed 75 K5Y1s, to bring overall production of these two models to 5768. These served throughout the war years, equipping the home-based training Kokutais (air corps) at Kashima, Kasumigaura, Suzuka and Tsuchiura, plus that at Shanghai on the Chinese mainland. In the Allied wartime system of codenaming Japanese trainers after trees, the K5Y was known as 'Willow'. In weapons training roles, it could be armed with a single forward-firing, fixed 7.7-mm (0.303-in) Type 89 machine-gun, a movable Type 92 gun of the same calibre in the rear cockpit, and a modest bombload—typically, ten 10-kg (22-lb) bombs or a pair of 30-kg (66-lb) bombs.

Two K5Y3 twin-float prototypes were completed by Nihon Hikoki, each with an uprated Amakaze 21 engine of 515 hp. No production of this model was undertaken, and plans for higher-powered K5Y4 and K5Y5 landplane versions were never implemented.

(K5Y1) *Span:* 11 m (36 ft 1 in) *Length:* 8.05 m (26 ft 5 in) *Gross weight:* 1500 kg (3310 lb) *Maximum speed:* 212 km/h (132 mph)

K.8

Dutch submarine class built 1917-23. These boats were authorized for the East Indies marine under the 1916 Programme and were numbered *K.8-10.* They were a modified Electric Boat company design with increased bunkerage for service in the East Indies. All three boats were built by de Schelde.

The vessels were slightly larger than the Hay-Denny *K.2* Class, and did not have the revolving torpedo tubes in the deck casing. For the first time an 88-mm (3.5-in) deck gun was provided. *K.8* received her MAN diesels from Germany but her two sisters had to be engined with Sulzer engines of slightly lower power.

All three boats survived to serve in the Second World War but they were overwhelmed in the Japanese attack on the East Indies. *K.8* escaped to Australia in August 1942 but was so badly damaged that she was paid off and scrapped. *K.9* was hulked when she reached Australia, and was wrecked in June 1945. *K.10* was depth-charged by a Japanese patrol craft north of Java on March 1, 1942, and had to be abandoned and scuttled the following day.

Displacement: 521/712 tons (surfaced/submerged) *Length:* 64.2 m (210 ft 8 in) oa *Beam:* 5.5 m (18 ft) *Draught:* 3.6 m (11 ft 10 in) *Machinery:* 2-shaft diesel/electric, 1500 bhp/630 shp (*K.8,* 1800 bhp/630 shp) =15/9.5 knots (surfaced/submerged) *Armament:* 1 88-mm (3.5-in) AA; 4 45-cm (17.7-in) torpedo tubes (2 bow, 2 stern) *Crew:* 31

K9W, Kyushu Japanese navy version of Bücker Jungmann German trainer aircraft

See **Jungmann**

K10W, Kyushu

Japanese naval training aircraft. Development of the K10W followed the importation by Mitsubishi in 1937 of two examples of the US North American NA-16 advanced trainer, a low-wing, single-engined, fixed-undercarriage relative of the AT-6 Texan ordered for the US Army Air Corps. After evaluation, the Japanese naval air force obtained a manufacturing licence for the NA-16-4R, entrusting the design of a suitably modified version to the Watanabe company (later known as Kyushu). With redesigned fin and rudder, and a 600-hp Nakajima Kotobuki 2 Kai Jupiter engine in place of the US Wright Whirlwind, it was placed in production in 1941 as the K10W1 or Navy Type 2 Intermediate Trainer. However, the Watanabe/Kyushu factory produced only 26 before handing over production to Nihon Hikoki, which built a further 150 during 1943-44. The K10W1 supplemented the Yokosuka K5Y as a standard wartime JNAF trainer and was known as 'Oak' in the Allied Pacific codenaming system. Pupil and instructor sat in tandem cockpits under a long 'greenhouse' canopy. For armament training, the K10W1 was fitted with a single 7.7-mm (0.303-in) Type 97 machine-gun.

Span: 12.36 m (40 ft 7 in) *Length:* 8.84 m (29 ft) *Gross weight:* 2093 kg (4615 lb) *Maximum speed:* 282 km/h (175 mph)

K.11

Dutch submarine class, built 1922-25. Three boats, *K.11-13,* were ordered from the Fijenoord yard, Rotterdam, under the 1918 Naval Programme, for service with the East Indies marine.

For the first time design was entrusted to the navy, and several novel features were introduced. To increase the weight of armament two 53-cm (21-in) torpedo tubes were carried forward, in addition to the 45-cm (17.7-in) tubes of the previous *K.8* Class. The submarines' gun armament comprised one 88-mm (3.5-in) AA and one 12.7-mm (0.5-in) machine-gun.

The class was intended to have a high endurance and this was demonstrated between May-December 1926, when *K.13* travelled from Amsterdam to Soerabaya, Indonesia, through the Panama Canal, without an escort. All three boats of the class were present in the East Indies when Japan attacked in December 1941. *K.13* suffered an internal explosion while lying at Singapore on December 24, 1941, and was towed back to Soerabaya, but had to be scuttled there on March 2, 1942. *K.11* and *K.12* were paid off in Australia in 1944-45 and scrapped.

Displacement: 611/815 tons (surfaced/submerged) *Length:* 66.7 m (218 ft 10 in) oa *Beam:*

5.7 m (18 ft 9 in) *Draught:* 3.7 m (12 ft 2 in) *Machinery:* 2-shaft diesel/electric, 2400 bhp/725 shp=15/8 knots (surfaced/submerged) *Armament:* 1 88-mm (3.5-in) AA; 1 12.7-mm (0.5-in) machine-gun; 2 53-cm (21-in) torpedo tubes (bow), 4 torpedoes; 4 45-cm (17.7-in) torpedo tubes (2 bow, 2 stern), 8 torpedoes *Crew:* 31

K11W, Kyushu

Japanese naval training aircraft. A total of 798 examples of this single-engined aircrew trainer were built during the Second World War, in two basic models (the K11W1 and K11W2). It was still in production when the war ended. Known to the Japanese by the name *Shiragiku* (white chrysanthemum), its existence apparently remained unknown to the Allies, and it was one of the few combat types not included in their wartime list of codenames for Japanese aircraft. A midwing, retractable-undercarriage monoplane, the K11W1 featured a deep-bellied fuselage, in appearance not unlike that of the North American O-47 upon which it was based. Produced to a Japanese naval air force 15-Shi (1940) requirement, it was intended for the training of bomber crews, and could accommodate a total of five persons: a pilot and radio operator/gunner in the upper cockpits, beneath a long 'greenhouse'-type canopy, and navigator and bomb-aimer trainees with their instructor in the belly compartment. Access to this was by a separate door in the port side of the fuselage. The Shiragiku was designed by the Watanabe company (hence the 'W' in its designation), and flew for the first time in November 1942, quickly completing an uneventful flight test programme. In 1943, Watanabe was reorganized as the Kyushu Hikoki K.K., receiving a substantial order for the K11W1 shortly afterwards. This model, which was of all-metal construction, except for the fabric-covered control surfaces, entered service in mid-1943 and was the principal version built. The K11W2 differed only in being of all-wood construction and was introduced in an attempt to conserve available metal supplies for front-line combat types. Both models were powered by a 515-hp Hitachi Amakaze 21 nine-cylinder radial engine. As operational trainers, the K11Ws were armed with a single 7.7-mm (0.303-in) Type 92 machine-gun on a movable mounting in the rear cockpit, and could carry a pair of 30-kg (66-lb) bombs externally. Towards the end of the war, in common with most other serviceable Japanese aircraft types, the K11W was adapted for kamikaze suicide missions, for which it was loaded with a single 250-kg (550-lb) bomb and, of course, flown as a single-seater. Some K11W2s were adapted as utility transports, and a few others as stopgap antisubmarine aircraft. This last role prompted the design of a purpose-built two-seat ASW model, known as the Q3W1 Nankai (South Sea), but development of this was suspended in January 1945, after an accident to the only prototype.

Span: 14.98 m (49 ft 2 in) *Length:* 10.24 m (33 ft 7 in) *Gross weight:* 2800 kg (6175 lb) *Maximum speed:* 230 km/h (143 mph)

K.14

Dutch submarine class, built 1929-34. Five submarines, *K.14-18* were authorized in 1929-30 for the East Indies marine. They were developed from the *O.12* Class, also with welded hulls for deep diving, but carried a heavier armament and had higher endurance. The feature introduced in the *O.12*s, a pair of 40-mm (1.57-in) Bofors AA guns in disappearing mountings at either end of the conning tower, was continued.

Three of the boats were early losses. *K.17* was lost from an unknown cause—probably a mine—east of Malacca, in the Malay Peninsula, and the official date of loss was presumed to be December 19, 1941; *K.16* was torpedoed by a Japanese submarine off Kuching, Sarawak, six days later, while *K.18* was depth-charged by Japanese escorts off Balikpapan and so badly damaged that she was scuttled at Soerabaya on March 3, 1942. The other two, *K.14* and *K.15*, served successfully in Eastern waters and were paid off in the East Indies in 1946. Both boats were sold for scrapping in 1950-51.

See also *O.12*.

Displacement: 771-782/1000-1024 tons (surfaced/submerged) *Length:* 74 m (242 ft 9 in) oa *Beam:* 7.6 m (25 ft) *Draught:* 3.9 m (12 ft 10 in) *Machinery:* 2-shaft diesel/electric, 3200 bhp/1000 shp=17/9 knots (surfaced/submerged) *Armament:* 1 88-mm (3.5-in) AA; 2 40-mm (1.57-in) AA (2×1); 8 53-cm (21-in) torpedo tubes (1 bow, 4 stern, 2×1 external, amidships; 14 torpedoes carried) *Crew:* 38

K.26

British submarine, built 1918-23. An improved 'K' Class of six units, numbered *K.23-28*, was ordered in 1918. They were broadly similar to the original steam-driven boats, with a heavier armament of six 21-in (53-cm) torpedo tubes in the bow, four 18-in (46-cm) beam tubes, and three 4-in (102-mm) guns. As the steam plant of the 'K' Class was used on a bigger displacement the speed was slightly reduced.

On November 23, 1918, the orders were cancelled, but on December 31 the frames of *K.24-26* and *K.28* were dismantled and moved to Chatham for completion. This new order was later rescinded, and only *K.26* was completed, the last steam-driven submarine in the Royal Navy until the advent of nuclear power. She was completed in September 1923, and served for nearly eight years before being scrapped. She was quite successful and showed her enormous endurance by cruising to Colombo, Ceylon, and back from January-August 1924.

Displacement: 2140/2770 tons (surfaced/submerged) *Length:* 107.14 m (351 ft 6 in) oa *Beam:* 11.58 m (38 ft) *Draught:* 5.08 m (16 ft 8 in) *Machinery:* 2-shaft steam turbine/diesel-electric, 10 000 shp/1400 shp=23.5/9 knots (surfaced/submerged) *Armament:* 6 21-in (53-cm) torpedo tubes (bow); 4 18-in (46-cm) torpedo tubes (beam); 3 4-in (102-mm) QF guns (3×1) *Crew:* 58

HM Submarine *K.26*, which was the last steam-powered submarine to serve in the Royal Navy before the advent of nuclear-powered vessels

IWM

Ka-1, Kayaba

Japanese autogyro. Based on a US design and powered by a German engine, the two-seat Kayaba Ka-1 was one of the comparatively few rotorcraft to see operational service during the Second World War. Developed by the Kayaba Seisakusho at Sendai, it followed the general configuration of the Kellett KD-1A. A machine of this type had been purchased from the US in 1939 but destroyed shortly afterwards in a crash. The Ka-1 prototype, powered by a Japanese-built 240-hp Argus As 10C eight-cylinder inverted-V engine driving a two-blade propeller, made its first flight on May 26, 1941, and about 240 were subsequently built for the Japanese army.

Intended as unarmed artillery spotters and liaison aircraft, they had tandem open cockpits, a three-blade rotor, a fixed undercarriage, and a high-mounted tailplane beneath which were twin egg-shaped fins. In an attempt to counteract heavy shipping losses during the middle years of the war, some were also employed as antisubmarine aircraft, operating in Japanese inshore waters from the light escort carrier *Akitsu Maru,* a converted merchantman. In this role they were flown as single-seaters, carrying a pair of 60-kg (132-lb) depth charges. Experimental variants included the Ka-1-KAI, with a small solid-fuel rocket at the tip of each rotor blade to increase lift; and the Ka-2, identical to the Ka-1 except for a 240-hp Jacobs radial engine. The Ka-1 had a takeoff run of about 30 m (100 ft) and a range of 280 km (170 miles).

Rotor diameter: 12.2 m (40 ft) *Length:* 9.2 m (30 ft 1 in) *Gross weight:* 1170 kg (2580 lb) *Maximum speed:* 164 km/h (102 mph)

Ka-10, Kamov Soviet helicopter See **Hat**

Ka-15, Kamov Soviet helicopter See **Hen**

Ka-20, Kamov Soviet helicopter See **Harp**

Ka-25, Kamov Soviet helicopter See **Hormone**

Kaba

Japanese destroyer class. When Japan declared war on Germany in 1914 in response to the terms of the British-Japanese alliance, the Japanese fleet was found to be woefully short of fleet destroyers. A crash programme of construction was instituted in September 1914. There was no time to prepare a new design for a fleet destroyer and so the most recent design, that of the 2nd Class *Sakura*-type destroyers, was taken and modified for use as a 1st Class fleet destroyer.

The hull and general layout of *Sakura* was retained, but the vessels were fitted with more modern machinery. More efficient boilers of a smaller pattern than those in *Sakura* were installed. Only four were fitted as opposed to the five in *Sakura,* without loss of performance. The main armament layout of a single 4.7-in (120-mm) gun and two twin 18-in (46-cm) torpedo tubes was retained, but the 12-pdr guns of *Sakura* were replaced with 3-in (76-mm) models. Bunkerage was increased to enable the vessels to operate in support of fleet units, and with other improvements the displacement rose by 60 tons.

The ships were ordered under the 1914 War Emergency Programme and were laid down between November 1914-April 1915.

Kasa—built Yokosuka navy yard
Kaede—built Maizuru navy yard
Kashiwa, Matsu—built Mitsubishi, Nagasaki
Katsura—built Kure navy yard
Kiri—built Uraga
Kusumoki, Ume—built Kawasaki, Kobe
Sakaki—built Sasebo navy yard
Sugi—built Osaka

All were launched in 1915. On completion they were sent to the Mediterranean where units of the Royal Navy were heavily engaged in the Dardanelles operations. This left the central Mediterranean practically undefended, the Italian fleet being fully engaged in countering the Austro-Hungarian fleet. The Japanese destroyers were mainly based at Malta and were used to cover the numerous Allied convoys passing reinforcements to the Eastern Mediterranean. Evidence of the value of the Japanese destroyers to the Allied effort is provided by France's decision to order 12 ships of the same type, known as the Type Japonais.

Sakaki was damaged by a torpedo from the Austrian submarine *U 27* on June 11, 1917. Her bow was destroyed as far back as the bridge, though she returned to service after repair. All vessels of the class were removed from service in November 1931.

See also *Arabe.*

Displacement: 665 tons (normal), 850 tons (full load) *Length:* 83.5 m (274 ft) oa *Beam:* 7.3 m (24 ft) *Draught:* 2.6 m (8 ft 6 in) *Machinery:* 3-shaft reciprocating vertical triple-expansion, 9500 ihp=30 knots *Armament:* 1 4.7-in (120-mm); 4 3-in (76-mm); 4 18-in (46-cm) torpedo tubes (2×2) *Crew:* 92

Kadett, Heinkel He 72

German trainer aircraft. One of the first aircraft built to a *Reichsluftfahrtministerium* (air ministry) specification, the He 72 was a staple product of the Heinkel company, more than 4900 being built in 1933-37. Many were exported or used as German club and touring machines, but most of them went to Luftwaffe elementary flying schools, where in the majority of cases they were the first aircraft used.

There were many variants of this trim fabric-covered biplane, and the standard Luftwaffe trainer was the He 72B-1 with 160-hp Siemens Sh 14A radial engine. In winter, skis were often used. Some aircraft carried a blind-flying hood. The Kadett did not, so far as is known, serve on the Eastern Front in the light night-attack role.

Span: 9 m (29 ft 6 in) *Length:* 7.52 m (24 ft 8 in) *Gross weight:* 900 kg (1985 lb) *Maximum speed:* 195 km/h (121 mph)

The Japanese destroyer *Ume* at Corfu on April 18, 1917, while she was on escort duties with Allied convoys in the eastern Mediterranean

IWM

Real Photographs

The Japanese carrier *Kaga* which was laid down as a battleship in 1921 and was converted in the mid-1920s. She was lost at Midway in 1942 after four hits by US Navy Dauntless dive-bombers

IWM

Kaga

Japanese aircraft carrier. Laid down in 1918 as one of the battleships which would give Japan naval equality with the US, *Kaga* was launched on November 17, 1921. Had she been completed, she would have been the largest, heaviest and most powerfully-armed battleship in the world, with a main armament of ten 16-in (406-mm) guns.

Within months of launching, however, the Washington Naval Treaty brought a halt to the naval arms race, work ceased on *Kaga* and she was laid up awaiting scrapping. In September 1923, however, a severe earthquake severely damaged the unlaunched hull of a battlecruiser scheduled for completion as an aircraft carrier *Amagi* and it was decided that *Kaga* would be substituted.

Conversion and completion took four and a half years at the Yokosuka navy yard, where she was towed from the original Kobe launching yard. The finished product bore close resemblance to the earlier *Akagi*, with a flush flight deck over two hangars, each of which opened on to a short flying-off deck, giving the forward third of the ship a 'terraced' appearance. Two twin 8-in (203-mm) turrets were positioned one on either side of the upper hangar flying-off deck, and six more were fitted in single casemates, three on either quarter. Heavy AA armament consisted of three twin 4.7-in (120-mm) dual-purpose mountings on each side, amidships.

A major difference between the two carriers lay in the funnel arrangements. Whereas *Akagi* had her uptakes led across to the starboard side from all boilers, *Kaga*'s were divided to port and starboard, led up to the gallery deck and then ducted aft to exhaust outboard in line with the after end of the hangar. The original battleship four-shaft machinery was retained and a speed of 27.5 knots was attained on trials.

Although she was commissioned on March 31, 1928, trials revealed the need for modifications in many areas and minor defects required continuous attention, so that it was not until the beginning of 1930 that she finally joined the fleet. She was employed extensively in the waters off North China between 1931 and 1933, during the succession of 'incidents' which accompanied Japanese expansion in the area; on February 22, 1932, three of her fighters destroyed a Chinese Boeing fighter to give the navy the first victory scored by Japanese fighters.

In June 1935, *Kaga* was taken in hand at Sasebo navy yard for modernization. The hull was lengthened by 10.4 m (34 ft) and the flight deck was extended to stretch the full length of the ship, thus eliminating the flying-off decks, which had become less useful with the introduction of heavier aircraft needing longer takeoff runs. The hangars were also extended forward to create space for an extra 30 aircraft, depending on type. Aircraft complement, including reserve stowage, went up from 60 to 90 and a third lift was fitted to handle the extra number. The gallery deck funnel ducting was deleted and a single large downward-angled funnel was installed on the starboard side amidships, abaft a diminutive island, the first to appear as a permanent feature on a Japanese carrier. The four 8-in (203-mm) guns displaced by the hangar extension were remounted in casemates aft, giving the ship five single guns on either quarter. Mounted only 5 m (16 ft) above the waterline, it is difficult to imagine how they would have been used in bad weather. Standard tonnage rose by nearly 9000 tons and draught by 1.5 m (5 ft) and to preserve the original speed, more powerful modern machinery was installed, giving 127 400 shp on trials, compared with the original 91 000 shp. Speed increased by nearly a knot and although nearly double the fuel load was carried, the radius of action increased by only 25%, to 16 100 km (10 000 miles).

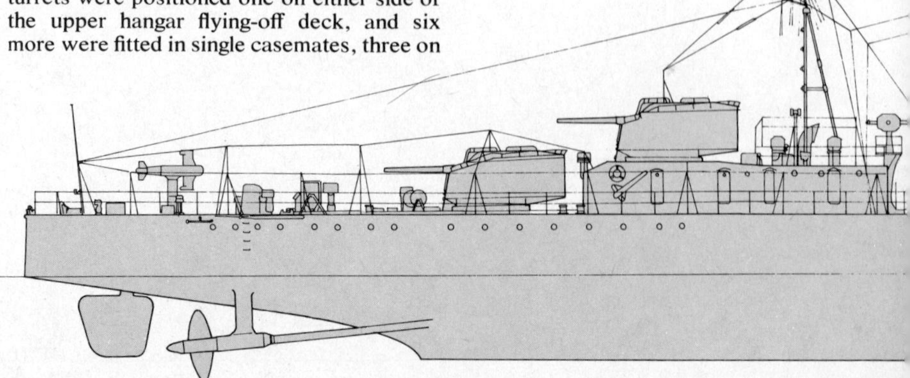

The AA armament was much improved, the six twin 4.7-in (120-mm) guns giving way to eight of the modern twin 5-in (127-mm) DP mountings; provision was also made for the fitting of 11 twin 25-mm (1-in) AA guns, when these French-designed guns should become available.

The modernization took only one year to complete, in spite of its extent, and by the end of 1935 *Kaga* was back with the fleet. In August 1937, she was off Shanghai when Japanese forces began their assault and her aircraft joined shore-based bombers in raids on the Chinese city. The defending Chinese fighters made a better initial showing than in 1932, and on August 17, *Kaga* lost all but one out of a dozen Yokosuka B4Y 'Jean' torpedo-bombers sent out on such a raid. The carrier's new Mitsubishi A5M 'Claude' fighters quickly won back air superiority, however, and by mid-September *Kaga* was no longer needed for direct action; Japanese naval air force units were by then based ashore in the Shanghai area.

Kaga saw further service off China between 1937 and 1940, but in 1941, with the hardening of US attitudes towards Japanese aggression in the Far East, the carrier fleet began to prepare for the pre-emptive strike against the US Pacific Fleet. Since 1939, she had been paired with *Akagi* in Carrier Division 1 and during the year which followed the beginning of the intensive training for the strike on Pearl Harbor they were separated for only one operation.

On December 7, 1941, *Kaga* launched a first wave of 27 Nakajima B5N 'Kates' against Pearl Harbor. Twelve were armed with shallow-running torpedoes and the remainder with 14-in (356-mm) shells adapted for use as armour-piercing bombs. The second wave consisted of 18 Mitsubishi 'Zero' fighters as escort; these would overtake the Kates and then remain in the target area to cover the third deck-load of 26 Aichi 'Val' dive-bombers. Nine of these aircraft failed to return, four of which were fighters. Claims of achievements of *Kaga*'s strikes on the warships at the Hawaiian naval base cannot be sorted out from the general success shared by Carrier Division 1 and Carrier Division 2 (*Soryu* and *Hiryu*).

Carrier Division 1 returned to Japan for a two-week rest and replenishment period, then proceeded to Truk to await the next operation. Between January 20 and 23, 1942, the carriers prepared for and then covered the invasion of Rabaul. Four weeks later, on February 19, Darwin was the target of a devastating strike which eliminated any possibility of interference from Australia with the forthcoming invasion of Java. Between February 24 and March 9, Carrier Divisions 1 and 2 operated to the south of Java, intercepting evacuation shipping and, on March 5, sending 180 aircraft to raid Tjilatjap, Java, the last major port in Allied hands. The carrier force put into Staring Bay, Celebes, on March 10, but before it left a fortnight later for the Ceylon operation, *Kaga* was detached to Japan to make good defects, including damage sustained when she had run aground at Peleliu on February 9.

Kaga rejoined Carrier Division 1 at the end of May 1942 and sailed with *Akagi, Hiryu* and *Soryu* to take part in the Midway invasion operation. On June 4, 1942, each carrier launched 18 bombers and nine fighters for a dawn strike on the airfield at Midway. Before these aircraft returned, Midway-based dive- and torpedo-bombers made a series of unsuccessful attacks, the nearest bomb to *Kaga* falling 18 m (20 yards) off her starboard quarter.

Two hours later, as *Kaga* was preparing to fly off a strike against the US carriers, she was attacked by 12 Douglas Dauntless dive-bombers from *Enterprise*. Four direct hits were scored on the carrier's unarmoured deck and five very near misses bracketed her, fracturing petrol lines which fed the fires started among the fuelled and bombed-up aircraft in the hangars and on the flight deck. *Kaga*, like *Akagi* and *Soryu*, had to be abandoned within 30 minutes of the attack and she burned for another nine hours. Finally, at dusk, the fires reached her magazines and she blew up and sank almost immediately. She took with her some 800 men who had been killed by the bombs or who had been trapped by the fires when she was abandoned.

See also *Akagi*.

(1930) *Displacement:* 29600 tons ('official' displacement was 26000 tons, as declared for Treaty purposes), 33160 tons (trials displacement—full load in excess of 35000 tons) *Length:* 238.2 m (781 ft 6 in) oa *Beam:* 29.6 m (97 ft) wl *Draught:* 7.9 m (25 ft 11 in) *Machinery:* 4 sets geared turbines, 4 shafts, 91000 shp=27.5 knots *Aircraft:* 60 *Armament:* 10 8-in (203-mm) (2×2, 6×1); 12 4.7-in (120-mm)/45-cal AA (6×2) *Crew:* 1340

(1941) *Displacement:* 38200 tons (standard), 43650 tons (full load) *Length:* 248.56 m (815 ft 6 in) oa *Beam:* 32.51 m (106 ft 8 in) wl *Draught:* 9.45 m (31 ft) *Machinery:* 4 sets geared turbines, 4 shafts, 127400 shp=28.34 knots *Aircraft:* 90 *Armament:* 10 8-in (203-mm) (10×1); 16 5-in (127-mm) (8×2); 22 25-mm (1-in) AA (11×2) *Crew:* 2016

Kagero

Japanese destroyer class. Known as the Type A destroyers, the 15 vessels of the class were ordered under the 1937 and 1939 Programmes, and laid down between August 1937 and April 1940. The design was practically identical with the preceding *Asashio* Class but improved boilers and other minor alterations increased the displacement by 72 tons. The three improved Kanpon boilers developed a steam pressure of 30 kg/sq cm (427 lb/sq in) at 350°C, resulting in a maximum output from the turbines of 52020 shp, and a trials speed of 35 knots. (Compared with 22 kg/sq cm [284 lb/sq in] at 300°C, 50 100 shp and 35 knots in the *Asashios*.) The bunkerage of 400 tons of oil fuel, and the radius of action of 5000 nautical miles at 18 knots both remained the same.

The problems of instability caused by excessive topweight, encountered in the previous Special-type destroyers, were largely overcome. The bridge was much smaller than in earlier designs, as were the engine-room vents, which were sited lower down the

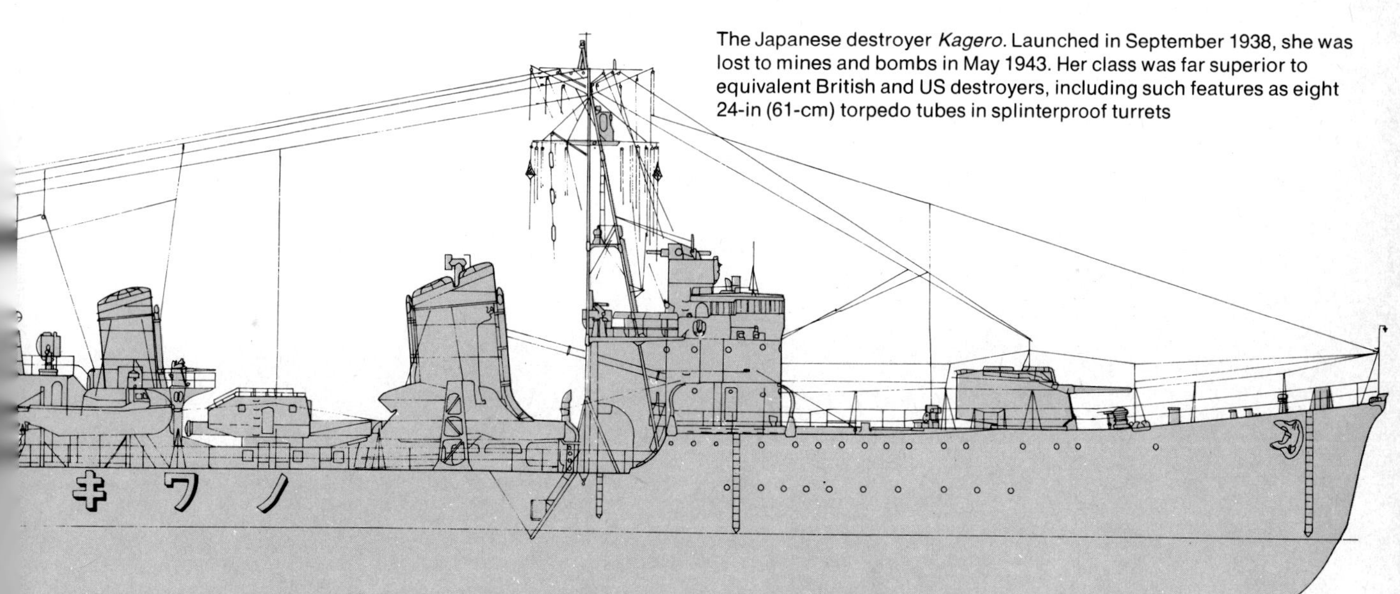

The Japanese destroyer *Kagero*. Launched in September 1938, she was lost to mines and bombs in May 1943. Her class was far superior to equivalent British and US destroyers, including such features as eight 24-in (61-cm) torpedo tubes in splinterproof turrets

funnel. The forward torpedo reloads were sited two on each side of the forefunnel, rather than in the single bank of four mounted to one side found in earlier designs.

The final design conformed well to the specifications and requirements laid down by the Japanese naval staff. The *Kagero* Class were far superior to British and US destroyers, the heavy torpedo armament being mounted in splinterproof turrets with a full set of spare torpedoes which could be reloaded in 15 minutes. The gun armament was also superior, the heavy calibre dual-purpose weapons being mounted in enclosed turrets.

Amatsukaze was used as a testbed for developing a new superheated high-pressure boiler. These small boilers occupied much less space than previous models and delivered steam at 40 kg/sq cm (569 lb/sq in) at 400°C. On trials, the turbines in *Amatsukaze* developed a maximum of 52 150 shp to give a speed of 34.55 knots on a displacement of 2553 tons.

The destroyers entered service between November 1939-July 1941 and were extensively used throughout the Pacific during the war. Five yards were engaged in the construction of the *Kagero* Class.

Amatsukaze, Arashi, Kagero, Nowaki and *Oyashio*—built Maizure navy yard
Hagikaze Hamakaze, Hayashio, Shiranui and *Tokitsukaze*—built Uraga
Hatsukaze—built Kawasaki
Isokaze and *Yukikaze*—built Sasebo navy yard
Kuroshio, Maikaze, Natsushio, Tanikaze and *Urakaze*—built Fujinagata

Name	launched	fate
Amatsukaze	10/39	sunk USAAF 6/4/45
Arashi	4/40	sunk USN destroyers *Dunlap, Craven, Maurey* 7/8/43
Hagikaze	6/40	sunk with *Arashi*
Hamakaze	11/40	sunk US aircraft of *Hornet, Cabot* 7/4/45
Hatsukaze	1/39	sunk US destroyers *Spence, Ausburne, Dyson, Claxton, Stanley* 2/11/43
Hayashio	4/39	sunk USAAF 24/11/42
Isokaze	6/39	war loss 7/4/45
Kagero	9/38	mined and bombed 8/5/43
Kuroshio	10/38	sunk with *Kagero*
Maikaze	3/41	war loss 17/2/44
Natsushio	2/39	torpedoed US submarine 8/2/42
Nowaki	9/40	sunk US destroyers *Owen, Miller* 26/10/44
Oyashio	11/38	sunk with *Kagero*
Shiranui	6/38	war loss 27/10/44
Tanikaze	11/40	torpedoed US submarine *Harder* 9/6/44
Tokitsukaze	11/39	sunk USAAF 3/3/43
Urakaze	4/40	torpedoed US submarine *Sealion* 21/11/44
Yukikaze	3/39	surrendered. Chinese *Tan Yang* 1947; scrapped 1971

With the increasing dominance of US aircraft in the Pacific many of the class had X turret removed in 1943-44 and replaced by two triple 25-mm (1-in) AA. In addition the minelaying equipment was replaced by depth-charge equipment. Following the disastrous Marianas battle in June 1944, when US aircraft swept the remnants of Japanese naval aircraft out of the sky, all surviving units had their AA substantially increased, mounting between 18-28 25-mm (1-in) AA.

Displacement: 2490 tons (normal), 2033 tons (full load) *Length:* 118.4 m (388 ft 6 in) *Beam:* 10.8 m (35 ft 5 in) *Draught:* 3.8 m (12 ft 5 in) *Machinery:* 2-shaft geared turbines, 52 000 shp=35 knots *Armament:* 6 5-in (127-mm) (3×2); 4 25-mm (1-in) (2×2); 8 24-in (61-cm) torpedo tubes (2×4) *Crew:* 240

Kaibokan

Japanese escort vessel type. The heavy losses suffered both by Japanese merchant shipping and the navy as a result of US submarine operations compelled the Japanese naval authorities to institute a crash programme of A/S escort construction. To mass produce units as rapidly as possible,

The *Hamakaze* on June 30, 1941. By 1943-44 her class had received additional AA armament and depth charges, X turret being deleted

The Austro-Hungarian torpedo boat 50E or *Kaiman*. The suffix 'E' indicated that the boat had been built in the English yard of Yarrow

utilizing electric-welding techniques to the utmost, the design was made as basic and free from refinements as possible, and that of the earlier *Mikura* Class was recast in a simplified form, known as the Type C. Overall length was reduced, and all flare, sheer or any form of streamlining dispensed with, the structure being completely angular. All non-essential items of equipment, embellishments of accommodation, etc were omitted. Lower-powered diesels resulted in a loss of 3 knots compared to the *Mikura*. By adopting these measures it was hoped that each unit could be completed in three to four months, but shortages of materials sometimes increased this to eight to nine months.

The ships entered service between the end of February 1944 and August 1945. Once the design was completed, orders for the *Ukura* Class escorts (a modified *Mikura*) were cancelled. Large numbers of *Kaibokan* were ordered: a total of 131 vessels under the 1943-44 War Programme, with a further 168 planned for the 1944-45 War Programme.

Shortly after orders for the Type C had been placed, doubts were expressed as to the capability of Japanese industry to produce the large number of diesel engines required. The design was therefore modified to incorporate a single geared turbine instead of the diesel engine. The new design was known as the Type D, and apart from a slight increase in length there was little difference between it and the Type C, armament remaining the same. The Type D showed a much higher fuel consumption, however, and radius of action fell by 2000 nautical miles to 4500 nautical miles at 14 knots. Towards the end of the war the severe oil shortage led to some turbine-powered units being adapted to burn coal.

A total of 143 Type D escorts was ordered under the 1943-44 War Programme, construction running parallel with the Type C. A further 60 units were planned for the 1944-45 War Programme.

The Type C escorts were given odd numbers from *1-263*, while the Type D were even-numbered from *2-286*. The units of both types planned under the 1944-45 Programme were never ordered. The following units, although ordered, were subsequently cancelled before construction had started: Type C *91, 99, 103, 111, 113, 115, 117, 119-203, 209, 211, 231, 233, 237-263;* Type D *86-100, 108, 110, 114, 120, 128, 136, 140, 146, 148, 152, 162-184, 188, 206-286.* The following Type C and Type D units, although laid down, were never completed: *70, 80, 83, 89, 93, 97, 101, 122, 229, 235.*

Of the units completed the vessels listed below were all sunk during the war, the remainder being surrendered and scrapped:

Torpedoed by US submarines: *4, 7, 9, 13, 15, 21, 25, 31, 41, 47, 53, 73, 6, 10, 24, 28, 38, 42, 56, 64, 72, 84, 112, 144.*

Mined: *46, 63.*

Sunk by naval aircraft: *3, 5, 17, 19, 23, 33, 35, 43, 51, 65, 219, 2, 30, 54, 68, 74, 186.*

Sunk by US Air Force: *1, 11, 39, 18, 20, 66, 130, 134, 138.*

Marine casualty: *69, 75.*

Sunk by Soviet aircraft: *213, 82.*

(Type C) *Displacement:* 745 tons (standard), 810 tons (full load) *Length:* 67.5 m (221 ft 6 in) oa *Beam:* 8.4 m (27 ft 7 in) *Draught:* 2.9 m (9 ft 6 in) *Machinery:* 2-shaft diesels, 1900 bhp=16.5 knots *Armament:* 2 120-mm (4.7-in) (2×1); 6 25-mm (1-in) (2×3) AA; 1 3-in (76-mm) A/S mortar; 1 depth-charge rack, 12 depth-charge throwers, 120 depth charges *Crew:* 136

(Type D) *Displacement:* 740 tons (standard), 940 tons (full load) *Length:* 69.5 m (228 ft) oa *Beam:* 8.6 m (28 ft 3 in) *Draught:* 3.6 m (11 ft 10 in) *Machinery:* 1-shaft geared turbine, 2500 shp=17.5 knots *Armament:* As Type C *Crew:* 160

Kaiman

Austro-Hungarian torpedo boat class, built 1904-10. The prototype, *Kaiman,* was ordered in 1904 from Yarrow, followed by a further 13 from Stabilimento Tecnico, Trieste, in 1905-07: *Anaconda, Alligator, Krokodil, Wal, Seehund, Delphin, Narwal, Hai, Möve, Schwalbe, Pinguin, Drache* and *Greif.* In 1907-09 a further ten were ordered from Danubius, Fiume: *Triton, Hydra, Skorpion, Phönix, Krake, Polyp, Echse, Molch, Kormoran* and *Alk.*

On January 1, 1914, the whole class was renumbered, with suffix 'E' for England, 'T' for Trieste and 'F' for Fiume, the suffix indicating place of building. Thus *Kaiman* became *50E,* the *Anaconda-Greif* series became *51T* to *63T,* and the *Triton-Alk* series became *64F* to *73F.* In the autumn of 1918 it was planned to replace the after torpedo tube with a 66-mm (2.6-in) AA gun, but it is not known how many were thus rearmed. Only one, *52T* (ex-*Alligator*), was lost when she ran aground off Spalato, Yugoslavia, in December 1918. Four—*60T, 61T, 69F* and *54T*—were handed over to the fledgling Yugoslav navy as *torpiljarka* (torpedo boat) *T.9-12,* and served until scrapped in 1928-30. The rest were allocated to Great Britain, who sold them for scrap in Italy.

Displacement: 210 tons (normal) *Length:* 56 m (183 ft 9 in) pp *Beam:* 5.5 m (18 ft) *Draught:* 1.3 m (4 ft 3 in) *Machinery:* 2-shaft reciprocating steam, 3000 ihp = 26 knots *Armament:* 4 47-mm (1.85-in)/33-cal (4×1); 3 45-cm (17.7-in) torpedo tubes (3×1) *Crew:* 31

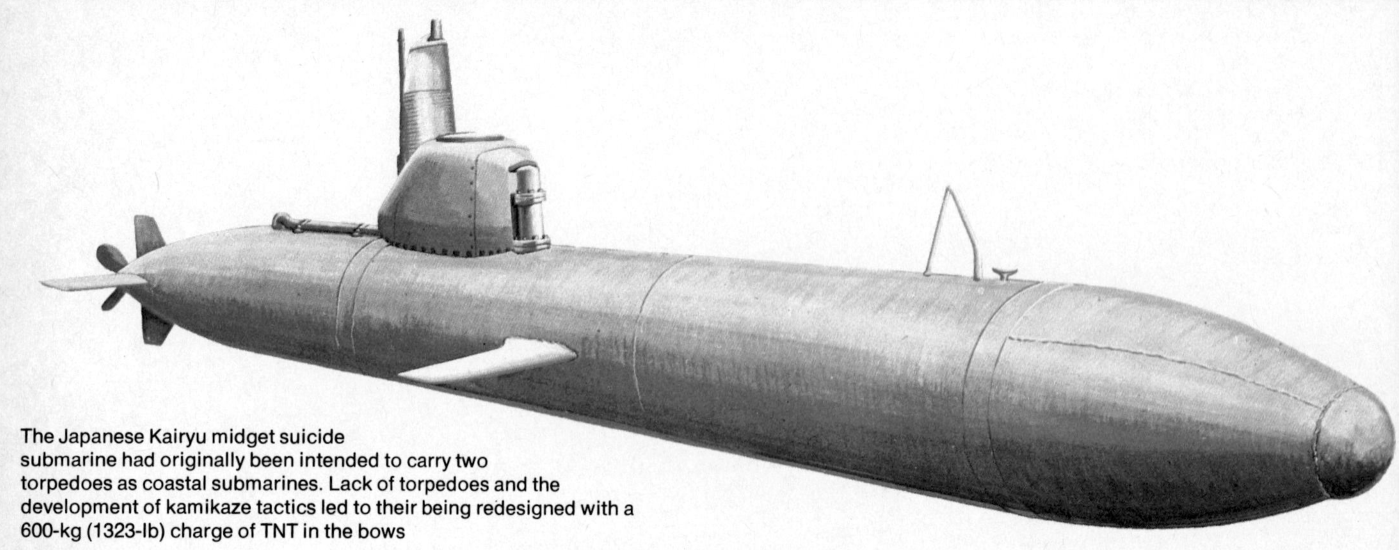

The Japanese Kairyu midget suicide submarine had originally been intended to carry two torpedoes as coastal submarines. Lack of torpedoes and the development of kamikaze tactics led to their being redesigned with a 600-kg (1323-lb) charge of TNT in the bows

Kairyu

Japanese midget submarine class. Following the construction in 1943 and 1944 of two small experimental midget submarines with fixed side-hydroplanes, a preproduction model, known as Kairyu, was ordered. The design was developed from the Type A midget submarine, and retained the torpedo-shaped hull of the two experimental models. Production Kairyu differed from the experimental models in having a conning tower housing the periscope standard. The normal torpedo-type hydroplane and rudder were sited aft while fixed hydroplanes were fitted abreast the conning tower on either side of the main pressure hull.

Kairyu were originally designed for a defence role, operating with Koryu craft around the coastline of Japan, and they were intended to carry two 46-cm (18-in) torpedoes slung beneath the hull to port and starboard. A shortage of torpedoes, however, meant that they were usually armed with a heavy explosive charge in the bows, and used as suicide craft. For such small craft they were very strongly constructed, and the maximum submerged depth when armed was 100 m (330 ft).

Full production of the Kairyu commenced in 1944, ten yards being responsible for the final assembly. Shortages of materials led to many minor differences between individual craft, this being particularly true of the propulsion units. The Kairyu craft were mass produced in three sections and welded together in a machine shop ashore, construction time being about 30 days. A production run of 760 Kairyu was projected for completion by September 1945, but by the end of the war in August only 215 craft had been completed, while a further 207 were still under construction.

Displacement: 19.25 tons (submerged) *Length:* 17.3 m (56 ft 9 in) *Beam:* 1.4 m (4 ft 7 in) *Draught:* 1.4 m (4 ft 7 in) *Machinery:* 1-shaft Isuzu gasoline motor/1 electric motor, 85 hp/80 hp=7.5/10 knots (surfaced/submerged) *Armament:* 2 46-cm (18-in) torpedoes or 600 kg (1325 lb) TNT *Crew:* 2

The *Prinzregent Luitpold.* This *Kaiser* Class battleship saw action at the Battle of Jutland. Scuttled at Scapa Flow in 1919, she was raised and scrapped in 1931-33. Her turbine propulsion allowed her to carry a total of ten 305-mm guns

Friedrich der Grosse became the flagship of the German High Seas Fleet from 1914 to 1917. Like her sisters she could fire a full broadside of her ten 305-mm (12-in) guns. She is shown prior to her refit in 1914 when she received a heavy tubular foremast and an enlarged gunnery spotting top

Kaiser

German Dreadnought battleship class, built 1910-13. The faults of the *Helgoland* Class were rectified in this class: steam turbines replaced the less reliable reciprocating machinery and the main armament was mounted to better effect. Following the lead given by the British *Neptune,* the after 305-mm (12-in) gun turrets were arranged with one superimposed over the other, and the two midships turrets were mounted en echelon on the beam. A theoretical maximum of ten guns could be fired on the broadside as against only eight in *Helgoland,* but the magazines could have been better laid out.

The German navy was not convinced that the Parsons turbine was the answer to the problem of propulsion, and to achieve greater fuel economy Krupp's Germania works was asked to produce a big six-cylinder diesel motor for the centre shaft of the third ship, *Prinzregent Luitpold.* This was too advanced an idea for 1910, and Krupps never delivered the diesel motor; *Prinzregent Luitpold* went to sea without a centre shaft and, with 5000 hp less, was slower than her sisters.

Friedrich der Grosse was the first to be laid down, in January 1910, and she was launched by AG Vulcan, Hamburg on June 10, 1911. She was followed by the *Kaiserin* from Howaldt, Kiel, *König Albert* from Schichau, Elbing, *Prinzregent Luitpold* from the Germania yard, Kiel, and *Kaiser* from the Royal Dockyard, Kiel. *Kaiser* was the first to commission, in August 1912, and *König Albert* did not join the fleet until July 1913.

Friedrich der Grosse was refitted in 1914 to serve as flagship of the High Sea Fleet, with a heavy tubular foremast and enlarged gunnery spotting top. She fought at Jutland, suffering no damage, and at the end of 1916 she was relieved by *Baden* to join the 4th Battle Squadron. *Kaiser, Kaiserin* and *Prinzregent Luitpold* saw action with the 3rd Battle Squadron at Jutland, and *Kaiser* was hit twice. *König Albert* missed the battle as she had trouble with her condensers, but for the rest of the war she served with her sisters in the 3rd Battle Squadron. In November 1917 *Kaiser* and *Kaiserin* engaged British cruisers when they raided German outposts in the Heligoland Bight.

All five were surrendered under the terms of the Armistice, and were interned at Scapa Flow. On June 21, 1919, they were scuttled, and the wrecks were raised between 1930 and 1936.

The class underwent few changes in appearance. The 88-mm (3.46-in) guns were progressively removed, and were replaced by four 88-mm antiaircraft guns in 1916-17; the torpedo nets were removed after Jutland; and *Kaiser* was given a tubular foremast like *Friedrich der Grosse.*

Displacement: 24 380 tons (normal), 26 573 tons (full load) *Length:* 171.9 m (564 ft) pp *Beam:* 29 m (95 ft 2 in) *Draught:* 8.3 m (27 ft 3 in) *Machinery:* 3-shaft steam turbines, 31 000 shp=20 knots (*Prinzregent Luitpold* 2-shaft turbines, 26 000 shp=19 knots) *Protection:* 349-197

***Friedrich der Grosse* as a flagship after her refit in 1914. Like her sisters she was scuttled at Scapa Flow in 1919 and scrapped in 1937**

mm (13¾-7¾ in) belt, 76 mm (3 in) decks, 298 mm (11¾ in) turrets *Armament:* 10 305-mm (12-in)/50-cal (5×2); 14 150-mm (5.9-in)/45-cal (14×1); 12 88-mm (3.46-in) (12×1); 5 50-cm (19.7-in) torpedo tubes (submerged; 1 bow, 4 beam) *Crew:* 1084

Kaiser Franz Josef I

Austro-Hungarian protected cruiser class, built 1888-92. *Kaiser Franz Josef I* and *Kaiserin Elisabeth* were built at Trieste and Pola respectively and commissioned in 1890 and 1892. As completed they had single 240-mm (9.4-in) guns but they were modernized in 1905-06 with light and more powerful guns, and improved boilers to reduce the enormous coal consumption.

In 1914 *Kaiserin Elisabeth* was stationed in China, and she helped to defend the German base at Tsingtao by landing her 150-mm (5.9-in) and 47-mm (1.85-in) guns for shore operations. She was scuttled on November 2 to prevent her from falling into Japanese hands.

Her sister served as guardship at Cattaro (now Kotor), and in 1916 many of her guns were removed. In 1917 she was completely disarmed to become a headquarters ship. After falling into French hands after the Armistice she foundered off Kumbor in October 1919.

Displacement: 4030 tons (normal) *Length:* 103.9 m (340 ft 11 in) *Beam:* 14.8 m (48 ft 7 in) *Draught:* 5.6 m (18 ft 4 in) *Machinery:* 2-shaft reciprocating steam, 8000 ihp=20 knots *Protection:* 57 mm (2.24 in) deck *Armament:* (As built) 2 240-mm (9.4-in)/35-cal (2×1); 6 150-mm (5.9-in)/35-cal BL (6×1); 5 47-mm (1.85-in) QF (5×1); 10 37-mm (1.46-in) (10×1); 4 36-cm (14-in) torpedo tubes (beam, above water) (As rearmed) 2 150-mm (5.9-in)/40-cal QF (2×1); 6 150-mm (5.9-in)/35-cal (6×1); 16 47-mm (1.85-in) QF (16×1); 1 machine-gun; 4 36-cm (14-in) torpedo tubes *Crew:* 450

Kaiser Franz Josef I with awnings over the after deck during a cruise in the Mediterranean

Kaiser Friedrich III

German battleship class, built 1895-1901. Five 1st Class battleships were laid down in 1895-98: *Kaiser Friedrich III (Ersatz Preussen), Kaiser Wilhelm II (Ersatz Friedrich der Grosse), Kaiser Wilhelm der Grosse (Ersatz König Wilhelm), Kaiser Karl der Grosse (Schiff 'B')* and *Kaiser Barbarossa (Schiff 'A').*

When completed the class was well regarded as good seaboats with good manoeuvrability, but they were still more suited for coastal waters rather than the North Sea, and were slower and weaker in gun power than contemporary front-line ships abroad. *Kaiser Wilhelm II* was fleet flagship until 1906, and when war broke out all five were mobilized for coast defence. However, they were soon laid up. *Kaiser Friedrich III* was an accommodation hulk at Kiel from the end of 1914, and housed Allied PoWs from 1916. *Kaiser Wilhelm der Grosse* was used for torpedo training at Kiel from 1916; *Kaiser Barbarossa* and *Kaiser Karl der Grosse* became prison hulks in the same year. In 1915 *Kaiser Wilhelm II* became a headquarters ship for the Fleet Staff.

The class was stricken in 1919-21 and sold for scrap.

The German battleship _Kaiser Friedrich III_ during the operational phase of her career. She became a prison hulk in Kiel from 1916

Displacement: 11 098 tons (normal), 11 894 tons (full load) *Length:* 120.88 m (396 ft 7 in) wl *Beam:* 19.96 m (65 ft 6 in) *Draught:* 8.23 m (27 ft) max *Machinery:* 3-shaft reciprocating steam, 14 000 ihp=18 knots *Protection:* 305-102 mm (12-4 in) belt, 254 mm (10 in) turrets, 76 mm (3 in) decks *Armament:* 4 240-mm (9.4-in)/40-cal (2×2); 18/14 150-mm (5.9-in)/40-cal (18/14×1); 12/14 88-mm (3.5-in)/30-cal (12/14×1); 12 machine-guns; 6 50-cm (19.7-in) torpedo tubes (submerged; 1 bow, 1 stern, 4 beam) *Crew:* 658

Kaiser Karl VI

Austro-Hungarian armoured cruiser, built 1896-1900. A single unit was ordered from Stabilimento Tecnico, Trieste in 1896 and commissioned in May 1900. Like many Austrian designs she was an attractive and well-armed ship, but over-gunned for her displacement. By 1914 there was no role for her to play in the Adriatic, as the Austro-Hungarian navy needed light, fast cruisers to spearhead their destroyers, and she played no part in the First World War. In March 1918 she paid off to become headquarters ship for the Sebenico naval district. She was sold for scrap in Italy in 1920.

Displacement: 6325 tons (normal) *Length:* 119 m (390 ft 5 in) wl *Beam:* 17.2 m (56 ft 5 in) *Draught:* 6.2 m (20 ft 4 in) *Machinery:* 2-shaft reciprocating steam, 12 300 ihp=20 knots *Protection:* 220 mm (8.7 in) belt, 60 mm (2.4 in) deck, 200 mm (7.9 in) turrets *Armament:* 2 240-mm (9.4-in)/40-cal (2×1); 8 150-mm (5.9-in)/40-cal (8×1); 16 47-mm (1.85-in) QF (16×1); 2 75-mm (2.95-in) AA (replaced two 47-mm in 1914); 2 45-cm (17.7-in) torpedo tubes (above water, beam) *Crew:* 548

Foto Droppel

The German cruiser *Kaiserin Augusta* under way. She became a gunnery training ship in 1914

Kaiserin Augusta

German armoured cruiser, built 1890-92. This was the first large cruiser built for the German navy, and was originally classed as a cruising corvette. Laid down as *Schiff H* at the Germania yard, she was launched on January 15, 1892, and entered service later the same year. Until 1902 she served abroad. Her original temporary armament of four 150-mm (5.9-in) guns was increased to 12 150-mm guns in 1896, at the expense of the 105-mm (4.1-in). From 1907 four above-water 36-cm (14-in) torpedo tubes were removed leaving a single tube underneath the ram bow.

Kaiserin Augusta was regarded as a good seaboat, although she had to be strengthened after completion. She was the first ship in the German navy to use a triple propeller shaft installation.

In 1914 she became a gunnery training ship, and from 1916 mounted a variety of U-Boat weapons: a 150-mm (5.9-in)/45-cal, four 105-mm (4.1-in)/45-cal and various 88-mm (3.5-in) guns, etc. She was stricken in October 1919 and was scrapped at Kiel.

Displacement: 6056 tons (normal), 6318 tons (full load) *Length:* 123.2 m (404 ft 2 in) *Beam:* 15.6 m (51 ft 2 in) *Draught:* 7.4 m (24 ft 3 in) *Machinery:* 3-shaft reciprocating steam, 12 000 ihp=21 knots *Protection:* 70-50 mm (2.8-2 in) deck *Armament:* (As completed) 4 150-mm (5.9-in)/30-cal (4×1); 8 105-mm (4.1-in)/35-cal (8×1); 8 88-mm (3.5-in)/30-cal (8×1); 5 36-cm (14-in) torpedo tubes (4 broadside trainable, above

The attractive Austro-Hungarian armoured cruiser *Kaiser Karl VI*, which despite her heavy armament saw no action during the First World War

IWM

Kaiserin Augusta

The German armoured cruiser *Kaiserin Augusta* in 1895. Launched three years earlier she had been laid down as *Schiff H* at the Germania yard. In the years up to 1902 her attractive lines were seen in the waters off Germany's African colonies. Her armament was changed from four 150-mm (5.9-in) guns to 12 150-mm guns in 1896 when eight 105-mm (4.1-in) were removed. After her foreign cruises her above-water 36-cm torpedo tubes were removed leaving only a single tube beneath the ram bow. Though she was a good seaboat with a triple shaft, the first in the German navy, she was rather elderly by the beginning of the First World War. She was used as a gunnery training ship and in 1916 became the testbed for a variety of U-Boat weapons. These included a 150-mm (5.9-in)/45-cal, four 105-mm (4.1-in)/45-cal and various 88-mm (3.5-in) guns. She was stricken a year after the end of the war and scrapped at Kiel

IWM

water; 1 submerged, bow) (From 1896) 12 150-mm/35-cal (12×1); 8 88-mm/30-cal (8×1); 5 36-cm torpedo tubes (reduced to 1 bow in 1907) *Crew:* 430

Kaiserin Und Königin Maria Theresia

Austro-Hungarian armoured cruiser, built 1891-95. She was built at Stabilimento Tecnico, Trieste, and was reconstructed during 1909-10. The upperworks and masts were rebuilt to reduce topweight, and the two single 240-mm (9.4-in) guns were replaced by 190-mm (7.5-in).

The ship was too old and slow for front-line service in the First World War, and from August 1914 she was detached from the 1st Cruiser Division of the Austro-Hungarian Fleet to be used for local defence at Sebenico. She lost most of her light guns in 1915, and in January 1917 was completely disarmed for use as an accommodation hulk for German U-Boat personnel at Pola (now Pula). Along with other ships surrendered to Great Britain after the end of the First World War, *Kaiserin Und Königin Maria Theresia* was sold for scrap in Italy in 1920.

Displacement: 5200 tons (normal) *Length:* 114 m (374 ft) wl *Beam:* 16.2 m (53 ft 2 in) *Draught:* 6.5 m (21 ft 4 in) *Protection:* 100 mm (3.9 in) belt, 57 mm (2.24 in) deck, 100 mm turrets *Machinery:* 2-shaft reciprocating steam, 9000 ihp = 19 knots *Armament:* (As built) 2 240-mm (9.4-in)/35-cal (2×l); 8 150-mm (5.9-in)/35-cal (8×l); 18 47-mm (1.85-in) QF (18×l); 4 45-cm (17.7-in) torpedo tubes (beam, above water); (As reconstructed) 2 190-mm (7.5-in)/42-cal (2×1); 8 150-mm/35-cal (8×l); 16 47-mm/44-cal (16×l); 4 45-cm torpedo tubes *Crew:* 468

IWM

The Austro-Hungarian armoured cruiser *Kaiserin Und Königin Maria Theresia* in 1900. She was too old for front-line service in the First World War, and by 1917 was an accommodation hulk

Kaiten

Japanese suicide submarines. During the Solomons campaign of 1943 the Japanese were increasingly forced on the defensive, incurring heavy naval losses. This led a number of Japanese naval officers to study alternative means of attacking the heavily defended US warships which somehow always managed to evade Japanese naval forces. One of the new forms of attack suggested was the possibility of using manned torpedoes. These could be easily hidden among the numerous islands of the Pacific or transported to the area of operations aboard submarines and then launched to search for suitable targets. The theory behind the concept was that the enemy vessel, although able to take evading action, would be unable to escape, for the pilot aboard the torpedo would be able to counter any evasive manoeuvre and steer the torpedo directly onto its target.

The design of the new weapons was based around the body of the Type 93 torpedo and initial trials of the Kaiten, as the new weapon was called, were held in the spring of 1944. The initial Kaiten were completed with a watertight hatch which could be released from inside the craft, so that the pilot could abandon the craft after aiming it at the target. The system proved difficult to operate and it was soon realized that the enemy ships could still evade the weapon. Many of the volunteers who came forward to operate the

A store of Kaiten warheads captured by the Americans at Maizuru Naval Base, Japan

US Army

Japanese sailors ready a Kaiten 1 aboard a submarine. Early Kaitens allowed the pilot to escape once the craft was on course for a target, but later models sealed him inside

Kaiten indicated that they were more than willing to die for their country. Consequently the craft was modified and the watertight hatch was omitted. Instead an entry hatch was fitted underneath the craft so that the pilot could enter through a watertight tunnel in the parent submarine. Once the Kaiten pilot was seated at the controls the entrance was sealed off from the outside. The training of pilots for the suicide Kaiten involved a rigid psychological preparation and ritual on the final operation.

Once a pilot had set out on his one-way journey to the intended target he remained in radio contact with the commander of the submarine who passed him bearings and ranges of the target. When the pilot had sighted the target through his small periscope at about 180-m (600-ft) range he fully submerged his craft and locked the controls to set the torpedo on its target.

The first Kaiten operation was carried out in November 1944, and by the end of the war over 50 Kaiten attacks had been carried out. In spite of the dedication of the pilots only a few minor successes were achieved.

Many craft were never completed owing to a lack of torpedoes and the partially constructed craft, lacking a propulsion unit, were adapted for use as fuel tanks on transports.

Apart from the Kaiten 1, three other models were built during the war. The propulsion plant in the Kaiten 2 and 3 was powered by a hydrogen-peroxide system, basic details of which had been supplied by the Germans. Production problems with the engine and its novel fuel system seriously curtailed production of the Kaiten 2 and 3. Only one version of the Kaiten 3 was built and this was used as a testbed. Owing to the problems encountered with the hydrogen-peroxide propelled units many were completed with a standard torpedo propulsion unit, but with a much more powerful explosive charge. These craft were known as Kaiten 4. Continuing problems with the supply of torpedo units, however, resulted in many craft being found uncompleted at the end of the war.

(Kaiten 1) *Displacement:* 8.3 tons (submerged) *Length:* 14.8 m (48 ft 7 in) *Beam:* 1 m (3 ft 3 in) *Machinery:* 2 Type 93 torpedo engines, 550 hp=30 knots *Armament:* 1550 kg (3400 lb) TNT *Crew:* 1

(Kaiten 2) *Displacement:* 13.3 tons (submerged) *Length:* 16.5 m (54 ft 2 in) *Beam:* 1.3 m (4 ft 3 in) *Machinery:* 1-shaft hydro-hydrazine engine, 1500 hp=40 knots *Armament:* 1550 kg (3400 lb) TNT *Crew:* 2

(Kaiten 3) *Displacement:* 13.3 tons (submerged) *Length:* 16.5 m (54 ft 2 in) *Beam:* 1.3 m (4 ft 3 in) *Machinery:* 1-shaft peroxide-hydrazine engine, 1800 hp=30 knots *Armament:* 1500 kg (3300 lb) TNT *Crew:* 2

(Kaiten 4) *Displacement:* 18 tons (submerged) *Length:* 16.5 m (54 ft 2 in) *Beam:* 1.3 m (4 ft 3 in) *Machinery:* 1 torpedo engine, 1500 hp=40 knots *Armament:* 1800 kg (4000 lb) TNT *Crew:* 2

Kaiyo

Japanese escort carrier. Although the Japanese had more practical experience in the conversion of merchant ships to aircraft carriers, and commissioned their first auxiliary (escort) carrier as early as September 1941, the Imperial Japanese Navy devoted little effort to building up a force of such ships, in spite of heavy merchant shipping losses at the hands of US submarines. Only two new escort carriers were commissioned in 1942 but in that year, two 12 750-grt, 21-knot merchant vessels, built in 1938-39 and requisitioned as naval transports at the outbreak of war, were earmarked for conversion. *Brazil Maru* was sunk near Truk by a submarine in August 1942, but her sister *Argentina Maru*, built for OSK lines by Mitsubishi, Nagasaki, arrived at Kure in December 1942 to begin conversion and was renamed *Kaiyo*.

Unlike the US and British carrier conversions, which retained the original merchant design's main machinery, *Kaiyo* was equipped with destroyer-type steam turbines in place of the original diesel motors. A speed of 24 knots was demanded by the Japanese navy, while the Allied navies were satisfied with 17-19 knots. Gun armament was also more elaborate, for *Kaiyo* was armed with four twin 127-mm (5-in) dual-purpose guns and, initially, six triple 25-mm (1-in) AA mountings.

The passenger liner's superstructure was cut down to the forecastle-deck level. The navigating bridge was moved to a position at the forward end of a 113-m (370-ft) hangar erected on the forecastle deck, and the boiler uptakes were led to the starboard side, where the smoke was exhausted outboard and downward in the usual Japanese fashion. The hangar extended between two aircraft lifts and was intended to accommodate 24 aircraft.

The steel-plate flight deck was supported by the hangar walls and, fore and aft of the hangar, by pillars, thus leaving the forecastle and quarterdeck open to the weather. As was common in Japanese carriers, the deck tapered fore and aft, conforming approximately with the planform of the hull. Though this 'ship-shaped' flight deck was 166.6 m (546 ft 6 in) long, some 26.5 m (87 ft) longer than in the US Navy's *Casablanca* Class, the US ships' decks were slightly wider and were rectangular, giving a greater usable aircraft parking area. *Kaiyo* had no island, and aircraft control and gunnery fire-control was exercised from open positions at the deck-edges. Eight arrester wires were installed, as well as a safety barrier, but there was no catapult.

Kaiyo commissioned as an escort carrier on November 23, 1943, and after trials was allocated to the newly formed General Escort Command, organized in a belated effort to reduce US submarine successes. In spite of the urgent need for close air escort for convoys, *Kaiyo* was frequently diverted to aircraft transport duties, ferrying short-range aircraft to China, Formosa and more distant destinations around the South China Sea. She also carried out the training of replacement carrier pilots.

After the Allied invasion of Luzon in January 1945, all Japanese carriers remained in their home waters, venturing only as far as the Chinese ports in the Yellow Sea. On March 19, *Kaiyo* was one of the carriers which sustained slight damage during US carrier strikes on Kure. A month later she was paid off as a carrier, although her gun crews and a steaming crew were retained. On July 18, she was proceeding to a port on Kyushu when she sustained minor damage from a magnetic mine. She put into Beppu Bay, Kyushu, to effect repairs but she was found there and attacked by British carrier aircraft. On this occasion, she was severely damaged. Her hull was holed and her back broken, and she had to be beached and abandoned. The derelict *Kaiyo* was still in Beppu Bay at the end of the war and it was not until 1948 that a local firm completed the task of scrapping her.

See also *Hiyo, Taiyo*.

Displacement: 13 600 tons (standard) 18 000 tons (full load) *Length:* 166.6 m (546 ft 6 in) oa *Beam:* 21.9 m (72 ft) wl *Draught:* 8.2 m (27 ft) *Machinery:* 2 sets geared steam turbines, 2 shafts, 52 100 shp=23.8 knots (trials) *Aircraft:* 24 *Armament:* (1943) 8 127-mm (5-in) DP (4×2); 24 25-mm (1-in) AA (8×3); (From 1944) 8 127-mm (5-in) DP (4×2); 44 25-mm (1-in) AA; 168 12-cm (4.7-in) AA rocket launchers (6×28) *Crew:* 829

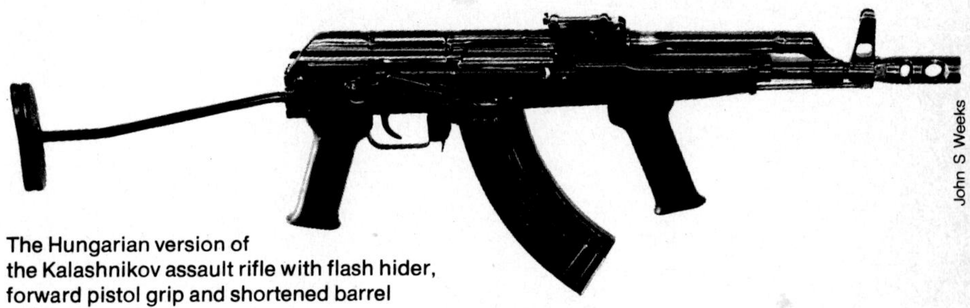
John S Weeks

The Hungarian version of the Kalashnikov assault rifle with flash hider, forward pistol grip and shortened barrel

Kalashnikov

Soviet assault rifles. The AK (Automat Kalashnikova) assault rifle was designed by Mikhail Kalashnikov and based on the weapons produced to fire the wartime M43 intermediate cartridge, a copy of the German 7.92-mm (0.312-in) kurz round. The first of the series to be produced was the AK-47, first issued to the Soviet army in 1950. By 1978 the Kalashnikov AKM (the modernized version of the AK-47) had replaced all other service rifles and submachine-guns and had become the standard weapon of the Soviet navy and air force ground troops, as well as those of the Warsaw Pact nations. There is also much evidence of Kalashnikovs in communist-inspired guerilla and nationalist movements. Manufacture has spread to several of the Warsaw Pact arsenals in Eastern Europe and an accurate estimate of the number produced is impossible, although it may be assumed to be in excess of ten million.

There are several features of the AK design which are unusual, but in general it is a

Soviet troops deploy from their BTR-60 APCs. They are armed with Kalashnikov AK47 assault rifles. This gas operated weapon has now been replaced by the simpler AKM. Both weapons use a rotating bolt which engages locking shoulders in the receiver to lock the action. The AKM has a stamped steel receiver and ribbed receiver cover and a cyclic rate reducer. Both weapons have a 30-round detachable box magazine. The advantages of these weapons are that they put automatic fire (about 600 rds/min) in one man's hands with a range of up to 400 m (440 yards) with a rifle which is robust and simple to service. The disadvantage is that the large magazine makes the rifle difficult to fire from a prone position and is almost twice the weight of most modern small-calibre arms. However the test of any weapon is its use in action and the AK has been used in Vietnam, the Middle East and Africa. The Israelis too have equipped their units from captured stocks

Novosti

simple, straightforward, robust and handy weapon of sound design and good workmanship. The layout and original inception perhaps owe something to the German Sturmgewehr of 1944, but it is quite different internally, and certainly better made. The AK is gas-operated with the piston permanently attached to the bolt carrier, and with no adjustment for the amount of gas tapped from the barrel. This probably means that it is set permanently with a little too much gas so that fouling and dirt can be overcome. The bolt locks by rotating and engaging forward lugs into recesses in the body and the 30-round curved magazine feeds upwards.

The barrel is chromed internally throughout, and on the original AK the bolt was polished, though it is parkerized on the modernized AKM. The AK body was machined from the solid, but the AKM uses pressed steel and some stampings held together with spot welds and pins. Even so there appear to be anomalies in the design since a small number of East German AKMs have been identified in recent years with machined bodies. A distinctive feature of the rifle is the long pivoted cover for the boltway on the right-hand side of the body. This cover also acts as a safety device since when it is closed it holds the bolt forward.

The great majority of the AKs and AKMs have wooden furniture, though the type of wood varies and in Romania it is laminated ply with a forehand grip. In East Germany the furniture is generally plastic; in Hungary it is a mixture of plastic and steel sheet and the butt is a steel folding skeleton. The Chinese use a poor-quality wood furniture and leave a folding bayonet permanently attached. The Hungarians have produced a short-barrelled version with a large muzzle brake.

All versions use the same basic mechanism and the same sights. These are a somewhat old-fashioned open backsight with a hooded post at the fore end, working over quite a short radius. However the Soviet teaching is that the effective range is 400 m (440 yards) and automatic fire should not be used beyond 300 m (330 yards) and at these ranges the short sight radius is unlikely to be noticeable.

The AK has an enviable reputation for reliability, largely due to its simplicity and the small number of moving parts and to the generous clearances and robust, but not highly stressed, components, and it seems likely that production of this extraordinarily successful weapon will continue.

(AK-47) *Calibre:* 7.62-mm (0.30-in) *Length:* 102 cm (40 in) *Rate of fire:* 20 rds/min *Muzzle velocity:* 735 m/sec (2410 ft/sec) *Maximum range:* 400 m (440 yards)

(AKM) *Calibre:* 7.62-mm (0.30-in) *Length:* 876 mm (34.5 in) *Barrel length:* 414 mm (16.3 in) *Magazine:* 30-round box *Rate of fire:* 600 rds/min (cyclic) *Muzzle velocity:* 715 m/sec (2345 ft/sec) *Maximum range:* 300 m (330 yards)

Kalashnikov

Soviet machine-guns. Mikhail Timofeyevich Kalashnikov followed up the success of his 7.62-mm (0.30-in) AKM assault rifle—a standard Soviet weapon—by producing, not unpredictably, a light machine-gun version. The 7.62-mm RPD (or Degtyarev LMG), introduced around 1953, had become a Red Army standard but by the 1960s was fast

becoming dated and needed to be replaced. Kalashnikov's RPK, designed to the same calibre as his assault rifle and using a large proportion of its components, was taken into service by the Red Army in the middle of the 1960s and fast became distributed throughout the Soviet bloc. It is an attractive weapon, clearly resembling the AKM, except that the barrel is heavier. The RPK's barrel, like that

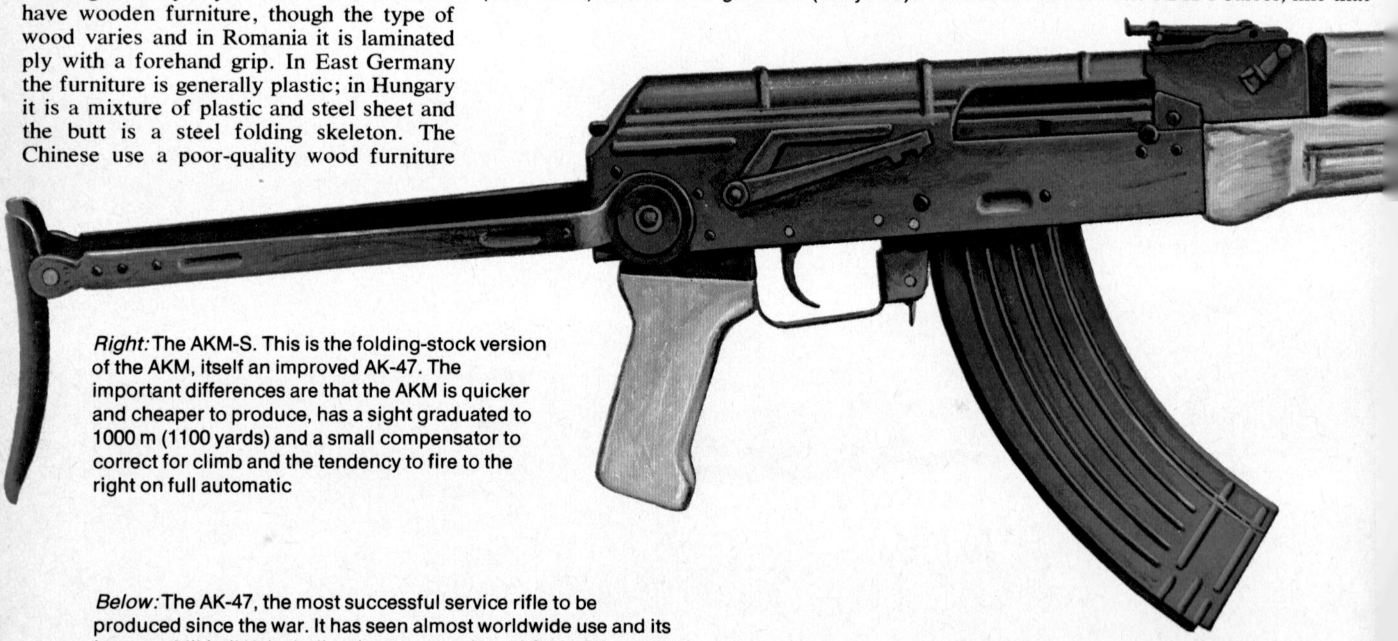

Right: The AKM-S. This is the folding-stock version of the AKM, itself an improved AK-47. The important differences are that the AKM is quicker and cheaper to produce, has a sight graduated to 1000 m (1100 yards) and a small compensator to correct for climb and the tendency to fire to the right on full automatic

Below: The AK-47, the most successful service rifle to be produced since the war. It has seen almost worldwide use and its inventor Mikhail Kalashnikov has won Lenin and State Prizes and the title of Hero of Socialist Labour. The AK-47 has also become the trademark of many terrorist and insurgent groups in Africa and the Middle East

Above: The Soviet PK GPMG, the original version of a gun that has been through six modifications for use in AFVs, as an MMG and as a lightened version. It fires a 7.62-mm (0.30-in) round and belt boxes for 50, 200 and 250 round belts are issued. The 50-round box can be clipped to the gun in the assault role

Soviet soldiers on exercise with an RPK LMG with the 40-round box magazine. The RPK is basically an AKM with a longer, sturdier barrel and light bipod but no barrel-change facility

John S Weeks

of the assault rifle, is fixed so that the gun cannot deliver continuous rapid fire. However it is used as a squad light automatic and must improve its firepower to a useful degree.

Normally the RPK is fitted with a 40-round version of the AKM magazine, but it can also take a 75-round drum, which is probably easier to handle since the 40-round magazine is so long that it touches the ground when the weapon is in the firing position. In an emergency, the riflemen's 30-round magazine can be used. To steady the weapon when firing long bursts there is a light bipod on the muzzle. For carrying, this folds up and clips to the barrel just forward of the handguard.

At almost the same time as the RPK appeared in the squad, another Kalashnikov gun was issued. This is the PK, and at first it was thought that it would be a straight replacement for the RP 46 company support gun. However, it turned out to be the first true Soviet general-purpose machine-gun (GPMG). It is a most interesting weapon, and combines a number of components and principles from existing guns, with complete success. The PK fires the old M1908 long round, which is rimmed and would normally be considered to be obsolete by now. The Soviets obviously believe it still has sufficient power to be useful, and in a GPMG the M43 short round would be definitely underpowered. The Guryonov mechanism has been adopted to feed the M1908 round. The barrel change system of the Guryonov has been taken over too. The feed pawls are powered by the piston—a reliable and safe principle, first used on the Czech M52. The bolt, locking system, piston and gas port come from the AK series, but are fitted upside down. The trigger and sear mechanism are taken directly from the RPD.

The PK has appeared in at least six versions and has a heavier and sturdier barrel for mounting in armoured vehicles. It is issued with a bipod, a tripod and an AA mounting. A bipod-mounted company support version was tested in the US and received glowing reports for its reliability and simplicity.

PK: the basic gun has a heavy fluted barrel, a feed cover constructed from both machined and stamped components, and a plain butt plate.

PKS: the basic gun mounted on a tripod. The 7.48 kg (16 lb 8 oz) tripod provides a stable mount for long-range ground fire, and it can also be opened up quickly to elevate the weapons for antiaircraft fire.

PKT: the basic weapon adopted for coaxial installation in armoured vehicles. Sights, stock, tripod and standard pattern trigger are deleted. A longer, heavier barrel is fitted and a solenoid is attached to the receiver back plate for remote triggering. A new emergency manual trigger and safety is also fitted.

PKM: a special lightweight version. Excess metal is machined away to reduce the weight to about 8.39 kg (18 lb 8 oz). The barrel is fluted, the feed cover constructed entirely from stamping and a hinged butt rest is fitted to the butt plate.

PKMS: a tripod-mounted version of the PKM.

PKB: a PKM with tripod, butt stock and trigger mechanism removed and replaced by twin spade grips and a butterfly trigger. (Possibly also designated PKMB.)

It seems likely that the weapon will remain in service for many years to come. With both the company machine-guns and the assault rifle coming from the Kalashnikov drawing board, Kalashnikov enjoys a virtual monopoly of the Soviet infantry small arms.

(RPK) *Weight unloaded:* 4.76 kg (10 lb 8 oz) *Calibre:* 7.62 mm (0.30 in) *Length:* 104.1 cm (3 ft 5 in) *Barrel length:* 589 mm (1 ft 11 in) *Operation:* gas *Cartridge:* 7.62 mm patron obr 1943g (M43) *Magazine:* 30- or 40-round box, or 75-round drum *Rate of fire:* 600 rds/min *Muzzle velocity:* 731 m/sec (2400 ft/sec)

(PKM) *Weight unloaded:* 8.9 kg (19 lb 10 oz) *Calibre:* 7.62 mm (0.30 in) *Length:* 119.3 cm (3 ft 11 in) *Barrel length:* 660 mm (2 ft 2 in) *Operation:* gas *Cartridge:* 7.62 mm patron obr 1891g (M1908) *Magazine:* 200- or 250-round belt *Rate of fire:* 650 rds/min *Muzzle velocity:* 822 m/sec (2700 ft/sec)

Kalinin

Soviet destroyer class, built 1913-27. These destroyers, otherwise known as Type III, were the survivors of the *Avtroil* group of the *Azard* Class, modernized after the civil war of 1917-22. The *Kalinin* (ex-*Pryemislav*) was completed in 1916. In the Second World War both were early casualties, *Kalinin* being mined off Cape Juminda in the Baltic on August 28, 1941, and *Karl Marx* being bombed by German aircraft in Loksa Bight on August 8, 1941.

See also *Azard*.

Displacement: 1757 tons (normal), 2200 tons (full load) *Length:* 107 m (351 ft) oa *Beam:* 9.5 m (31 ft 2 in) *Draught:* 4.9 m (16 ft) *Machinery:* 2-shaft steam turbines, 32 700 shp=28 knots *Armament:* 5 102-mm (4-in) (5×1); 1 75-mm (2.95-in) AA; 1 37-mm (1.46-in) AA; 2 machine-guns; 6 45-cm (17.7-in) torpedo tubes (2×3); 80 Model 1926 mines *Crew:* 168

KAM-3D, Kawasaki

Japanese antitank missile. KAM-3D, designated Type 64 ATM or ATM-1 by the Japanese ground self-defence force, is a first-generation wire-guided weapon with manual control. Development began in 1957 under contract to the Japan defence agency's Technical Research and Development Institute. Following test firings of several hundred rounds the missile was accepted into service in 1964. KAM-3D can be fired from infantry-portable launchers or from vehicle installations on Jeeps or helicopters. More than 300 have been built.

The round is fired from a box launcher elevated at 15°. The two-stage Daicel (Dai-Nippon Celluloid) solid-propellant rocket motor burns for 0.8 sec to accelerate the missile out of the launcher, the cruise speed of 85 m/sec (280 ft/sec) being maintained by the sustainer section. The operator sights his target visually with binoculars and steers the round by means of a joystick, the command signals being transmitted via wires to operate spoilers on the wing trailing edges. A flare on the missile's rear assists visual tracking in daylight, and at night the rocket-motor exhaust indicates position. KAM-3D carries a hollow-charge warhead.

Length: 1 m (3 ft 3 in) *Span:* 60 cm (2 ft) *Diameter:* 12 cm (4.7 in) *Weight:* 15.7 kg (34 lb 10 oz) *Minimum/maximum range:* 350/2000 m (1150/6550 ft)

Minekaze. **The *Kamikaze* Class bore such a close resemblance to the *Minekaze* Class that they were known by the Allies as *Minekaze II* Class**

Fujifotos

KAM-9, Kawasaki

Japanese antitank missile. KAM-9, also known as TAN-SSM, is a longer-range development of the same manufacturer's KAM-3D and employs semiautomatic command to line-of-sight guidance. (The operator merely tracks the target with his sight and steering commands are automatically generated by a small computer and transmitted over wires to the missile.) Development began in 1964 and the weapon entered service with the Japanese ground self-defence force following completion of operational evaluation in the mid-1970s.

KAM-9 is fired from a tubular container which is also used for storage and transport of the missile. A solid-propellant Nippon Oils and Fats boost motor ejects the round from its container and, once cruising speed is reached, propulsion is assumed by the Daicel sustainer motor. The operator keeps the target in his optical sight, and an infrared sensor adjusted to the sightline detects a flare on the rear of the missile. The miniature computer in the tracker unit calculates the steering commands which are needed to bring the round back on line to the target, and these are passed down wires trailing behind the missile. The 1.9 kg (4lb 3oz) hollow-charge warhead can penetrate more than 500 mm (20 in) of armour plating, and KAM-9 is intended to engage landing craft in addition to armoured vehicles.

Length: 1.5 m (4 ft 11 in) *Span:* 33 cm (13 in) *Diameter:* 15 cm (6 in) *Range:* 3000 m (3300 yards)

Kamikaze

Japanese destroyer class. Nine vessels of the *Kamikaze* Class were laid down between December 1921 and October 1923. The first five ships had originally been ordered under the 1920 Programme, the names *Okaze, Makaze, Tsumikaze, Soyakaze* and *Suyukaze* being assigned. The order was subsequently transferred to the 1921-22 Programme when a further four ships were ordered and all were given numbers instead of names, the numbers assigned to the units being: *1, 3, 5, 7, 9, 11, 13, 15* and *17*. They entered service between December 1922 and December 1925, and in 1928 they were all assigned names.

The design was a virtual repeat of the last three vessels of the *Minekaze* Class but these destroyers were completed with an updated armament. In place of the old 4.7-in (120-mm)/45-cal weapon the new 4.7-in/50-cal gun was mounted.

The ships were refitted between 1941-42 when the after 4.7-in was removed and replaced with 25-mm (1-in) AA. Altogether the ships mounted between six and ten 25-mm AA and in addition shipped 18 depth charges and four depth-charge throwers. Normal displacement rose to 1500 tons with the new equipment. During the summer of 1944 the light AA of surviving units was further increased to 13-20 25-mm.

Name	launched	fate
Asakaze (ex-*3*)	12/22	torpedoed US *Haddo*, 8/44
Asanagi (ex-*15*)	4/24	torpedoed US *Pollack*, 5/44
Harukaze (ex-*5*)	12/22	surrendered; scrapped 1947
Hatakaze (ex-*9*)	3/24	sunk in air raid on Formosa, 1/45
Hayate (ex-*13*)	3/25	sunk Wake Island, 12/41
Kamikaze (ex-*1*)	9/22	surrendered; scrapped 1946
Matsukaze (ex-*7*)	10/23	torpedoed US *Swordfish*, 6/44
Oite (ex-*11*)	11/24	sunk in air raid on Truk, 2/44
Yunagi (ex-*17*)	4/24	torpedoed US *Picuda*, 8/44

Displacement: 1400 tons (normal), 1720 tons (full load) *Length:* 102.4 m (336 ft) *Beam:* 9.7 m (31 ft 10 in) *Draught:* 2.9 m (9 ft 6 in) *Machinery:* 2-shaft geared turbines, 38 500 shp=37.25 knots *Armament:* 4 4.7-in (120-mm) (4×1); 2 7.7-mm (0.303-in); 6 21-in (53-cm) torpedo tubes (3×2) *Crew:* 148

Kamov Soviet helicopters
See **Harp, Hat, Hen, Hormone**

Kangaroo

British armoured personnel carrier. In August 1944 the 2nd Canadian Corps were confronted with a strong German position across the Caen-Falaise road, and mounted Operation Totalize to break through. Lieutenant-General Simonds, the corps commander, hit on the idea of using armoured carriers to put the infantry onto their objectives and began looking for some suitable vehicles. At that time the three field artillery regiments of the 3rd Canadian Division had just handed in their M7 Priest self-propelled 105-mm (4.1-in) howitzers, to be re-equipped with towed 25-pdr guns. The barrels of the Priest equipments were worn out, and Simonds obtained permission to convert these self-propelled howitzers into carriers.

The howitzer, mantlet, seats and ammunition racks were stripped out and a piece of armour plate welded across the front opening. This work was done by an advanced workshop detachment whose codename happened to be Kangaroo, and the vehicles were named after the workshop. The infantry only had one day in which to practise and familiarize themselves with their new transport. The drivers of the Kangaroos were mostly Royal Canadian Artillery drivers who drove them as Priests a few days before.

The conversion and the operation were both a success, and the term Kangaroos came to be applied to any conversion of a tank to an armoured personnel carrier. In September 1944 the 1st Canadian Armoured Carrier Regiment was formed, using Ram tanks with the turrets removed. In Italy, more Priests and a number of old Sherman tanks were converted. The 79th Armoured Division, responsible for various peculiar armoured vehicles, took over the APC task and the 49th Royal Tank Regiment was reformed as the 49th APC Regiment late in 1944.

The Kangaroo was an overweight and extravagant way of moving ten infantrymen, but it worked, and utilized vehicles which otherwise would probably have been scrapped out of hand. It gave an early insight into the whole question of providing infantry with APCs. Several of the wartime Kangaroos

The Kangaroo began life as a stop-gap with the Canadians, but after its debut in Normandy it was accepted as an APC and old Sherman and Sherman Ram hulls were converted. Several wartime Kangaroos remained in service with the British Army of the Rhine after the war

IWM

remained in British service for some years after the war, finally being replaced by purpose-built carriers.

Kangaroo

Soviet air-to-surface missile. The strategic stand-off missile known variously as Kangaroo and AS-3 in the West made its public debut at the 1961 Soviet aviation day, held at Tushino outside Moscow. It had probably entered service the previous year though some sources give the initial operational date as 1963. The missile uses major components of the Su-7 Fitter-A fighter-bomber, with a redesigned tail unit: the dorsal fin is reduced in size, allowing the weapon to fit into the bomb bay of its Tu-95 Bear-B launch aircraft, and a ventral strake has been added to restore directional stability.

Kangaroo, though by then obsolescent, was still carried in the late 1970s by Bear-Bs of the Soviet air force's long-range aviation and naval aviation arms. The weapon is relatively inaccurate, since no terminal homing is employed, but accuracy is relatively unimportant since a large thermonuclear warhead is used. Typical targets would be sprawling facilities such as railway marshalling yards, port complexes and centres of population. A secondary antiship role is also likely, especially against convoys and nuclear task forces.

Kangaroo is the largest Soviet stand-off missile, and is powered by an afterburning turbojet. The weapon is too large to fit completely inside the Bear's bomb bay and is carried partially recessed. The fixed inlet in the missile's nose is covered by a fairing to reduce drag while being carried by the mother aircraft, and it may incorporate trunking to carry high-pressure air from the Bear's engines to start the Kangaroo's turbojet before launching.

All details of Soviet missile operation are speculative, but AS-3 is thought to be launched normally at a height of some 18 000 m (60 000 ft). When approximately 160 km (100 miles) from its target the Kangaroo begins its dive at about Mach 1.8, the top speed being limited by the inlet design, reaching a maximum range of 650 km (400 miles). A low-level flight profile, with the weapon cruising at about Mach 1, could also be flown.

The method of guidance employed during the early stages of the missile's flight is thought to be beam-riding, with rearward-facing aerials on the Kangaroo detecting emissions from a radar transmitter in the launch aircraft. The weapon steers itself into the centre of the beam, which is aligned with the target. This is only possible at comparatively short ranges, however, and the last phase of the mission is flown with the missile under autopilot control. Correction commands can be transmitted by radio from the launching bomber or from another aircraft if the missile wanders off course or is assigned to a different target while in flight.

Length: 14.9 m (48 ft 11 in) *Span:* 9.15 m (30 ft) *Diameter:* 1.85 m (6 ft) *Weight:* 11 000 kg (24 250 lb) *Range:* 650 km (400 miles) *Warhead:* 2300 kg (5070 lb) thermonuclear

Kangaroo, Blackburn

British bomber. The most important First World War product of the Blackburn Aeroplane & Motor Co of Leeds was this curiously named coastal patrol bomber. It was developed from the GP, a three-seat twin-float seaplane flown in July 1916, and went into production with an undercarriage having two lateral pairs of wheels and a tail skid, and folding unequal-span wings. The engines were two 250-hp Rolls-Royce Falcon II.

The crew of four in tandem cockpits all had a magnificent view, but the fuselage was so shallow that the nose and rear gunners could not aim their Lewis guns over the full available arc of fire; the fuselage twisted visibly in manoeuvres. Four 104-kg (230-lb) bombs were hung by their noses in the fuselage and three (in some cases four) more could be slung in a row underneath. Usual antisubmarine load was two bombs of 236 kg (520 lb).

Originally ordered by the Royal Naval Air Service, the Kangaroo was used only by the newly formed RAF, the first unit being 246 Squadron at Seaton Carew, County Durham, from late April 1918. Between May 1, 1918, and the end of the war the squadron flew convoy-protection missions and spotted 12 U-Boats and attacked 11. On August 28, aircraft B9983 found and bombed the German submarine *UC.70*, which was later finished off by the destroyer *Ouse*.

It is possible that some Kangaroos served in Belgium. At least 15 existed at the time of the Armistice in 1918, and survivors later served as commercial transports and trainers.

Span: (upper wing) 22.81 m (74 ft 10 in), (lower wing) 16.18 m (53 ft 1 in) *Length:* 14.02 m (46 ft) *Gross weight:* 3636 kg (8017 lb) *Maximum speed:* 161 km/h (100 mph)

'Kanin'

Soviet SAM destroyer class. The vessels of the class were originally members of the

The Blackburn Kangaroo antisubmarine patrol bomber which entered service with 246 Squadron of the newly formed RAF in April 1918

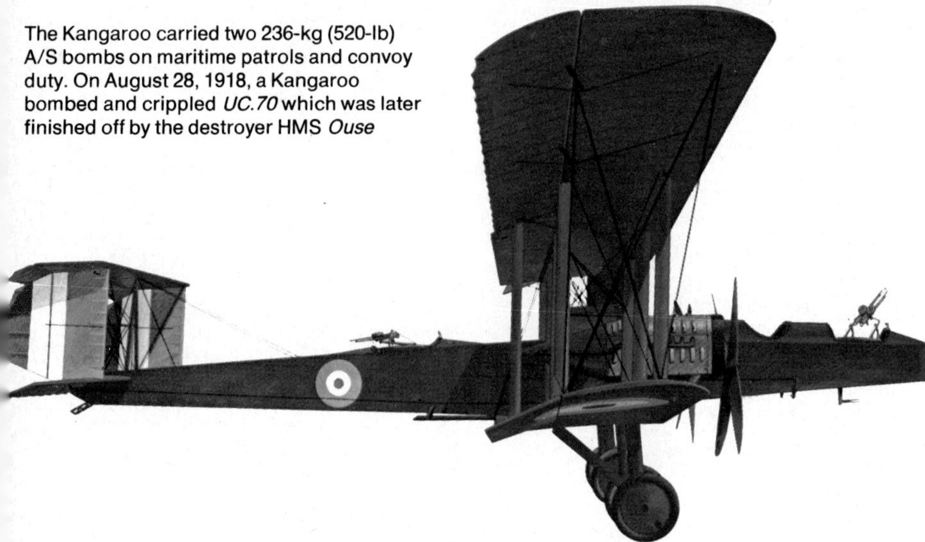

The Kangaroo carried two 236-kg (520-lb) A/S bombs on maritime patrols and convoy duty. On August 28, 1918, a Kangaroo bombed and crippled *UC.70* which was later finished off by the destroyer HMS *Ouse*

'Krupny' Class, which underwent a series of major conversions from 1967-68 into the early 1970s. At least six of the eight 'Krupny' Class vessels have been converted to 'Kanins', and are named *Boiky, Derzhky Gnevny, Gremyashchy, Zhguchy* and *Zorky.* It is probable that Baltic yards have been responsible for the conversion work and rebuilding of the superstructure.

The radical modernization involved the replacement of the two SS-N-1 Scrubber launchers and their magazines by a single SA-N-1 Goa launcher for surface-to-air missiles in an installation which resembles that of the 'Kotlin SAM' modification. The launcher was placed on top of its magazine. The 'Krupnys' lattice mast amidships was replaced by a short pyramidal tower carrying the Peel Group guidance radar. The after 57-mm (2.24-in) mounting was shifted forward in a return to the 'Kildin'-type layout, while the two mountings amidships were replaced by 12-barrelled A/S mortars. A third mortar was placed on the forecastle, while the triple torpedo tubes were replaced by quintuple mountings. A bow sonar was fitted to complement this increase in antisubmarine capability, the shape of the bow being changed accordingly. The helicopter deck was enlarged and moved further forward, becoming an extension of the shelter deck aft. Some ships have subsequently been fitted with four twin 30-mm (1.18-in) guns with accompanying Drum Tilt directors on platforms projecting from the radar tower—a feature also of some ships of the 'Kotlin SAM' Class.

With the advantage of the larger 'Krupny'-type hull, the 'Kanin' conversion is undoubtedly more successful than the 'Kotlin SAM' modification. In 1978, ships of the 'Kanin' Class were distributed evenly between the Northern, Baltic and Pacific fleets, and carried pennant numbers in the 200, 500 and 900 ranges.

Displacement: 3650 tons (standard), 4500 tons (full load) *Length:* 139.5 m (457 ft 8 in) oa *Beam:* 14.6 m (47 ft 11 in) *Draught:* 5 m (16 ft 5 in) *Machinery:* 2-shaft steam turbines, 80 000 shp=34 knots *Armament:* 2 SA-N-1 launchers (1×2); 8 57-mm (2.24-in) AA (2×4); 8 30-mm (1.18-in) AA (4×2) (some ships only); 10 53-cm (21-in) torpedo tubes (2×5); 36 MBU 2500A A/S mortars (3×12) *Crew:* 350

'Kara'

Soviet missile cruiser class. *Nikolayev*, the first ship of the class, was laid down in 1969 and completed in 1973; *Ochakov, Kerch, Azov* and *Petropavlovsk* followed at yearly intervals. (*Azov* is reported to be a modified version.)

Developed from the 'Kresta-II' design, the 'Kara' Class is apparently intended to accompany the new aircraft carriers, for which they provide added defence against aircraft and submarines. The hull has been lengthened by 16 m (52 ft 6 in), the increase being accounted for by an extra section inserted between the forward Head Light radar and the main radar tower. The change of layout appears to have been dictated by the change to gas-turbine propulsion, evidenced by the massive square funnel. Since the back-to-back search radar

A Soviet 'Kanin' Class guided missile destroyer shadows the Commando Carrier HMS *Hermes* during a NATO exercise in October 1973

A Soviet 'Kara' Class guided-missile cruiser photographed by an RAF Nimrod during a naval exercise in the Mediterranean. This 'Kara' Class vessel, probably the *Kerch*, is armed with surface-to-surface and surface-to-air missiles as well as medium and close-range AA guns. She also carries A/S weapons. Her rear deck is used as a helicopter deck for a Hormone A or B which is housed in a hangar. This is the first class of large cruisers to be built since the *Sverdlovs* apart from the specialized *Moskva*. The class was first seen when the *Nikolaev* entered the Mediterranean in March 1973. The clutter of radar visible amidships includes Top Sail and Head Net C for surveillance, Head Light for SA-N-3 control, Pop Group for SA-N-4 control, Owl Screech for 76-mm gun control and Drum Tilt for the Gatling-type guns. A full ECM outfit appears to be installed on the bridge and mast. The class is known as Bolshoy Protivolodochny Korabl which means Large Anti-Submarine Ship

MOD

A 'Kara' Class guided missile destroyer belonging to the Soviet navy photographed by an RAF Nimrod during an exercise in the Mediterranean

could no longer be accommodated above the uptakes because of the hot exhaust gases, it has had to be moved forward to the after end of an enlarged bridge structure on a lattice mast modelled on that of the 'Krivaks'.

While the main armament of SA-N-3 Goblet surface-to-air missiles and SS-N-14 antisubmarine missiles has remained identical in layout to that of the 'Kresta-II', advantage has been taken of the added section amidships to ship two twin 76-mm (3-in) mountings, the twin 57-mm (2.24-in) of the 'Krestas' being omitted. This in turn has freed space abreast and aft of the funnel which, with the increase in beam, has been used to resite the four Gatling close-range mountings and to add two SA-N-4 'pop-up' launchers for short-range surface-to-air missiles together with their Pop Group directors. As there has been no change in the main armament of the ships, the main sensor outfit is identical to that of the 'Krestas', the only significant addition being the variable-depth sonar beneath the flight deck on the stern. The complex helicopter-handling arrangements of the earlier design have been retained, presumably to avoid having to increase the height of the hangar with attendant effects on the siting of the after SA-N-3 Goblet launcher and its guidance radar. Similarly, no attempt has been made to rationalize the rambling system of shelter decks of the 'Krestas', which distinguishes them from modern Western warships. The 'Kara' Class are almost certainly slower than earlier missile cruisers, partly because there is less need for high speed in ships such as these and the new carriers built for an ocean-going role, but presumably also because of the problems in getting the necessary power from a maximum of four gas turbines. Given the present state of the art, these are probably rated at about 25000 hp each, with two on each shaft. The 'Kara' Class were the largest ships in the world to be powered exclusively by gas turbines, a distinction which remained with them until after the completion of *Invincible* for the Royal Navy.

Displacement: 8200 tons (standard), 9500 tons (full load) *Length:* 174 m (570 ft 10 in) oa *Beam:* 18 m (59 ft) *Draught:* 6 m (19 ft 8 in) *Machinery:* 4 gas turbines, 2 shafts, 100000 shp=30+ knots *Armament:* 4 SA-N-3 launchers (2×2); 8 SS-N-14 launchers (2×4); 4 SA-N-4 launchers (2×2); 4 76-mm (3-in) AA (2×2); 4 Gatling-type guns; 10 53-cm (21-in) torpedo tubes (2×5); 24 MBU 2500A A/S mortars (2×12); 12 MBU 4500A A/S mortars (2×6); Hormone A ASW helicopter *Crew:* 500

Karaś, PZL P.23

Polish bomber and reconnaissance aircraft. In the 1930s the Lotnictwo Wojskowe (Polish military aviation) was one of the most powerful and efficient air forces in the world, yet its offensive strength was made up almost entirely of this single-engined aircraft. Like the PZL monoplane fighters it was a most advanced design for its day; and, like them, the desperate need for it came at a time when it had become obsolescent.

Designed during 1931-32 by a team headed by Stanisław Prauss, the prototype was under construction before 1933, but engineering changes delayed the first flight until August 1934. In the second prototype the bomb bay was deleted, the heavy bombload of 700 kg (1543 lb) being slung under the fuselage and inner wings. The 580-hp PZL-built Pegasus II engine was mounted lower down to improve pilot view. The crew of three each had a 7.7-mm (0.303-in) gun, the upper and lower rear weapons being aimed by PZL hydraulically-powered mounts. The observer/bombardier could sight for level bombing through the front of a ventral bathtub. The advanced stressed-skin structure used rigid sandwich skin panels over large areas. The landing gear was fixed.

By 1935 the P.23 had reached the definitive standard, and orders were placed for 40 of the P.23A model, with Pegasus II engines, and 210 of the P.23B model with 680-hp Pegasus VIII engines. The service type-name was Karaś (crucian carp). The Karaś B was the chief operational version, entering bomber regiments in mid-1937 and eventually equipping no fewer than 14. Of these, 12 were still operational when the German invasion began on September 1, 1939. Seven regiments were attached to land armies and the other five formed the Independent Bomber Brigade with the first four Los heavy-bomber regiments. Upon the Karaś fell almost the entire burden of aerial attack on the invading German armies, and despite its age the type acquitted itself very well. Though some 80 were lost in action they inflicted severe losses on German army and airforce units, and a handful of both A and B models succeeded in escaping to Romania towards the end of September as Polish resistance collapsed. Later these aircraft were taken into the Romanian air force and used on the Eastern Front against the Soviet Union.

In 1936 the Bulgarian air force ordered a derivative of the Karaś as its standard tactical bomber. Known as the P.43A, it differed chiefly in being powered by a 930-hp Gnome-Rhône 14Kfs two-row radial. It also had a second forward-firing gun and other changes. Twelve were delivered in late 1937, when a further 42 aircraft designated P.43B were ordered, powered by the 980-hp Gnome-Rhône 14N1. Most of these had been delivered by September 1939.

In October 1938 PZL flew the more powerful prototype P.46 Sum, features of which—including the twin-finned tail—were tested in a production P.23B, which failed to reach the Polish regiments in time.

Span: 13.95 m (45 ft 9 in) *Length:* 9.68 m (31 ft 9 in) *Gross weight:* (P.23B) 3526 kg (7773 lb) *Maximum speed:* (P.23B) 350 km/h (217 mph)

In about 1930 the German General Staff detected a loophole in the provisions of the Versailles Treaty: the German army were forbidden to develop heavy artillery, but nothing in the terms of the treaty forbade them developing rockets. A Rocket Research Station was set up at Kummersdorf Artillery Proving Ground to take advantage of this, and the best-known fruit of their labours was the A-4 missile. A lesser-publicized weapon was the Nebelwerfer ('fog-thrower' or smoke mortar) field artillery rocket and its derivatives.

15-cm Nebelwerfer 41

One of the first projects given to Kummersdorf was the development of a bombardment weapon with a range of 5-8 km (3-5 miles), and out of this grew a programme of investigation into the stabilizing of the rocket in flight by spinning it, rather than by using fins. This had been pioneered by the British Army's Hale War Rocket in the 1870s and then followed up by the Swedish inventor Baron Unge, but neither was particularly successful and the idea was dropped. The Kummersdorf group, under the guidance of General Walter Dornberger, examined the idea afresh and came to the conclusion that one defect of the old designs was that the rocket thrust was applied at the base of the missile, and this thrust tended to push the nose of the rocket off-course if the motor burned at all erratically—which it usually did in the early days. Moreover, the rate of spin had been allowed to fall where it liked, rather than having been scientifically worked out.

The Kummersdorf designers produced a radically new solution by putting the rocket motor in front of the explosive payload, with 26 venturi outlets arranged around the rocket body. These outlets were canted at 14° so that as well as delivering the forward thrust, they also spun the rocket. The combination of front drive and spin produced a rocket of unparalleled accuracy for its day.

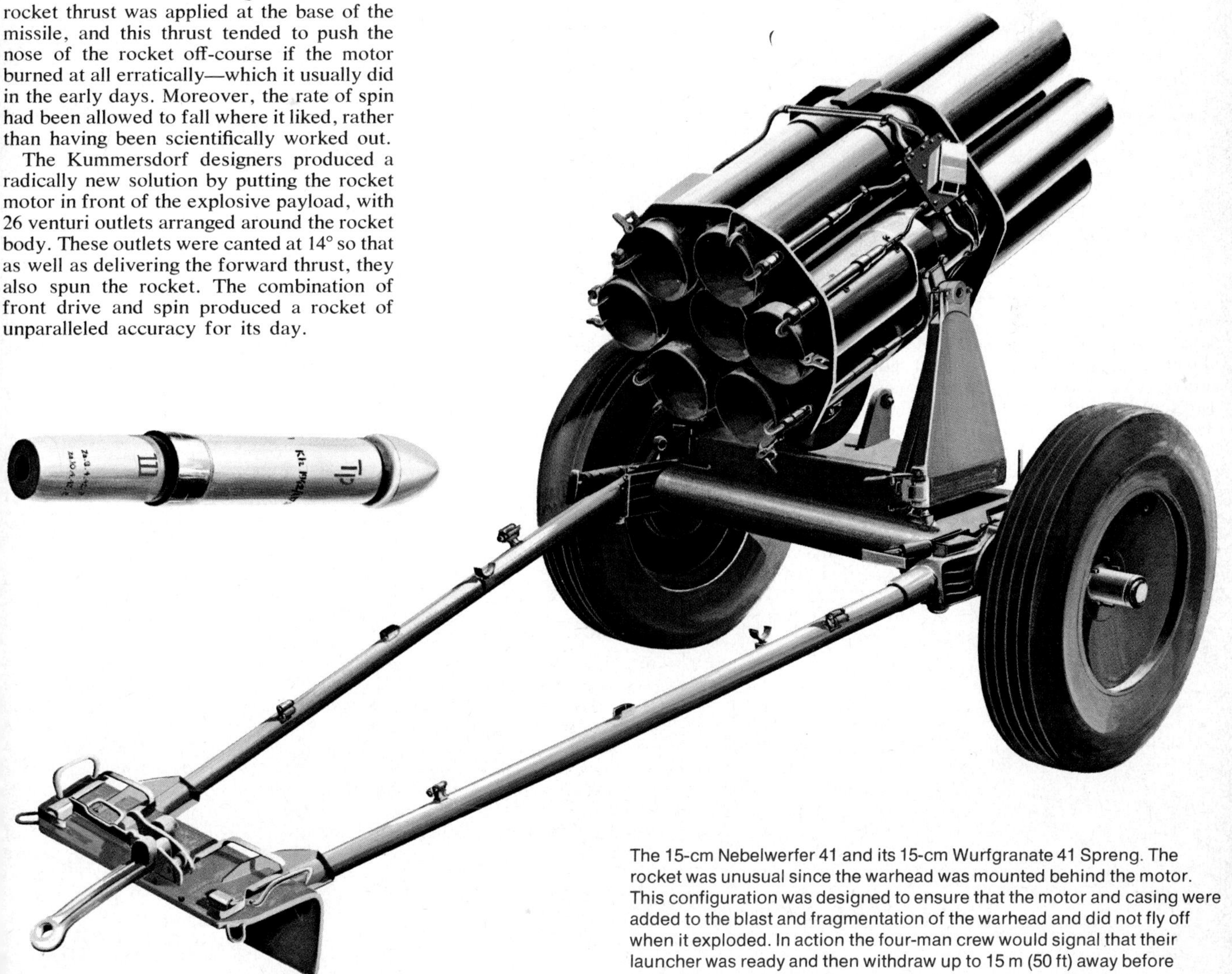

IWM

The crew of a 15-cm Nebelwerfer 41 quickly withdraw to cover before firing the rocket salvo

The 15-cm Nebelwerfer 41 and its 15-cm Wurfgranate 41 Spreng. The rocket was unusual since the warhead was mounted behind the motor. This configuration was designed to ensure that the motor and casing were added to the blast and fragmentation of the warhead and did not fly off when it exploded. In action the four-man crew would signal that their launcher was ready and then withdraw up to 15 m (50 ft) away before firing. The rockets were fired electrically at two-second intervals

J G Moore Collection

J G Moore Collection

Top left: A crew member picks up a 31.8-kg (70-lb) 15-cm Wurfgranate 41 Spreng from a stack of uncrated rockets. *Top right:* The barrels of the 15-cm Nebelwerfer. The advantage of rocket equipment was that it did not need to withstand the stresses of the explosion of an artillery round and so was quick and cheap to construct. *Below left:* Loading a Nebelwerfer—the Allies called it a 'Moaning Minnie'. *Below right:* Connecting the electrical circuit fired an ERZ 39 igniter, which in turn ignited a cellulose stick

J G Moore Collection

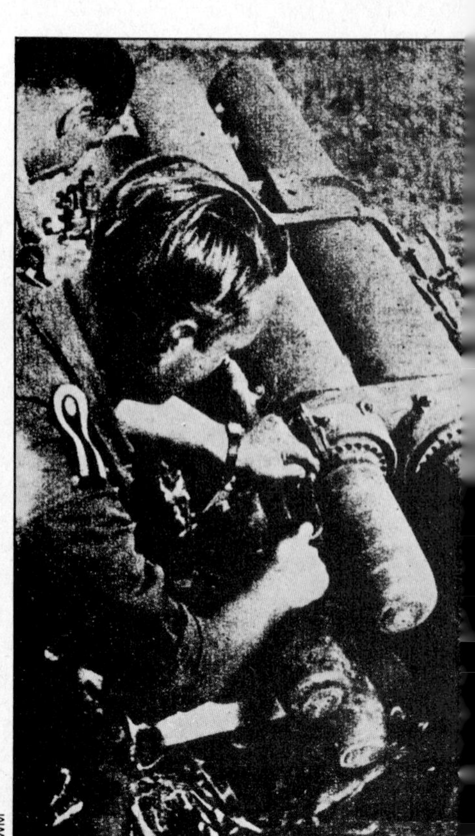

IWM

Below: A crude version of the SdKfz 251/1, which normally had a mounting known as a Schwerer Wurfrahmen 40 bolted on the hull sides allowing the wooden crates for the 28/32-cm rockets to be elevated

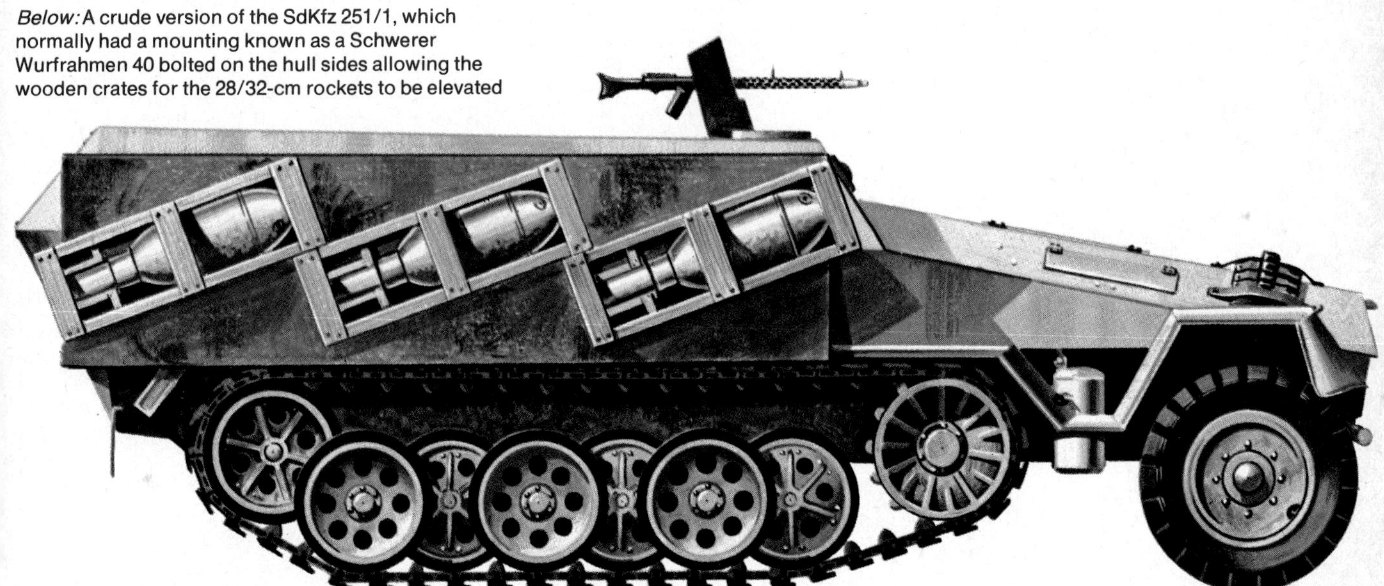

The launcher for this rocket was relatively light and simple equipment, a cluster of six tubes mounted on a split-trail carriage with two wheels, adapted from the carriage designed for the 3.7-cm (1.46-in) PAK antitank gun. The rockets were loaded into the rear of the tube; an electric ignitor was placed into one of the venturis; the weapon aimed in the same way as a normal artillery piece; and the rockets fired electrically from a position about 15 m (50 ft) away so as to avoid injury by back-blast.

Having developed this weapon, the next task was to persuade the Army to use it, since there was considerable resistance to such a revolutionary weapon. As it happened, at that time the Nebeltruppen, special units armed with mortars and intended to lay down gas and smoke barrages, were looking for a weapon to replace their ageing 10-cm (3.9-in) mortar. The replacement they had been offered was a complex and heavy mortar, which did not appeal to them, and someone hit upon the idea of producing a smoke payload rocket and issuing the new rocket discharger to them. As a result the new weapon was introduced into service as the 15-cm (5.9-in) Nebelwerfer D (or Smoke-thrower, Dornberger) though this title was soon changed to 15-cm Nebelwerfer 41 in line with the usual nomenclature methods.

The new weapon was highly successful in action on the Soviet Front, firing both explosive and smoke rockets, and the German army managed to keep it secret for quite a long time. It was not until January 1943 that the USSR captured a specimen.

21-cm Nebelwerfer 42

In view of the 15-cm model's success, the Germans began developing a larger one in 21-cm (8.27-in) calibre. There was not time to engage in long development, so a quick solution was achieved by simply placing the motor behind the warhead and reverting to the old pusher type of missile. Its accuracy was not up to the standard of the 15-cm model, but by 1943, when the 21-cm version appeared, accuracy was less important than volume of fire in this application.

With the issue of the new model, Nebelwerfer brigades were formed, armed with a total of 384 15-cm and 325 21-cm barrels; according to one German document, a medium Werfer Regiment could fire 476 rockets in five seconds, producing the firepower equivalent of 81 batteries of field howitzers.

32-cm Wurfkörper Flamm

In 1941 a cumbersome one-shot bombardment rocket had appeared, the Wurfkörper Flamm (flame mortar), a 32-cm (12.6-in) warhead of bulbous form containing 22 kg (48.5 lb) of incendiary mixture and propelled by a slender motor. This was supplied in a combined carrying crate and launcher which was laid on the ground, elevated by a pair of folding legs, and the rocket fired electrically.

28/32-cm Nebelwerfer 41

In 1943 it was decided to provide this with a multiple launcher, and the 28/32-cm NbW 41 appeared. This consisted of six open-frame launch racks mounted on the usual two-wheeled trailer: the dual calibre nomenclature came from the fact that it could fire the 32-cm Wurfkörper Flamm and also a new 28-cm (11-in) Wurfkörper Spreng (high-explosive mortar), the same rocket motor with a smaller high-explosive warhead.

30-cm Wurfkörper Spreng

While both these rockets were efficient, their range was short, and the research departments now laboured to produce a heavy-weight with good range. Close study of aerodynamics resulted in the 30-cm Wurfkörper Spreng, which could reach to 6500 m (7100 yards). This was provided with a new launcher which was more or less the 28/32-cm model but with six launch frames suited to the new design of motor.

COMPARATIVE DATA

Projectile	Weight of complete missile (kg/lb)	Weight of warhead (kg/lb)	Weight of propellant (kg/lb)	Length (cm/in)	Maximum range (m/yards)
15-cm WGr 41	34.1/75.2	10/22	5.9/13	93/36.6	6700/7300
21-cm WGr 42	112.5/248	47.2/104.1	17.9/39.5	125/49.2	7850/8600
28-cm WKrS 42	83.7/184.5	61/134.5	6.57/14.5	125/49.2	1925/2100
30-cm WKrS 42	125.6/277	66.33/146.2	15.4/34	124/48.8	4550/5000
32-cm Wkr Flamm	78.4/172.8	55.8/123	6.6/14.6	130/51.2	2200/2400

German Rocket Artillery

The last improvement in the Nebelwerfer system was the provision of a self-propelled launcher consisting of ten tubes mounted on the roof of an armoured semitracked Maultier vehicle, firing the standard 15-cm rocket.

While the Nebelwerfer equipments were the principal rocket artillery used by the Germans, there were one or two other, minor developments of interest. A 7.3-cm (2.9-in) spin-stabilized Propaganda Rakete was produced and used in small numbers to dispense leaflets over enemy lines, and towards the end of the war the rocket, redesigned with an explosive warhead, was adapted to an antiaircraft role, though very few were actually built. At the end of the war documents were found relating to a Schwere Wurfgranat 10 Spreng of 215-cm (84.6-in) calibre carrying a 10-ton warhead to a range of 4000 m (4400 yards) but it seems that this idea never got beyond the drawing board.

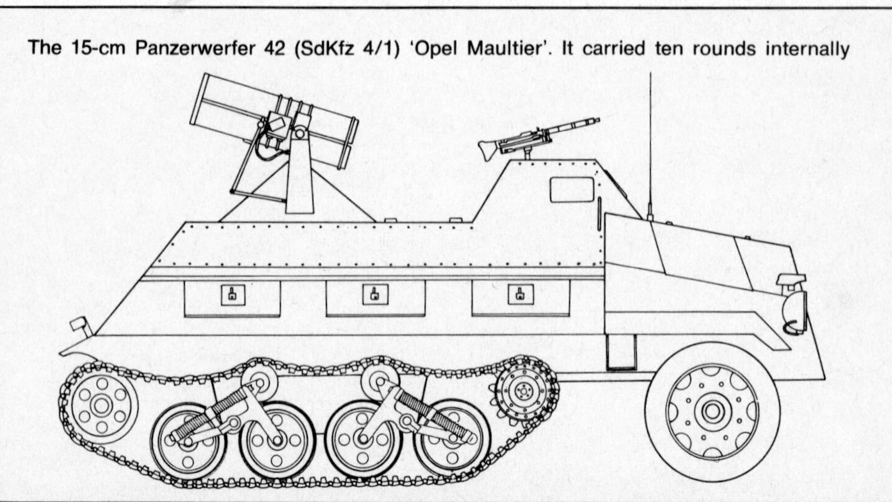
The 15-cm Panzerwerfer 42 (SdKfz 4/1) 'Opel Maultier'. It carried ten rounds internally

Unconventional Artillery

Since Sir William Armstrong perfected the first breech-loading built-up gun in the 1850s, most of the world's artillery has followed along more or less the same lines, and even such weapons as Gustav or the Paris Gun, for all their size or performance, have been conventional as far as their system of operation went. Now and then, however, a new idea comes along, and very occasionally it proves sufficiently attractive to be worthwhile trying out. And of these few experiments, it is a rare one indeed which produces something of lasting value; the only such example which springs readily to mind is the recoilless gun. However, some of the other ideas have come close to success in the past, and they are worth recording, even if only as a salutary warning to other would-be innovators.

Multi-chamber Guns

In 1870 two Americans, Lyman and Haskell, came up with a novel idea which, like all such novel ideas, appeared theoretically impeccable. They proposed a long-barrelled gun which would have the usual chamber at the back end for the propelling charge, but would also have a number of auxiliary chambers connected to the gun barrel, each of which would be loaded with an additional charge. A shell would be loaded and the first charge fired in the normal manner; then, as the shell passed the entrance to the first auxiliary chamber, the charge therein would be fired, adding more gas and more propulsive power to the shell; and as the shell passed each of the other chambers, so their charges would fire, until the shell had been boosted to whatever velocity the designer wished, after which it would travel up the rest of the gun barrel before emerging at a very high velocity so as to attain a much greater range than would be possible with a normal gun.

The Lyman & Haskell gun was built and test-fired at Frankfurt arsenal, but the results were at variance with the theory. Instead of emerging at high velocity the shell actually achieved only 335 m/sec (1100 ft/sec), much worse than an ordinary Armstrong gun of the same calibre. At the same time, the pressure in the barrel reached a massive 36 tons/sq in (5670 kg/sq cm), which should have delivered more velocity. Eventually it was discovered that the flame from the first cartridge was washing over the shell and igniting the auxiliary charges too soon, so that instead of boosting the shell they were actually impeding it. After some more experiments, which did nothing to improve the design, the Lyman & Haskell gun was dropped.

But in later years other people rediscovered the idea and proposed it. As recently as 1938 a Czech called Lugendhat offered the British government his Multiplex Gun, which was the same idea, and duly had it turned down. One of Lugendhat's most intriguing details, though, was his suggestion that it should be extremely long and, instead of mounting it on any sort of carriage, it was to be concreted into a hillside in order to give it support.

Whether Lugendhat offered his idea elsewhere is not known, but at much the same time a German engineer named Conders began experimenting along the same lines. Conders was the Chief Engineer of the Röchling Stahlwerk AG, who had produced a number of fin-stabilized anticoncrete shells for conventional guns, and it would seem likely that Conders was trying to find a way of delivering these shells at high velocity over long ranges. By May 1943 he had built and fired a 2-cm (0.79-in) scale model of a multiple-chambered gun and, via Reichsminister Speer, he received Hitler's blessing for the idea. A full-sized gun in 15-cm (5.9-in) calibre was designed, and it was planned to build a complex of 50 barrels, each 150 m (492 ft) long, dug into a hillside and aimed at London.

The original plan was to fire the auxiliary charges electrically, but this was dropped in favour of allowing the flash behind the shell to do the ignition. While work went ahead near Calais in building the 'High Pressure Pump', as it was codenamed, a prototype gun was built at Misdroy, on the Baltic, for experimental firing and to train crews. Special fin-stabilized shells were manufactured by the thousand.

Unfortunately, the project went awry. The prototype gun repeatedly blew up, while the giant installation at Calais was detected and subjected to intense aerial bombing. Eventually the Calais area was captured by Allied troops and the installation, after careful examination, was demolished. Two shortened versions of the Conders gun were produced and were reputed to have been put into action and to have fired a few rounds,

IWM

Above and right: Fleissiges Lieschen (Busy Lizzie). The design of this unusual gun was intended to boost a shell up a long barrel with a series of charges fired from lateral chambers. Described as a V-weapon it was to use non-alloy cast steel but since this occurred in the closing stages of the war no record appears to have been made of their performance.

The basic defect of the multiple-chamber gun is simply the question of timing the ignition of the auxiliary charges. Even with perfect electrical ignition, the charge does not build up its force for about 0.020 of a second, and in that short space of time the projectile will have moved some 15-20 m (50-65 ft) in the barrel. So that except by placing the chambers at impractically great distances apart, the multiple charges cannot be controlled. Further, there is an element of erosive wear at the mouths of the auxiliary chambers which leads to irregular gas flow, and this, in turn, leads to sporadic peaks of high pressure in the bore as the various gas impulses meet and combine. Even so, there is no doubt that another inventor will come up with the idea in the future.

Centrifugal Guns

Several inventors have come up with ideas to replace conventional propellants with some other propulsive force. One hardy annual is the centrifugal gun, in which a disc is spun at high speed and a ball-shaped projectile is then dropped into the centre. It then runs out to the edge of the spinning disc, gathering momentum, and is then flung off at high speed. The most obvious problem here is that of directing the projectile towards the target. Less obvious, but much more fundamental, is the age-old mechanical rule that you can get no more out of a machine than you put into it, and the amount of horse-power needed to produce the spinning disc usually requires some large array of machinery. Several inventors have suggested nothing more involved than a hand crank and gearing, and many of these appeared before the Ordnance Board during the First World War. Their defects were summed up by this body pointing out that one such device, in order to produce the necessary power to discharge the suggested missile, would need a soldier to crank it for about five hours for each shot.

Pneumatic Guns

Another suggestion was to use compressed air as the propulsive medium. This actually reached service in the US in the 1890s with the adoption of the Zalinski Dynamite Torpedo Cannon as a coast-defence gun and as a naval weapon. The weapon took its name from the fact that Zalinski, the promoter, envisaged firing heavy dynamite-filled contact mines (then known as torpedoes) in the coast-defence role. Three Zalinski guns were installed in the USS *Vesuvius* in 1890. Of 15-in (381-mm) calibre, they threw a 454-kg (1000-lb) fin-stabilized shell, but the maximum range was not comparable with conventional guns. Five 15-in coast-defence guns were built and installed but, once again, the rapid improvements in conventional ordnance in the 1890s soon made the dynamite gun obsolete. One great drawback was that each gun demanded a building about 30 m (100 ft) long to house the steam engines and compressors.

The object behind all this equipment was simply to devise a method of launching a shell carrying a heavy payload of highly sensitive explosive—dynamite—at a time when the difficulty of devising a suitable HE shell for conventional guns seemed insuperable. But with the arrival of Lyddite, Amatol and TNT, all explosives capable of sustaining fierce acceleration, the need for such weapons died away. Not before it had been tried out in a field gun, though; during the Spanish-American War some 15 Sims-Dudley Pneumatic Field Cannon were taken into use by the US Army. These used an explosive cartridge fired into an expansion chamber beneath the barrel to generate high-pressure

I V Hogg

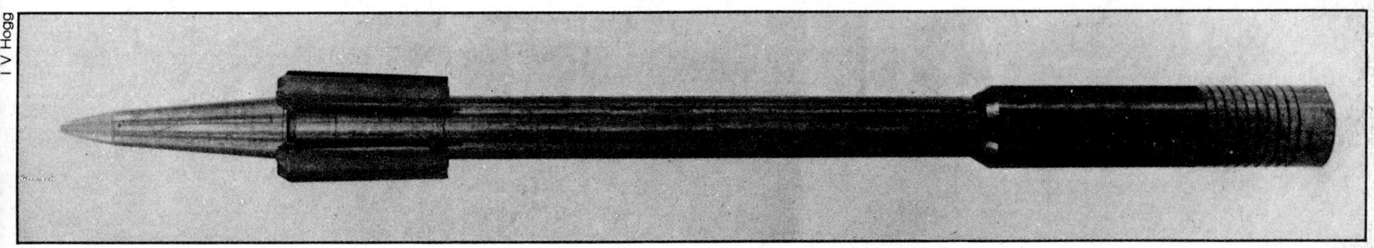

Fin-stabilized shell developed at Misdroy for the Busy Lizzie or High Pressure Pump

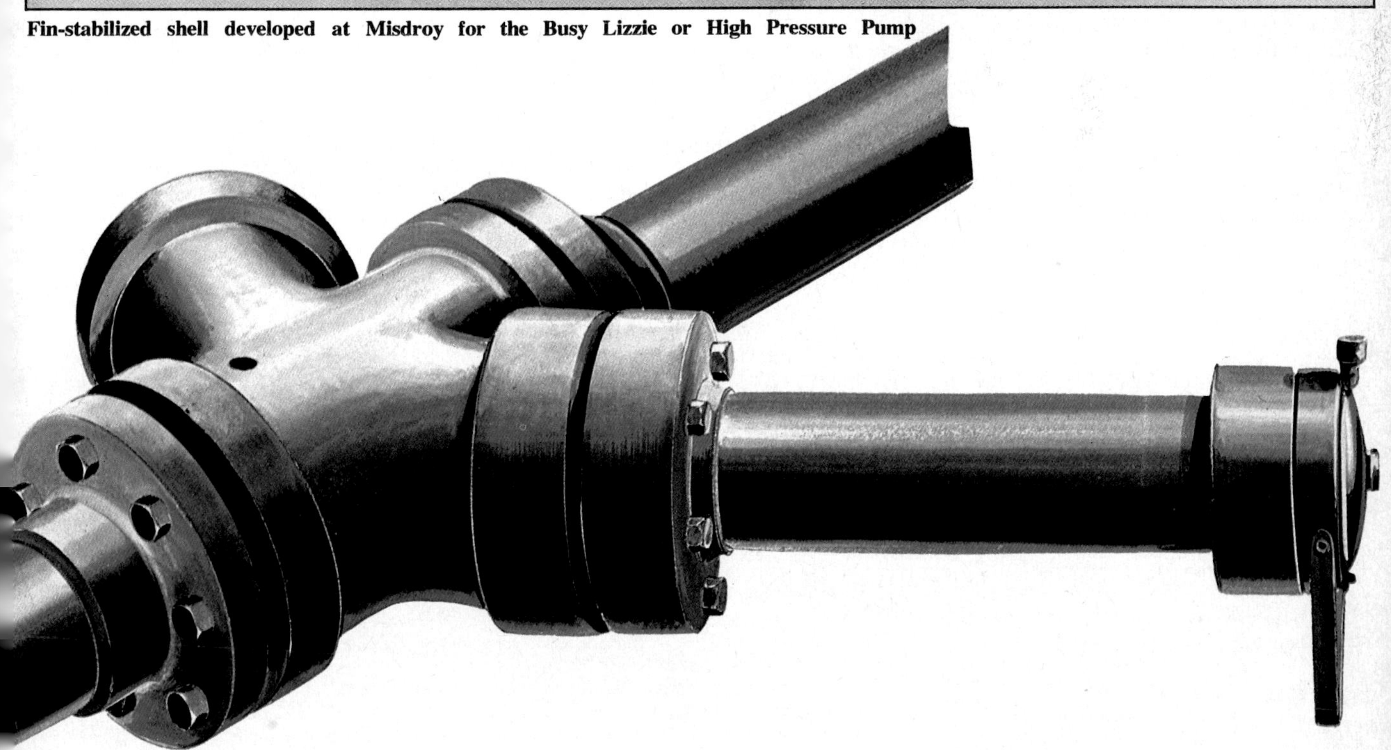

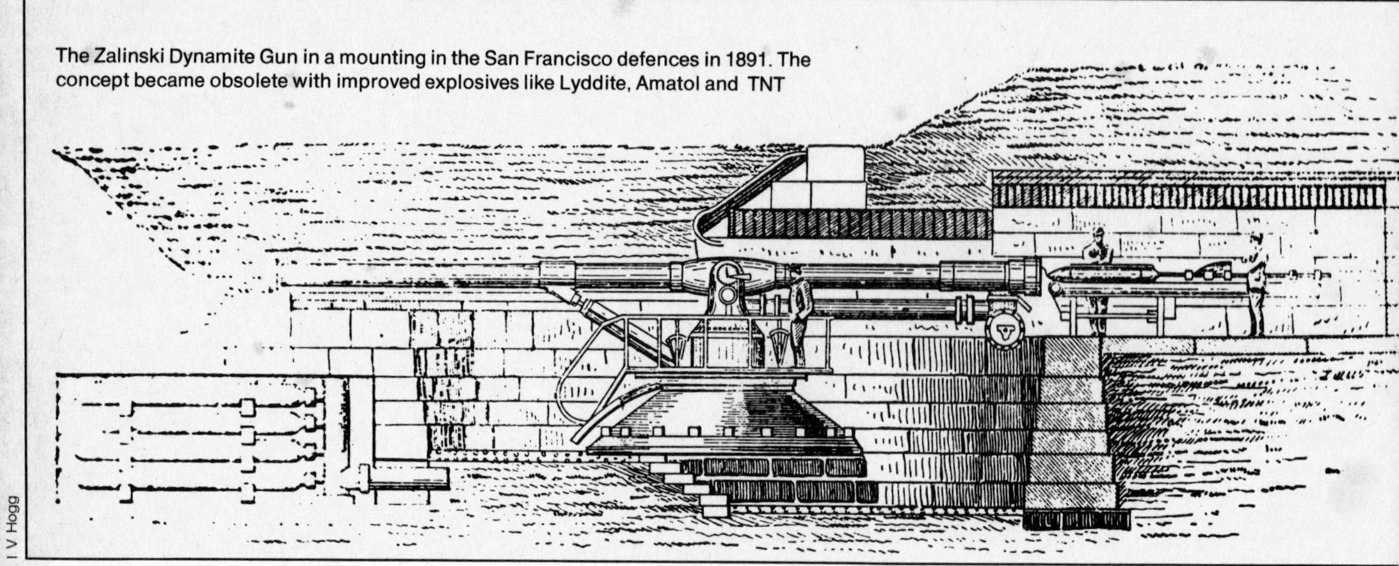
The Zalinski Dynamite Gun in a mounting in the San Francisco defences in 1891. The concept became obsolete with improved explosives like Lyddite, Amatol and TNT

I V Hogg

gas which was then leaked into the gun barrel to deliver gentle acceleration to the shell. According to the official history the guns were deployed at the battle of San Juan Hill but did not fire because nobody could find the ammunition. A few must have remained in the manufacturer's hands, since they were offered to the British Army in 1915, though without being accepted.

A close relative of the Sims-Dudley was the German High-and-Low Pressure Gun developed in 1943-44 by Rheinmetall-Borsig. This was a light smoothbore weapon, intended for infantry antitank use, which fired a finned hollow charge bomb to a range of about 800 m (880 yards) with quite respectable accuracy. Propulsion was by a 10.5-cm (4.1-in) howitzer cartridge fitted with a heavy steel closing plate pierced with four venturi holes. This confined the high-pressure side of the cartridge explosion to the gun chamber, which was suitably reinforced, and bled the gases into the gun barrel at low pressure to propel the bomb, so that a lightweight barrel could be used. Although successful, the idea was not pursued after the war by the major powers, and only the Swiss developed a similar weapon for use in an armoured car. More recently however, a gun on similar lines has appeared on the Soviet BMP-1 MICV.

Electric Guns

One idea which attracted innumerable theorists around the turn of the century was the prospect of using electricity to propel a missile, using the basic principle of the solenoid and magnetic field. The idea usually put forward was to surround the gun barrel with a massive coil of wire, feed this with a surge of current, and have the magnetic field throw the shell up the bore and out of the gun. The practical drawbacks to such an idea are legion, and nobody ever got very far with it.

In 1917, however, a Frenchman named Fauchon-Villeplee devised a new way of doing it. In simple terms, his idea was to make the 'barrel' from two parallel metal rails, and make the projectile with wings which rested on these rails. By inducing a powerful current into the rails he built up a magnetic current which caused the missile to move along the rails and launch itself at high velocity. He built a working model, obtained military backing for a service-sized prototype, but the war ended before he could get it working and the flow of money dried up, leaving him without the means to carry his idea to success. In more recent years this principle has been refined into the 'linear motor' idea, but before that had come along a German engineer had put up proposals for an electric gun.

In 1937 Otto Muck, a consultant with the Siemens company, began looking afresh at the electric gun, having in mind the many advances in electrical engineering which had taken place in the late 1920s and early 1930s. Finally, in 1943, he submitted detailed plans for a massive gun "which can fire without flash or detonation 12 shells a minute at a range of over 250 km (155 miles). The shells are of 15-cm (5.9-in) calibre and 200 kg (440 lb) in weight . . . They are specially adapted for continuous bombardment of immobile targets of great area. For this purpose the 100-m (328-ft) barrel is set up out of sight in a steep shaft inclined at 55°. The power supply (100000 kW) and installations . . . are arranged underground. Main purpose: the destruction of Greater London . . ."

Unfortunately for Herr Muck, his calculations contained some assumptions which were not tenable, and he did not know of the secret rocket programme in Germany, aimed at the same target and promising greater flexibility. His ideas were therefore turned down. But they appear to have started others thinking, and in 1944 another engineer, named Hansler, put up a proposal for a much less ambitious weapon, a 4-cm (1.57-in) electric antiaircraft gun using the linear motor principle. His ideas seemed feasible and the Luftwaffe gave him a development contract, but, as with his French predecessor, the war ended before practical results were achieved.

As might be imagined, a good deal of interest was shown by the Allies in this weapon after the war, but extensive investigation finally revealed that each gun would have required its own power station to provide the necessary current—about 1 500 000 amperes. The electric gun has, therefore, receded into the background once more, like every other unconventional weapon.

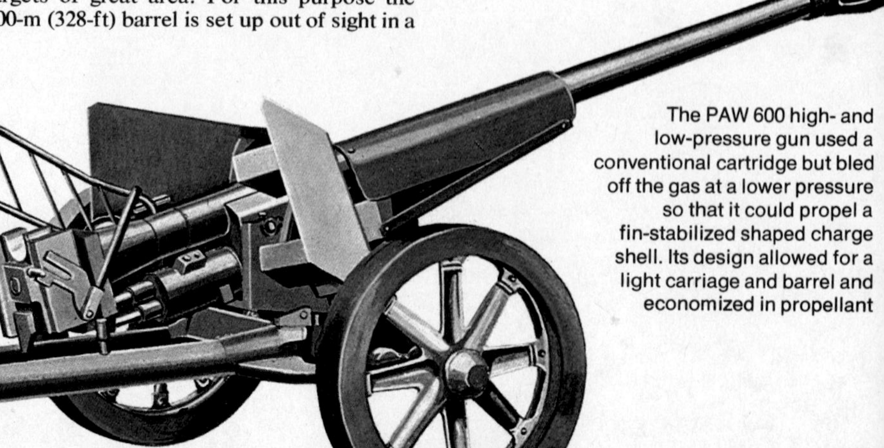
The PAW 600 high- and low-pressure gun used a conventional cartridge but bled off the gas at a lower pressure so that it could propel a fin-stabilized shaped charge shell. Its design allowed for a light carriage and barrel and economized in propellant

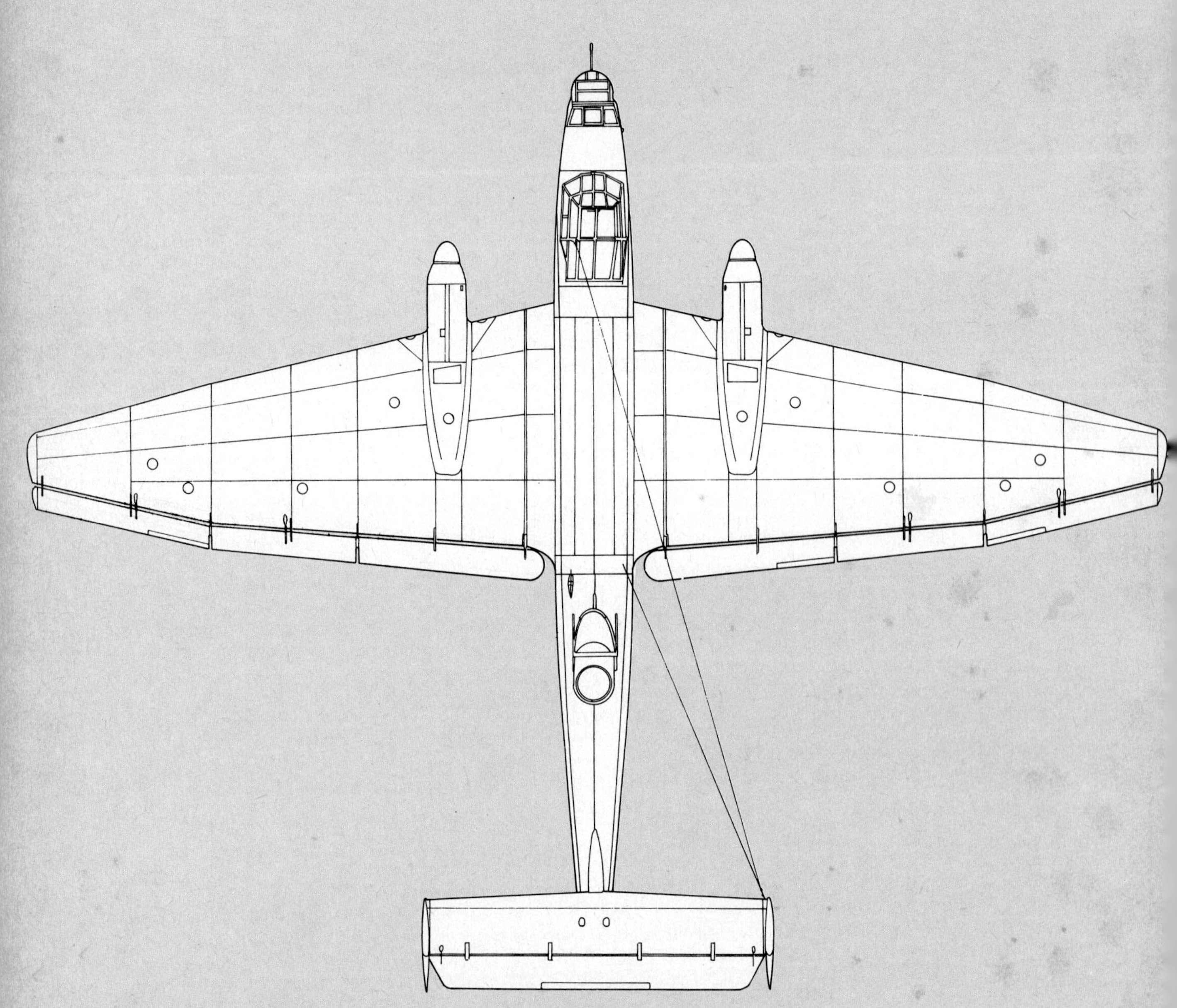